# Heroin addiction care and control: the British System 1916-1984

### H.B.Spear

### Edited by Joy Mott

Published by:

**DrugScope**

32 Loman Street, London SE1 0EE

Tel: 0207 928 1211  Fax: 0207 928 1771

E-mail: services@drugscope.org.uk

Web site: http://www.drugscope.org.uk

First published 2002

British Library Cataloguing in Publication Data.

A catalogue record for this book is available from the British Library.

Designed and typeset by Andrew Haig & Associates

**Printed and bound by Antony Rowe Ltd, Eastbourne**

ISBN 1 90431 904 1

# Heroin addiction care and control:

## the British System

# 1916
# 1984

## H.B. Spear

## Edited by Joy Mott

# Contents

# Editor's foreword

Henry Bryan (Bing) Spear died on 9th July 1995 after many years of ill health. At the time of his death he had almost completed the first draft of this book. He bequeathed the draft to me. Some sections were obviously incomplete but by using his notes and my memories of many discussions with him I have tried to complete his book as I hope he would have done.

Since the early 1960s a meeting with Bing Spear at the Home Office was an imperative for drug researchers and others who was interested in the nature and operation of the British system for treating addicts. He was uniquely qualified to discuss such matters having joined the Home Office Drugs Inspectorate in 1952, and was Chief Inspector from 1977 until he retired in 1986. During his career he worked with men who had been closely involved in the monitoring of the British system since the early years of the 20th century. His predecessors included F. T. Thornton (Chief Inspector 1943–1956) who had transferred to the Home Office in 1917 from the Board of Trade where he had issued licences for the export of cocaine and opium. Thornton was succeeded by A. L. Dyke (Chief Inspector 1956–1964) who had joined the Inspectorate in 1941 from the Metropolitan Police where he had been the first specialist drugs officer.

Bing Spear had another advantage which is denied to later commentators and policy analysts of the British drug scene since the 1950s. He knew well many of the London addicts and the general practitioners who were willing to treat them before 1968, including Lady Frankau and John Petro who were notorious for their generous and eccentric prescribing of heroin. He was in close touch with the pharmacists who dispensed the addicts' prescriptions for heroin and cocaine and with the 'chemist sergeants' who inspected their Dangerous Drugs registers, as well as with the police drug squads.

His book is written from the perspective of the Home Office Drugs Inspectorate but it is not simply the reminiscences and memoirs of a retired Home Office official. It is a detailed critical account of the two most active periods of the formulation and implementation of British policy for dealing with addiction to heroin and other dangerous drugs: between 1916 and 1926 when the foundations of the policy which came to be known as the 'British system' were laid by Sir Malcolm Delevingne and the Departmental Committee on Morphine and Heroin

Addiction (the Rolleston Committee), and the modifications to that policy which flowed from the recommendations of Lord Brain's reconvened Interdepartmental Committee on Drug Addiction in 1965.

The sources Bing Spear used in writing his book, as well as the Parliamentary record and other published reports and scientific papers, included his own memories of events and meetings of officials as well as reports and memoranda he and his colleagues in the Drugs Inspectorate prepared to advise the Home Office administrators and Ministers of the day and the Advisory Council on the Misuse of Drugs. The conclusions he draws from this material are his own and not those of the Home Office.

Bing Spear was proud of his Cornish origins. He used the story of the Cornish giant Jan Tregeagle who, for his sins, was doomed to bale out a moorland pool, Dozmary Pool, with a limpet shell with a hole in it to draw the analogy with his attempts to explain 'the British system' to visitors from abroad. This book is his attempt to use a limpet shell without a hole to bale out the pool of myths that still persist about the origins and evolution of the British System for dealing with heroin and other opioid addiction as it operated until 1984.

**Joy Mott**
June 2002

*Acknowledgements: On behalf of the author, his editor thanks all those people who shared with him their memories of the United Kingdom drug scene in the 1960s and 1970s as well as the librarians, especially John Witton (formerly of DrugScope), who assisted in locating much of the published material referred to here.*

# Bing Spear: Appreciations

## David Musto

Bing Spear was a friend of everyone who wanted to understand the evolution of British drug policy. In the Home Office he commanded an excellent position from which to view changes and held that position for a long time. His experience began before the explosion of American-style drug use in Britain in the 1960s. Prior to that time, drug users often came to notice by way of medical treatment and those known to the Home Office were in the hundreds, not in the many thousands estimated today. Bing participated in the painful adjustments to an enormous growth in the scale of the drug problem. The impact of size on drug policy is insufficiently appreciated.

Bing cared a great deal that an accurate history be written about what Americans call 'the British System' and, in fact, all aspects of British drug policy. I think being part of the Home Office frustrated him because government policies curtailed his ability, as a civil servant, to speak out. Some recent historical work on the origins of drug control at the time of World War One particularly irritated him. He also felt that the Rolleston Committee (1924–1926), which is frequently credited with establishing policies in contrast to American drug control legislation, had been misunderstood. He particularly defended Sir Malcolm Delevingne whom some had accused of wanting to criminalise excessively the provision of drugs to those addicted to their use. Finally, Bing was angry that in the creation of clinics for drug users in the 1960s 'the moral high ground was seized by a small group within the medical establishment, and by psychiatrists in particular, who, over the years, succeeded in imposing their own ethical and judgmental values on treatment policy'. He concluded that 'the treatment centre era was an unmitigated disaster'. These quoted phrases from his book are familiar echoes of my last conversation with him in the fall of 1994.

In America, the British System has been a topic of discussion for more than 60 years. Critics of the punitive drug policy pursued by the U. S. Federal Bureau of Narcotics interpreted the policy of permitting opiates to be prescribed for maintenance as the reason Britain had so few addicts compared with the United States. Some Americans explained the passage of the British Dangerous Drugs Act of 1920 as a response to a serious drug problem (although, in fact, no such problem existed) rather than as a requirement of the Versailles Treaty ending World War One. This misconception led to the assumption that heroin used to maintain addiction reduced the number of addicts to a few by the 1930s. Edward Brecher argued this latter point in a popular book published in 1973, *Licit and Illicit Drugs*, by saying 'The results (of prescribing opiates to addicts) can best be described as magnificent. By 1935, the United Kingdom reported ... that there were only 700 addicts left in the entire country'.

The crux of this debate lay in the enormous disparity in the numbers of addicts between the United States and Britain. The small population of addicts in Britain from the 1920s through the 1950s seemed to refute a common American belief that the same addictive drug would have a similar effect in any culture. In the controversy, American admirers of the British System generally held that the details of the drug law and regulations explained the difference and that if the United States adopted the more medical view of the Rolleston Committee the result would be similar to that in Britain. On the other hand, to explain the disparity on the basis of culture was vague, offered little hope for change, and also was not nourishing to the American ego. In this book Bing Spear described the actual circumstances of the Rolleston Committee and goes on to clarify a number of relevant British administrative and legal procedures American observers seldom appreciate.

Whenever I came to Britain I tried to see Bing. I recall first meeting him in the 1970s in his office as Chief Inspector of the Drugs Branch of the Home Office. Even then he had serious health problems and was on kidney dialysis. As the years went by and he retired, he became more openly critical of the British and Americans he believed were trying to impose their own ideological views on British drug policy. He was determined to write an account of the British approach to dangerous drugs that refuted those in error. During what turned out to be our last meeting we spent a day driving around Dartmoor talking about 'the book'. He was having problems finishing it. My only advice, other than to write the book, was to suggest he moderate expressions about people with whom he disagreed. This he seems to have done, but not to the extent that his authentic voice is lost.

It was against illness and the difficulties of obtaining records that he struggled to complete his study. He did not succeed. Fortunately his friend Joy Mott has been able to put the book together as, I believe, Bing would have wanted.

To the growing number of scholars and writers who pursue the history of drug policy Bing was always available for discussion. He had a unique perspective and now everyone can benefit from his thorough research and extensive practical experience. This is a book of great importance. It brushes away fantasies about British drug policy and brings us close to the difficult and persisting problem of an appropriate social and legal response.

Professor of Child Psychiatry
Yale School of Medicine, New Haven


## The Reverend Ken Leech

I first met Bing Spear in 1964 at a conference on heroin addiction. I was a newly ordained curate in Hoxton, part of the old Borough of Shoreditch, and had recently become involved with two local heroin addicts. Through them, I had got to know most of the intravenous addicts in Hackney, Bethnal Green and

Whitechapel. The East End was a late arrival on the intravenous scene, and the Home Office was only just beginning to take an interest in it. Bing often reminded me that, at the conference, I embarrassed him by a question I asked which 'put him on the spot'. I have no recollection of what this was, but we became close friends soon after, and remained in contact until his death.

Bing was a most unusual civil servant. The Home Office Drugs Branch, where he was Deputy Chief Inspector and then Chief Inspector, was located, in the 1960s, in Parliament Street. These were the days of open access, and there was no security on the door. Addicts would often invite themselves to tea with Bing and his superior Charles Jeffrey. The Branch became a kind of clearing house for addicts in difficulties as well as an advice centre and a 'human face' of government. Spear knew many – in the early days most – of the London addicts personally and would visit them in their homes. His commitment and concern spread far beyond the obligations of his work.

All of us who worked with addicts in those years regarded Bing Spear as a colleague, a friend, an ally, and a source of information and advice. He was a regular participant in our Tuesday night seminars on drug problems at St Anne's House in Soho from 1967 to 1971. I recall a certain alarm on the face of one speaker, head of the marketing division of a pharmaceutical company, when he recognised Bing in the audience. When two members of a drugs squad in a northern city secretly followed a mental health social worker to check on what she would tell the seminar about their local drug scene, Bing blew their cover by welcoming them in a voice loud enough for everyone to identify them

Spear was not afraid to engage in controversy, particularly where issues of truth and honesty were at stake. At the time when the Ministry of Health was claiming the existence of treatment facilities which all informed people knew did not exist, I asked him to come to Boot's all-night chemist at Piccadilly Circus and direct addicts in difficulties to St Anne's. When a newspaper correspondent, whom I had also invited, recognised Spear and asked him, 'Why don't you direct them to one of the thirteen treatment centres described by the Ministry of Health?', Spear smiled and said, 'It isn't for me to criticise another government department, is it? I am directing them to St Anne's, Soho. It's the only place I know.' We could not have wished for a better ally in the campaign for improved facilities.

During his many years at the Home Office, Bing Spear acquired a massive range of knowledge, expertise and wisdom, much of which is contained in these pages. But to those of us who knew him, what was so impressive was the personal qualities of the man: his kindness and care about each person, his unflappable, solid reliability, his stability and consistency over many years, and his utter dedication to the work of seeking to embody justice, responsibility and (in its true sense) pragmatism in drug policies.

He was highly critical of what he once described as a slavish 'following of

American drug polices in all the areas where they have most conspicuously failed'. After he had retired from the Home Office, Bing, together with the psychiatrist John Marks, the criminologist Philip Bean, myself and others, founded the Drug Policy Review Group to consider, and make recommendations in the area of, the reform of drug policies. The group, which included doctors, economists, psychologists and others, people of widely differing viewpoints, yet united by the belief that current drug policies were counterproductive, and that alternative approaches must be sought and studied. Bing had no doubt that all drugs are capable of doing grave harm. That was not at issue. The question for him was whether the policies did more or less harm than the drugs themselves. He would have been pleased that, in recent months, at least some people have finally awoken to the truth of what he was saying for so long.

Community theologian
St Botolph's Church, Aldgate, London

## Arnold Trebach

### The infamous Bing Spear

For over a quarter of a century, Bing Spear was the compassionate heart and soul of British drug control policy. He was my mentor and my inspiration for writing about drugs in the United Kingdom. In this position of great debt I am not alone. It is important that he be remembered by all those who are seeking a sensible and humane way through the emotional turmoil attendant upon dealing with drugs in modern society. His life's work is a model for the ages.

Bing served as a kindly and intelligent bridge between front line police and street addicts. Indeed, all came to him for advice. For many years he was acquainted with most of the established drug addicts in the country. As an American I was startled at the friends he brought to several of my London seminars: long-term injecting heroin addicts including one he had known for 35 years. I saw that addicts viewed the Drugs Inspectorate as friends, confidantes and allies. It would be a sign from heaven if American addicts could take their domestic and other troubles to their friendly local Drugs Enforcement Administration official.

The Drug Policy Foundation in Washington D. C. established an award in Bing's name in 1988. The H. B. Spear Award for Achievement in the Field of Control and Enforcement honours 'all those involved in drug control and enforcement whose activities have demonstrated a balanced regard for the needs of enforcement and also for the requirement of human compassion'. When I wrote to him of our decision and asked for his permission, he replied with characteristic modesty that he really did not deserve such recognition, that all he had been doing was 'keeping my bureaucratic nose clean for 34 years', adding 'I have merely been the custodian of the Rolleston tradition'. We are all better off because of the work of this mere custodian.

Almost to his dying day Bing attempted to make clear that the essence of the Rolleston tradition is that addiction is a medical problem and that doctors were protected by that tradition in their choices of drugs for their patients. He never said that drug *had* to be heroin, but that the drug chosen had to be the best for the patient in the professional judgement of the physician. He openly said on numerous occasions 'heroin is a benign drug' – a thought no modern American official has ever murmured. In this book Bing castigates those doctors, especially the psychiatric cartel in London, who led the charge away from injectables in the 1970s. Think of the contrast in American terms: a former top official drug expert telling the top addiction doctors that they failed in their medical duty by refusing to prescribe injectable drugs, including heroin, to their addict patients!

The move away from injectables and the great increase in the prescribing of oral methadone during the 1980s and 1990s has led many American and British experts to declare loudly that the old British system had become Americanised. Both Bing and I agreed that the spirit of Rolleston was being seriously harmed. We were both dismayed at the public criticisms by their colleagues of doctors whose prescribing did not conform to the current consensus. Two of them, Ann Dally and John Marks, had been introduced to me by Bing as examples of physicians who understood the message of Rolleston.

We both appreciated that the major source of attacks on doctors who believed in long-term prescribing to addicts came from within the medical profession. Unlike in America and in many other countries, the police led no doctors away in handcuffs because they prescribed for addicts – a fate suffered by thousands of American doctors during the 20th century. The main reason is there has been no criminal law in the United Kingdom that has been used to interfere directly with the right of a physician to prescribe whatever drugs he or she decides is professionally wise. Few American officials seem able to ingest this salient fact.

The partial Americanisation of British prescribing practices has taken place largely within the medical profession. The errors in recent years have not been imposed on doctors by the police or the criminal law, nor has there been a highly politicised national war on drugs filling the prisons with drug offenders as happened at the same time across the big pond. Rather, as Bing points out, the errors in the strategy were self-inflicted wounds by the medical leaders of the country. This is demonstrated most clearly in the series of clinical guidelines for the treatment of drug dependence published since 1984, the latest appearing in 1999. The worst part of this last worst set of guidelines is contained in a Foreword where it is stated 'The Guidelines have no defined legal position ... However, any doctor not fulfilling the standards and quality of care in the appropriate treatment of drug misusers that are set out in these Clinical Guidelines, will have this taken into account if, for any reason, consideration of (sic) their performance in this clinical area is undertaken'.

These thoughts are not only ungrammatical; they are also irrational and threatening. The group of doctors who produced these guidelines had no legal power. However, in the event of a doctor being hauled before the Professional Conduct Committee of the General Medical Council, or some other disciplinary body, each section of the guidelines will be treated as if they were contained in a statutory instrument enacted by Parliament. That had been happening with the previous guidelines but this was the first time the threat was made explicit.

Bing had no complaint about published guidelines to assist doctors in treating addicts. Nor do I. His complaint and mine, is that the guidelines should have remained as advice and not treated as canonical doctrine or laws. He bemoaned the rigidity of each set of guidelines and their increasing tendency to treat all addicts in the same way and contributing to the erosion of the independence of British physicians, and to the destruction of the careers of those doctors who were openly opposed to the dominant medical elite.

Since his untimely death, Bing's powerful ideas have been kept alive by many of his disciples, including me. I have never failed to cite my adherence to these concepts in my writing about the United Kingdom and in my appearances as an expert witness and an advisor to the defence in cases of doctors accused of improper prescribing by the General Medical Council. During the last case in which I played such a role, in 2001, the lead witness against the doctor was a well-respected clinic director who seemed to view the guidelines as holy writ. In an exchange during cross-examination by the accused doctor's counsel this witness described Bing Spear as 'the infamous ... he is the one Home Office Inspector that everybody knows ... he had been there since the 1950s, so he chronicled the whole history up until the late 1980s to the late 1990s'. When asked if he was critical of Bing when using the term 'infamous', the witness replied 'Not at all'. It is confusing to observe how this expert addiction doctor did not expect that the clear English meaning of 'infamous' would be seen as a critical comment.

What is not confusing is the fact that the ideals that Bing held dear are viewed as infamous and threatening by some of the leaders of British medicine today. This makes the publication of this volume all the more important. To those who say that the British have abandoned the British System, Bing replies that it never really existed in the way that many Americans believed and thus cannot be abandoned. The hodge-podge of practices and regulations continues along its uniquely British course. It is to be hoped that everyone who cares about the enduring goodness and effectiveness of the traditional British System will read his words very carefully and take them to heart.

Professor Emeritus
American University
Washington D. C.

# 1

# The origins of the British system

For over half a century there has been considerable interest in, and controversy about, what became known as the 'British system' for treating opiate drug addiction. The 1924–1926 Departmental Committee on Morphine and Heroin Addiction, known as the Rolleston Committee after its Chairman, Sir Humphrey Rolleston, is usually credited with establishing addiction as a medical matter and placing its control and treatment largely in the hands of doctors and sanctioning the long-term, or maintenance, prescribing of heroin to addicts.[1]

The term 'British system' is probably an American invention, dating from the 1950s, but its exact origin is uncertain. Alfred Lindesmith[2] quoted Dr E. W. Adams, one of the joint secretaries to the Rolleston Committee, as referring to a 'system of legalised purveying', which may have given rise to the term. Particularly in the United States, interest has centred on whether in fact there is a British system and if it does exist, how it has operated, and what has been its effect on the extent and nature of opiate addiction in Britain.

Whether what emerged from the Rolleston Committee's deliberations in the mid-1920s was actually a system, in the sense of an explicit set of rules, is debatable. It has been described as 'masterly inactivity'[3] and as 'pragmatic incoherence'.[4] In 1971 the *British Medical Journal*'s leader writer, in response to two American commentators, Glaser and Ball,[5] who had described the 'British system' as a 'myth', argued that 'a system which leaves much to the individual doctor, which leaves many matters undefined, is as much a system as one which is based on tightly defined legislative controls'.[6]

But British practice in the treatment of opiate addiction, whether or not a 'system', was not created by the Rolleston Committee. The Committee merely fine-tuned an approach which was already in existence. The fundamental ethos of that approach has always been that it is for doctors, not governments or bureaucrats, to decide how patients, whether terminally ill or addicted, should be treated and to determine which drugs to use in the course of that treatment. This is why in the United Kingdom (UK) heroin has always been 'legal' if prescribed by a doctor and why all attempts to prohibit its therapeutic use have encountered strong and successful opposition from the medical profession.

Berridge,[7, 8, 9, 10] in her detailed analysis of the development of British drug policy between 1916 and 1926, sees the Rolleston Committee as having frustrated the attempts of the Home Office in the person of Sir Malcolm Delevingne, an Assistant Under-Secretary of State at the time, to follow the American example and 'to establish a full-scale penal narcotics policy, involving criminal sanctions against both addicts and the doctors who prescribed to them'.[11] The essence of her thesis is that from the time the Home Office took responsibility for dangerous drugs matters in June 1916, when no other government department was willing to do so, Delevingne was determined to impose a penal policy, to control the medical profession and to deny the disease concept of addiction, but was forced to modify these objectives by the weight of medical opinion ranged against him.

Other commentators have made some highly questionable interpretations of the role of the Rolleston Committee. For example, Howitt[12] asserted that the Rolleston Committee made the recommendations that led to the 'British system being incorporated into British law'. This statement is not only inaccurate but it is also dangerously misleading because it offers support to others to similarly confuse interpretation and guidance with statutory authority. In fact, only three of the twenty Conclusions and Recommendations of the Rolleston Committee involved legislative action[13] and none of these related to treatment.

Before re-examining the evidence for Berridge's thesis it is important to try to clear up the confusion between national drug policy and medical practice, which appears to exist in the minds of so many policy analysts when examining the events and issues of 1916–1926. An undeniable right for the medical profession to be consulted on matters bearing on medical practice is not the same as an automatic right to be closely involved with the wider aspects of drug policy. Far too much has been written about the battle to preserve the interests of the medical profession, to ensure that doctors were involved in policy development and, quite rightly, to safeguard their clinical independence, in the face of what has been seen, quite wrongly, as Delevingne's onslaught. But far too little attention has been paid to the international background, or to the reasons for the controls that were introduced in 1916 and 1920, or to the practical difficulties of administering them which led to the convening of the Rolleston Committee.

## The International Opium Convention 1912

The foundations of British national drug policy, and that of many other countries, were laid by the International Opium Convention, signed by 12 nations including Great Britain, at The Hague on 23 January 1912, and usually known as the Hague Convention.

The basic aim of the Convention was 'to bring about the gradual suppression of the abuse of opium, morphine and cocaine' by limiting the manufacture of morphine and cocaine and their respective salts 'to medical and legitimate purposes.' (Certain preparations containing small amounts of the drugs were to be exempted.) Under Article 20, the signatory nations were required 'to examine the possibility of enacting laws or regulations making it a penal offence to be in illegal possession of raw opium, prepared opium, morphine, cocaine and their respective salts'. Thus, the Hague Convention, not the Dangerous Drugs Act of 1920 or the Dangerous Drugs Regulations of 1921 with which he was so closely associated, was the true origin of the 'penal policy' for which Delevingne has been condemned.

The Home Office was unwilling to take overall responsibility for the legislation needed to implement the provisions of the Hague Convention when the matter was discussed in 1914 and suggested that the Privy Council Office should deal with internal sales and the Board of Trade or Customs and Excise with external matters.[14] It was not until June 1916, at an interdepartmental meeting to discuss legislation to deal with cocaine and opium smuggling from British ports, and with growing anxiety about the use of cocaine by members of the armed forces, that the Home Office took responsibility for 'dangerous drugs' when the meeting agreed with Delevingne that dealing with these problems were 'police matters'.[15] For the next 25 years Delevingne was to play a major role in the development of both domestic and international drug policy.

While the Hague Convention laid the foundations of British drug control policy, it also laid the foundations for the difficulties which were to arise in the next few years. This was because the Convention did not define 'medical and legitimate purposes' and left it to each contracting party to interpret the terms as they thought fit. As subsequent events showed, although there was general agreement with the principles set out in the Convention, there was no such unanimity about how they should be applied in practice.

## Defence of the Realm Act 1914 Regulation 40B

The starting point for an examination of modern British drug policy has to be Defence of the Realm Act Regulation 40, which came into force on 22 December 1915. The Regulation made the gift or sale of 'intoxicants' (defined as any sedative, narcotic or stimulant) to a member of the armed forces with intent to make them drunk or incapable an offence punishable by a sentence of imprisonment up to six months. After it became apparent that cocaine was being used and peddled by prostitutes in the West End of London, and with evidence that the drug was being sold to Canadian soldiers, an order by the Army Council made on 11 May 1916 forbade the gift or sale of cocaine and other drugs (codeine, heroin, Indian Hemp (cannabis), morphine and opium) to a member of the armed forces unless prescribed by a doctor, with a written prescription signed and dated by the doctor and marked 'not to be repeated'. The medical profession welcomed this restriction on the availability of these drugs and suggested it should apply to all sections of the community.[16]

The sale to, and possession by, civilians of intoxicants could not be dealt with under the Army Council order. Most of the cocaine being misused was bought over the counter from pharmacists 'prepared to sell the drug without seeing a pre-scription or recording the purchaser's name'[17] and supplies from prescriptions for cocaine were not involved. Following the conviction of a number of men for being concerned with the sale of cocaine to Canadian soldiers, the Commissioner of Po-lice to the Metropolis, Sir Edward Henry, wrote to the Home Office on 20 July 1916 urging that 'to stamp out the evil, now rapidly assuming huge dimensions, special legislation is imperatively needed'.[18]

These fears of an epidemic of cocaine use were soon shown to be groundless when a Committee to enquire into the use of cocaine in dentistry was appointed on 16 November 1916. The Committee gathered evidence on the extent of cocaine misuse and reported on 20 February 1917. It came to the conclusion that there 'was no evidence of any kind to show that there is any serious or perhaps even notice-able prevalence of the cocaine habit amongst the civilian or military population of Great Britain ... apart from a small number of broken-down medical men'.[19]

On 28 July 1916 Defence of the Realm Act Regulation 40B (DORA 40B) was is-sued. The measures it introduced were primarily aimed at closing the hitherto un-regulated channels through which pharmaceutical cocaine was escaping, and at providing the police with new powers to deal with the illicit traffic. Under DORA 40B only specified persons were authorised to possess the drug: i.e. retail pharma-cists, medical practitioners, veterinary surgeons, persons holding general or spe-cial permits issued by the Secretary of State, or persons who had received cocaine on a doctor's prescription. Any other persons possessing cocaine would be com-mitting an offence. A prescription for cocaine was required to show the total amount to be supplied, be marked 'not to be repeated' and be dated and signed by the doctor with his or her full name, address and qualifications. DORA 40B also applied to opium except for the prescription provisions. On the same day, a proclamation was published prohibiting the import of cocaine and raw and pow-dered opium except under Home Office licence, and from 31 July all dealings in cocaine and opium had to be recorded on a special form.

DORA 40B did not refer to the circumstances under which cocaine could be prescribed, thus leaving totally unimpaired the clinical freedom of the medical profession to treat patients with cocaine when they considered it to be necessary. Berridge's comment[20] that the 'maintenance question' was 'casually passed over' is surely irrelevant because the prescribing of any drug, either for 'maintenance' or other reasons, was not an issue in 1916 and did not become one until September 1921 when the Regulations to the Dangerous Drugs 1920 came into operation. Then it was a problem which concerned the prescribing of morphine and heroin, not cocaine, in the treatment of addiction.

Berridge goes on to say that 'once the principle of restriction had been estab-lished, further regulation followed as a matter of course, and additional controls were added over the next twelve months'. The additional controls brought about by the amendments to DORA 40B on 5 December 1916 closed loopholes rather than introducing further restrictions. It then became an offence for a doctor to write a prescription for cocaine other than as specified by DORA 40B and empowered the Secretary of State to direct that 'an authorised person', such as a medical practitioner, who had been convicted of an offence against the Regulation, should cease to be authorised. A Home Office official was authorised to inspect all records required by DORA 40B and in May 1917 this authority was extended to a police officer not below the rank of inspector.

Berridge notes that despite these additional controls, not only was the response of the medical profession to DORA 40B 'universally favourable' but it argued for extending the controls to patent medicines and morphine. She concedes that the advice of the profession had been accepted on several points when drafting the Regulation, including the limitation on the number of times prescriptions could be dispensed. In fact, the Regulation had most practical consequences for pharmacists who, for the first time had to keep records which were subject to inspection, of the prescriptions they dispensed.

In January 1917 the Home Office asked police forces to report on the operation and effects of DORA 40B, on the action taken to enforce its provisions and the infringements which had come to their notice. The replies showed that the Regulation appeared to be working smoothly and there were few cases where the requirements were not being carried out. Moreover, as the frequency with which cocaine and opium preparations were being prescribed by doctors had reduced considerably, many chemists had ceased to hold stocks of the drugs. In the reports from forces outside London there were few references to cocaine or opium being misused.

The Metropolitan Police considered that the traffic in cocaine in London had been 'almost extinguished' and confidently believed that as long as the Regulation remained in force it could be prevented from 'breaking out into activity'.[21]

## The Dangerous Drugs Act 1920

According to Berridge, if DORA 40B did not sideline medical interests and was introduced to deal with a specific enforcement problem in wartime, it must therefore have been the Dangerous Drugs Act 1920 and the Dangerous Drugs Regulations 1921 by which the Home Office and Delevingne proposed to 'impose a policy completely penal in direction' and to subordinate 'the established medical view of addiction and the freedom of the profession itself'.[22]

The Dangerous Drugs Act 1920 (referred to hereinafter as the 1920 Act) and the Regulations of 1921 (referred to hereinafter as the 1921 Regulations) enacted into British domestic legislation the provisions of the Hague Convention, which had come into force in 1919 when the Convention was ratified under the Versailles

Peace Treaty. Delevingne was largely responsible for the drafting of the 1920 Act, but it should not be forgotten that it was passed by a Parliament where, as reference to Hansard shows, the medical profession had a strong and influential presence.

The 1920 Act came into force on 15 September 1920 and retained most of the provisions of DORA 40B. The production, import or export, possession, sale or distribution of opium, cocaine, morphine or heroin was prohibited except by persons licensed by the Home Secretary or otherwise authorised to do so. The prohibitions also applied to preparations containing at least 0.2 per cent of morphine or 0.1 per cent of cocaine, the lower limits set by the Hague Convention.

The 1920 Act and the 1921 Regulations were intended to meet both the letter and spirit of Britain's international obligations but with minimum interference with the legitimate medical uses of the drugs. They were aimed at monitoring the legitimate production and use of the drugs and ensuring that any leakages could be speedily detected and dealt with effectively. At the time, the most important element in the control and prevention of drug addiction was seen to be limiting the availability of drugs. Delevingne commented in 1934 that 'Drug addiction is at bottom a matter of supply'.[23] However, as he later realised, and as the history of the past 70 years has shown only too clearly, the doctor's prescription pad offers scope for the accidental, careless or deliberate leakage of drugs into the wrong hands.

## The 1921 Dangerous Drugs Regulations

Berridge's[24] suggestion that the 1921 Regulations 'aimed to impose stringent controls over the whole procedure of dispensing and prescribing' is a considerable exaggeration. Regulation 5, setting out the conditions with which prescriptions for dangerous drugs had to comply after 1 September 1921, had nothing to say about the medical purposes for which the prescription could be issued, and required of doctors only that they date and sign prescriptions with their full name and address. The rest, including the amount to be dispensed, could be completed by a secretary or receptionist (and in one surgery in the 1950s by the addict patient). This hardly amounts to major interference with a doctor's professional liberty. It is true that, for the first time, doctors were required to keep certain records but this was not an onerous clerical burden, and it is difficult to equate the reasonable precautions against forgery, introduced by Regulation 6, with 'stringent' control. This Regulation required that, before dispensing a prescription for a dangerous drug, a pharmacist should be acquainted with the signature of the prescriber or be acquainted with the patient, and have no reason to suppose the prescription was not genuine.

Berridge notes that the publication of the draft Regulations on 10 February

1921 unleashed 'a storm of professional protest', not least for what the *Pharmaceutical Journal* termed the 'bureaucratic arbitrariness and exclusiveness' with which they were drafted and issued. She implies that responsibility for the Regulations rested solely with the Home Office and 'the concern of the Ministry of Health for the liberty of the professional under narcotics law was disregarded' – although the Ministry of Health, as the Department in closest contact with professional interests, was sent a copy of the draft proposals for comment by the Home Office on 2 November 1920, three months before publication. In any case, Dr George McCleary, Deputy Senior Medical Officer at the Ministry of Health, had been very much involved in drawing up the Regulations. It was he and other Ministry of Health officials, not the Home Office, who were 'unsympathetic to pharmacists' complaints'.[25]

McCleary had, since 1919, become more closely involved with dangerous drugs policy following Delevingne's refusal to consider passing responsibility for administering and enforcing the dangerous drugs legislation from the Home Office to the newly created Ministry of Health. In his correspondence with the Ministry of Health, and quoted subsequently by his critics as evidence of his determination to pursue an American-style 'penal policy', Delevingne argued, as he had in 1916, that:

> The matter is very largely a police matter … the enforcement of the Regulations has in the main to be undertaken by the police, and there would be considerable objections to its being transferred to another Department which is not in close relations with the police …

This reaction had apparently not been anticipated by Ministry of Health officials and at first they considered referring the matter to ministers. However, it was decided that as a first step Sir George Newman, the Chief Medical Officer, should be asked to see Delevingne. The request to Sir George, by Sir Robert Morant, First Secretary at the Ministry of Health, in a minute dated 24 July 1919, was based on the belief that Sir George knew Delevingne 'pretty well' and could 'handle him', and because there were few in the Ministry 'with sufficient knowledge to cope effectively with Sir Malcolm's knowledge, plus obstinacy'.[26]

The outcome of this meeting was that 'Delevingne agreed amiably to active and continuous co-operation', and McCleary was appointed liaison officer to the Home Office. Consequently, when Captain Elliott MP enquired, immediately following publication of the draft Regulations, if the Ministry had been consulted or whether the Home Office had produced them on their own initiative, it was possible to confirm there had been close consultation between the two departments. After a meeting with Drs Smith Whitaker, McCleary and E. W. Adams, on 10 February 1921, Elliott agreed to use his influence with other medical members of Parliament:

... to dissuade them from lending themselves to any Parliamentary agitation until the critics of the Home Office Regulations have availed themselves of the opportunity given them by the Home Office of discussing their various points.

If there was merit in some of the objections to the draft Regulations, and to the tendency for the 'over-regulation of minor details', the public criticisms by the medical profession were less convincing. For the most part they stemmed from resentment that 'the self-regulating autonomy of the pre-war years was at an end'.[27] A typical protest came from the Council of the Metropolitan Counties Branch of the British Medical Association in a letter to *The Times* newspaper of 11 February 1921:

> ... nobody who represents the general views of the medical profession has been consulted in drawing up the Regulations which will render the daily work of medical practitioners almost intolerable and interfere most gravely with their powers of relieving cases of acute illness.

This 1921 version of today's more familiar 'patient care will suffer' was supported by another argument which, in modified form, was also heard in the 1990s, namely that the new Regulations 'will very seriously increase the cost to the public of many necessary medicines'.

The Portsmouth Branch of the British Medical Association saw the likely effect on patients rather differently. In a letter to *The Times* newspaper of 15 February 1921, it argued that the new Regulations 'would have a most detrimental psychic effect on our patients, that they are unnecessary [and] an intolerable interference with our rights and privileges [and] a slur upon our honour and *bona fides*'.

Berridge notes that the two major issues of concern were the 'attacks on doctors themselves and the issue of maintenance prescribing'.[28] Since bureaucratic authority and activity is circumscribed by the legislation approved by Parliament, what statutory authority did the Home Office have for this perceived assault on the medical profession?

The provisions of the 1921 Dangerous Drugs Regulations, far from interfering with, or posing a threat to, their clinical freedom, in fact, accorded the medical profession the monopoly position it had been seeking. Regulation 11 'ring-fenced' doctors' clinical independence to prescribe for patients as they felt necessary, as 'any duly qualified medical practitioner' was 'authorised *so far as is necessary for the practice of his profession or employment in such capacity* to be in possession of and supply the drugs', the words emphasised being the sole 'limitation' on doctors' clinical freedom. This maintained the position the medical profession had enjoyed before 1 September 1921 when the Regulations came into force: that it was for individual doctors, and no one else, to decide whether their patients required any of the drugs which were now subject to control. Regulation 11 is the bedrock upon which the British system is built.

## The use of dangerous drugs in medical treatment

The extension of controls by the 1920 Act to drugs such as morphine and heroin, both widely used in medical practice at the time, was soon to create difficulties for Delevingne and his Home Office colleagues who were responsible for ensuring that the will of Parliament was carried out. As the Rolleston Committee was to note, it was clearly Parliament's intention that 'the use of Dangerous Drugs should be confined to that which was necessary for medical treatment'.[29] The problem was that the 1921 Regulations offered no guidance on how the doctor's 'practice of his profession' was to be interpreted. In its report, the Committee appointed by the Home Office to consider objections to the draft Regulations had not commented on the proposed wording of Regulation 11.[30]

Moreover, although it was obvious that doctors should be able to use dangerous drugs for treatment of their patients, there was no authoritative definition of 'medical treatment'. No problem arose when the patient being treated was terminally ill or suffering from some painful organic condition. But was the supply of such drugs to someone who was addicted, perhaps even the doctor, really 'medical treatment' and a proper exercise of the authority conveyed by Regulation 11?

Although he was in no doubt about Parliament's intentions, Delevingne could not answer what were essentially medical questions and sought advice from the Ministry of Health. This approach has been interpreted by Berridge as the Home Office beginning to 'prepare the way for accommodation'[31] and the Ministry of Health having 'won a position of influence in deciding policy', although she concedes there was 'genuine Home Office uncertainty about what was legitimate medical practice'.[32]

The suggestion that the Ministry of Health had 'to win a position of influence in deciding policy' is based on a misunderstanding of the working relationships between government departments and their officials. There are few items of government business which fall entirely within the province of a single department and it is normal practice to consult other departments about matters which have a bearing on their interests or special expertise. For Delevingne to seek medical advice from the Ministry of Health was as natural as it was for him to consult the Foreign Office about international matters. In any case, the Chief Medical Officer at the Ministry of Health has always also been the Chief Medical Officer to the Home Office.

The fundamental problem facing Delevingne, which he first referred to the Ministry of Health in 1922, was later set out in the first two paragraphs of the memorandum the Home Office submitted to the Rolleston Committee:[33]

It is not expressly provided in the Regulations that prescriptions for the drugs must be for *bona fide* medical purposes – though this is of course the intention of the Regulations – and the absence of such a provision has given rise to difficulties in dealing with certain cases …

It will be seen that the full discretion of the medical practitioner to administer, supply or prescribe the drugs in whatever way he thinks best for his patients is not interfered with. On the other hand, the possession or supply of the drugs by a medical practitioner otherwise than for professional purposes is not covered and would constitute an offence against the Regulations. For instance, the supply of the drugs by a doctor to an addict to enable him to indulge in his addiction would be an offence punishable under the Acts.

The memorandum contained a number of examples of the types of cases which were causing the Home Office difficulty. These included the doctor who was supplying an addict with drugs with no pretence that he was attempting a cure, as well as the doctor who was himself addicted. There were also the essentially clinical questions of whether it was a legitimate use of a doctor's authority, under Regulation 11, to treat an addict by way of diminishing doses of the drug to which he or she was addicted, or to supply drugs over a long period to an addict for whom the prospects of cure were minimal and who could not otherwise function normally.

It also appeared to the Home Office that some doctors treating addicts had been extremely lax. For example, prescriptions were being sent by post, often to patients living long distances from the doctor's practice, without any fresh examination of the patients; batches of prescriptions were being given to cover the addict's needs over a long period of time; prescriptions were given where doctors had been 'actuated by pity for the addicts or have been wearied into giving them by their importunities'; and casual patients, previously unknown to the doctor, 'have successfully obtained prescriptions on the pretext of some acute pain requiring immediate relief'.

Parssinen[34] apart, the Home Office case has received short shrift from other commentators. Berridge[35] described the evidence which the Home Office put before the Rolleston Committee merely as 'a weighty memorandum which largely structured the proceedings'. Neither the fact that the Home Office had submitted a 'weighty memorandum', nor the fact that the Rolleston Committee was entirely medical in composition, should have surprised anyone. The Committee had been appointed solely to resolve important medical questions which were causing the Home Office considerable practical difficulty.

Yet, it is not only Delevingne's views, motives and actions that have been misrepresented and, at times, grossly distorted; so too has the sequence of events leading to the Committee's appointment. For example, Berridge[36] comments that the 'pressure' the Home Office put on the Ministry of Health was 'in part in the hope of obtaining medical support for an absolute line, a medical declaration that abrupt withdrawal was possible and maintenance prescribing improper' although she later revises this interpretation to: 'the Home Office was no longer demanding absolutism, but seeking medical advice'.[37]

The events of 1921–1926 can be read rather differently and Sir Malcolm Delevingne, by raising the issue of the validity of prescribing, and in particular of long-term prescribing, to addicts, can be seen as the true 'father' of the 'British system', rather than Sir Humphrey Rolleston. Such heresy demands substantiation.

## The alleged Home Office 'offensive' against the medical profession

Berridge's[38] main charges that under the 1920 Dangerous Drugs Act and the Regulations of 1921 and 1922 the Home Office conducted an 'offensive' against the medical profession were:

1  That doctors, as well as pharmacists, would be required to keep detailed records of purchases and supply of dangerous drugs.
2  That doctors not in actual practice were to be prohibited from prescribing dangerous drugs.
3  That doctors were forbidden to write prescriptions of dangerous drugs for themselves.

As further examples of the 'offensive' she included: Delevingne's proposal that a blacklist of addicts and doctors should be circulated by the police to wholesale pharmacists; disapproval of doctors who continued to write regular prescriptions for addicts who could not otherwise function; and a move to secure official confirmation that abrupt, rather than gradual, withdrawal was appropriate treatment. The latter two matters were dealt with by the Rolleston Committee.

To what extent does the evidence support these charges?

### Records to be kept by doctors

In the 1920s doctors themselves often supplied drugs and medicines to their patients. If retail pharmacists were to be required to keep records of their purchases and dispensing of prescriptions for dangerous drugs, then it was surely not unreasonable that doctors performing similar functions should also do so. The 1921 Regulations required doctors to keep a register in which had to be recorded details of the quantities of dangerous drugs they obtained and supplied to their patients, but they did not have to record details of drugs they personally administered or which were taken by a patient in their presence. (This exception was removed by the Misuse of Drugs Act 1971 Regulations of 1973.) Doctors who obtained and held only small stocks of such drugs for personal administration to their patients were not required to keep a register. This was later to be changed on the recommendation of the Rolleston Committee, who, following their discussion with the Director of Public Prosecutions, Sir Archibald Bodkin, proposed that these doctors too should keep a simple record of their purchases.[39] Doctors have never been required to keep records of their prescriptions.

### Prohibitions on doctors 'not in actual practice'

Neither the 1920 Act, nor the Regulations made under it, prohibited doctors not 'in actual practice' from prescribing dangerous drugs. The phrase was used in Clause 3 of the Dangerous Drugs and Poisons (Amendment) Bill of 1923 which proposed an amendment to the record-keeping provisions of Section 17 of the Pharmacy Act of 1868. Regulation 11 of the 1921 Regulations, which gave doctors their authority to possess and supply drugs, was not affected.

The purpose of Clause 3, as the then Home Secretary, W. C. Bridgeman, explained to the House of Commons in the Second Reading Debate on the Bill on 28 February 1923, was to ensure that drugs were not sold by pharmacists other than to registered medical practitioners 'in actual practice'.[40] Bridgeman anticipated the profession might wish 'some slight modification' to the clause, which he would be prepared to consider.

The medical profession had worked itself into a considerable state of agitation about the 'slur' cast on it by this proposal (and also to the amendment to the Dangerous Drugs Regulations, introduced in October 1922, which prohibited doctors from writing prescriptions for themselves) by the time the Bill reached the Standing Committee of the House of Commons on 27 March 1923. There, after hearing representations from a deputation of medical members of Parliament, Mr Bridgman moved an amendment to delete 'in actual practice' from Clause 3 of the Bill explaining that, as the words would be difficult to interpret, he had decided 'the best thing would be to leave them out'.[41]

### Doctor addicts and self-prescribing

The problem presented by the doctor addict was dealt with in paragraph 8 of the Home Office memorandum to the Rolleston Committee:

> The case of the medical practitioner who is himself addicted to the drugs is perhaps the most difficult with which the Home Office has to deal … In view of the cases coming to the notice of the Home Office in which medical practitioners were obtaining the drugs by means of prescriptions for addiction purposes, the Home Secretary made a Regulation that a prescription should not be given for the use of the prescriber himself. The Regulation, however, was objected to by the medical profession, and in view of the opposition was subsequently withdrawn.

It is surprising, in view of the weakness and illogicality of the arguments marshalled against the 1922 Regulation (S.I.1087), that it was withdrawn. The attack in the House of Commons had been led by Sir Sydney Russell-Wells, an eminent physician and a recent vice-chancellor of London University. He complained during the second Reading Debate on the Dangerous Drugs and Poisons (Amendment) Bill on 28 February 1923 that the Bill contained no provision for 'sweeping away this ridiculous regulation', which prohibited doctors from prescribing narcotics for themselves.[42] In his view, it had been introduced 'in order to deal with the very few, mostly retired medical men, who have given way to these habits', and was wrong: firstly, because it hampered the doctor by unnecessarily creating a new offence; and secondly, because as a preventive measure it was 'futile'. Precisely how doctors would be hampered in the day-to-day conduct of their practices by a Regulation which, in the next breath, Sir Sydney acknowledged did not prevent them from obtaining whatever drugs were needed for the treatment of their patients, was not explained.

The publication of the draft Regulation in the *London Gazette* on 4 August 1922, as procedure then required, had prompted *The Lancet* on 19 August 1922 to question whether it would 'achieve to any substantial degree the end which its framers have in view', although it was clear the journal's main complaint was against 'the slur upon the medical profession in general ... and considerable inconvenience to many of its members'.[43]

The Home Office had not acted unilaterally in proposing and introducing this amendment to Regulation 5 of the 1921 Regulations. The background is set out in a letter to the Ministry of Health dated 19 September 1922. Several cases had come to the notice of 'medical men who were the victims of the drug habit, purchasing considerable quantities of cocaine and morphine by giving prescriptions made out to themselves'. The view had therefore been taken that in these circumstances doctors were not acting in the practice of their profession. One doctor, obtaining cocaine in this way, had been prosecuted in Liverpool. He gave as his defence that he had originally used the cocaine for a painful disease of the arms but was now curing himself by using diminishing doses. The stipendiary magistrate had given him the benefit of the doubt but suggested that doctors should not prescribe the drugs for themselves and in case of need should obtain a prescription from a fellow practitioner. As a result of this case, no further prosecutions had been initiated and the Home Office decided to deal with the problem by way of an amendment to the Regulations. A letter from the Ministry of Health, dated 25 September 1922, confirmed that the Minister concurred with this proposal.

What has been omitted from the accounts of this episode is that the General Medical Council had been consulted about the proposed Regulation, and as a subsequent memorandum by Delevingne recorded, no formal objections had been received during the statutory period allowed following publication of the draft regulation in the *London Gazette*.

When the Secretary of the British Medical Association, Dr Cox, and an unidentified General Medical Council member came to see Delevingne they described the proposed Regulation as an 'undesirable limitation of the privilege of the registered medical practitioner, without any compensating advantage to the public, and derogatory to the medical profession'. As he later recorded, Delevingne thought their objections were not 'fundamental' and 'the Association's case was little more than a matter of *amour propre*'.[44]

Sir Sydney Russell-Wells' speech in the House of Commons in February 1923 was followed by a motion for the annulment of the 1922 Regulation put down by Major Molloy on 8 March. However, this was not pressed because, after meeting the Parliamentary deputation, the Home Secretary announced in the Standing Committee on 27 March 1923 that he intended to revoke the 1922 Regulation, confirming this two days later in an answer to a Parliamentary Question from Major Molloy.[45] The Home Secretary's decision was welcomed by the *Morning Star* on 28 March 1923, which quoted from a letter from Dr Cox, in which he wrote:

> It seems to the medical profession to be wrong and objectionable that difficulties should be put in the way of some thousands of perfectly respectable medical men in order to prevent a few addicts from obtaining drugs for self administration, as it is understood that the Home Office makes no charge of trafficking against the medical profession.

Although the doctors can be said to have won the day when the prohibition on their self-prescribing was withdrawn on 16 May 1923, one important question was left unanswered. Neither Sir Sydney Russell-Wells, nor any other critic of the 1922 Regulation, chose to explain why doctors alone had to be permitted to use their privileged position to initiate and sustain their own addiction. They were not, of course, being prevented from obtaining drugs for the treatment of their patients. The point was succinctly made by M. D. Perrins, one of Delevingne's colleagues, in a minute dated 16 June 1923 on the papers of the Boddy case,[46] when he wrote:

> This case is a good illustration of the weakness of our position with regard to doctors. Dr J. A. A. Boddy is undoubtedly an addict and there seems no way of obtaining a conviction. As we have just withdrawn a Regulation that doctors may not prescribe for themselves it may not be opportune to return to the charge. Unless, however, we are prepared to allow the medical profession to be the only class to be permitted addiction in drugs without hindrance, some way must be found to limit the amounts procurable by a doctor upon his own prescription or order.

The reaction of the profession to the 1922 Regulation not only confirmed Delevingne's view that their opposition to the new controls arose from resentment, rather than an objection in principle to what was being introduced, but also provided a good example of the flexible standards which from time to time operate in the medical world. Doctor addicts were to be free to obtain drugs as and when they chose but other addicts would have to obtain their drugs from doctors or from the almost non-existent illicit market, or enter hospital for withdrawal. Yet, not so long before, in April 1914, the end of self-medication of opiates by the general public (as a consequence of the restrictions on the availability of opiate preparations agreed at The Hague in 1912) had been welcomed on behalf on the profession by the same secretary of the British Medical Association, Dr Cox, in these words:[47]

> The advantage of restricting the sale of these substances in this way would be that the only legal way in which they could be obtained would be on the prescriptions of a body of men who by their education and training would on the whole, I think, respond to the responsibility.

This was the culmination of a long campaign by the medical and pharmaceutical professions against self-medication by the general population. However, as Berridge[48] suggests, their motives were as much concerned with 'professional consolidation and the elevation of the expert, whether pharmacist or doctor' and 'a sustained attempt to bring the paying patient to heel', as with the dangers of opiates. There remained the need for some limitation on the currency of prescriptions, which, until the Dangerous Drugs Act 1920, were the property of the patient, and could be redispensed at will. DORA 40B had a provision that a prescription for cocaine could be dispensed once only. The 1921 Dangerous Drugs Regulations, covering a wider range of drugs, relaxed this limitation by allowing a prescription to be dispensed a maximum of three times, the two 'repeats' to be at intervals specified by the prescriber.

If the 'objective dangers' of self-medication with opiates were subordinate to the doctors' intent to establish their monopoly, they were probably recognised. Although the Rolleston Committee endorsed what had always been the Home Office view, that doctor addicts were 'a source of special danger to the community' and that the withdrawal of the authorisation to possess the drugs was 'specially valuable in the interest of the practitioner himself',[49] they failed to caution practitioners against treating themselves. On the other hand, the Committee offered no comment which could be interpreted as a 'green light' for self-medication.

Whether Berridge's representation of the Home Office response to doctor addicts as an 'attack on doctors' is merely a little unfair or stems from a misreading of the facts, can best be judged from a re-examination of the charges that addict doctors were cut off from their supplies (prompting strong protests from the British Medical Association) and that doctors were, reportedly, 'on the run' from the police. Two cases have been cited in support of these charges, the two Drs Boddy, father and son in Manchester, as examples of the former, and Dr Grandy, of the latter. Both cases are worth a detailed account.

### The Boddy case

In February 1923 the Chief Constable of Manchester reported that regular supplies of hypodermic tablets of morphine, and less frequent supplies of morphine hydrochloride and morphine pills, were being made by a local wholesale chemist to Dr H. W. Boddy, a 75-year-old practitioner, whose son J. A. A. Boddy was also a doctor. Enquiries made by a Regional Medical Officer of the Ministry of Health disclosed that both doctors were taking morphine nightly, the father using one suppository, apparently obtained from another local wholesaler, and the son claiming to use one hypodermic tablet to 'counter diarrhoea'. The Regional Medical Officer considered the quantities taken by Dr H. W. were 'medicinal' but that the son was probably deceiving his father and was taking the main part of the drugs supplied to the practice. As it was not clear from the original report which doctor had actually ordered the drugs, the police were asked to make further enquiries. These revealed that, although the wholesaler's account was in the name of Dr H. W. Boddy, it was the son who usually signed the orders and collected the drugs.

At about the same time, and after the Regional Medical Officer's visit, J. F. Macfarlan, another supplier, reported to the Home Office their suspicions about supplies of Opoidine, a morphine preparation, they had been making to Dr J. A. A. Boddy. Macfarlans were told that the Home Office was already aware of the case, and, as it was doubtful whether the drugs were required for *bona fide* practice purposes, they were recommended to provide no further supplies. In Berridge's account of the Boddy case, this recommendation, which merely confirmed suspicions the supplier already entertained, is described as 'the Home Office ordered Macfarlans' not to send the Boddys any more morphine.[50]

Berridge goes on to say that, as the result of strong protests from the BMA 'at this interference with professional freedom', the Home Office resorted to a 'gentleman's agreement' so that Dr J. A. A. Boddy gave a written undertaking not to obtain further supplies and agreed to place himself under another doctor for treatment. The 'strong protests' from the British Medical Association were not, in fact, related to the correspondence between Macfarlan's and the Home Office but to the Boddys' dealings with another supplier, nor did they have any bearing on the decision to offer the younger Dr Boddy the opportunity of giving an undertaking.

The BMA's 'strong protest' was contained in a letter from Dr Cox to the Home Office dated 1 June 1923. He wrote that he had heard from the Association's Man-

chester branch that, following the visit of the Regional Medical Officer, when Dr
H. W. Boddy had next placed an order for morphine, his supplier (whom Dr Cox
did not identify) refused to fill the order on the grounds that they were 'under instructions from the Home Office not to supply him'. (Up to this point only one
Manchester wholesaler had been in contact with the Home Office and been 'recommended', as had J. F. Macfarlan, not to make any further supplies to Dr J. A. A.
Boddy.) The elder Dr Boddy felt he had satisfied the Regional Medical Officer
about his own use of morphine and that he was being penalised in mistake for his
son. Dr Cox's 'protest' was contained in the following paragraph of his letter:

> The point, however, I want to make is this; that if Dr Boddy's contention is true, that the
> first he heard of his supply being cut off was from the wholesale chemist, he seems to
> have been treated in rather a cavalier manner. One would have thought that in any case,
> other than a flagrant breach of the law, Dr Boddy would have been given a chance of
> mending his ways, or at any rate would have been given official information that his
> supplies were going to be cut off and not left to find it out from his wholesale chemist.

This, of course, is neither the language of 'strong protest', nor is it directed at
any interference with professional freedom. Dr Cox accepted an invitation to discuss the case with Delevingne and it was obvious that his primary concern was
that the Home Office would not advise the cutting off of supplies without first giving the doctor an opportunity to offer an explanation, as Delevingne's note of
their conversation records. Dr Cox apparently raised no objection to the Home
Office advising wholesalers to withhold further supplies and, in fact, in response
to a request from Delevingne, said he would always be willing, in similar cases, to
find out from local BMA branches the nature of a member's practice and the
amount of drugs he or she might be expected to require for legitimate purposes.[51]

The decision to seek an undertaking from the younger Dr Boddy resulted from
the inadequacy of the available evidence and difficulties over the interpretation of
the record-keeping requirements in the Regulations which made it impossible to
prosecute him for his failure to keep records of his purchases. The alternative of
charging him with possessing morphine otherwise than for *bona fide* medical purposes was also rejected. The implication that a 'gentleman's agreement' was a
face-saving device is similarly misleading. The undertaking procedure had, over
the years, provided the Home Office with an important, and often successful, option for dealing with doctor addicts. Nor do the warning letters sent to the Boddys
support the contention that the Home Office was determined that they would no
longer be able to obtain supplies. Dr J. A. A. Boddy was informed:

> (The Secretary of State) ... is willing to give you the opportunity of breaking yourself
> of the habit and retrieving your position, if you will give him a written undertaking that

you will not obtain any further supplies of morphine and that you will place yourself under the treatment of some other medical practitioner (other than your father) for as long as may be necessary.

In the case of his father, the warning letter was even less restrictive:

(The Secretary of State)… must receive a written assurance that you will in future obtain no supplies of morphine beyond the amount strictly required for the purposes of your profession and that you will neither supply your son nor assist him to obtain morphine or any other dangerous drug.

### Dr Grandy

Dr R. E. Grandy would appear to be one of the doctors Berridge referred to as 'on the run from the police'. This is presumably a reference to the fact that a warrant had been issued for his arrest, and the inclusion of his name in the 'blacklist' circulated to the police in 1924 by the Home Office. The circumstances were that Grandy had been issuing prescriptions to himself when the short-lived 1922 Regulations forbidding this came into effect. Instead of going to another doctor from whom he could have received prescriptions for his drugs perfectly legally, he chose to present to various pharmacies forged prescriptions, often written on notepaper stolen from other doctors. When last heard of he had been living in 'great poverty' in London but, at the time his name was circulated, his precise whereabouts were unknown.[52]

### The blacklist of addicts and doctors

Another of Delevingne's proposals used as an illustration of his anti-doctor bias was the suggestion that a confidential list should be given to the police of the names of doctor addicts thought to be obtaining 'concealed supplies', i.e. either from suppliers far removed from their practices or in small quantities from several different suppliers. Berridge has described this proposal as 'a blacklist of addicts and doctors' to be circulated 'by the police to wholesale pharmacists'.[53]

What was actually proposed was a follow-up to a circular which, in January 1924 with the approval of the Home Secretary, had been sent to all chief constables. This was a list, under 'very confidential' cover, containing the names of nine doctors and nine lay addicts, the latter thought likely to obtain supplies concurrently from a number of doctors. Delevingne explained his reason for the proposal in a minute dated 9 January 1924:[54]

I think the communication of this information to Chief Constables may be of some use, at any rate it seems a precaution we ought not to neglect and the circular will help to keep the necessity of regular inspection of records before the minds of Chief Constables.

The further circular to suppliers was also a Delevingne initiative. He proposed that it should be sent, in strict confidence, to the largest and most responsible firms and include only those names on police list. However, the then Permanent Under-Secretary of State, Sir John Anderson, while agreeing that the proposal, even if open to attack, could be justified, felt it might first be put to the Rolleston Committee. This was done in paragraph 8 of the memorandum submitted to the Committee by the Home Office but was not accepted.

### The Dangerous Drugs and Poisons (Amendment) Act 1923

Berridge includes this Act in her list of charges as evidence of Delevingne's determination to impose a strict penal drug control policy. This is yet another red herring. There was already strong pressure in Parliament for higher penalties for drug trafficking. In May 1922, in a Parliamentary Question, Mr Ramsden asked the Home Secretary if 'in view of the moral and physical damage caused by the illegal sale of cocaine and similar drugs' he could find his way, 'with a view of stopping this sale, to order that 12 strokes of the cat, in addition to imprisonment for 6 months or more, with hard labour, be given to all vendors who are caught illegally selling these drugs'.[55]

The changes introduced by the 1923 Act, the main one being an increase in the maximum penalty for trafficking from two to ten years' imprisonment, were not primarily aimed at the domestic situation, as was explained by the Home Secretary, during the second reading debate on the Bill in the House of Commons on 28 February, 1923:[56]

> Its object is to increase facilities and powers for dealing with the illicit traffic in drugs. This traffic is very largely of an international character. We believe a great deal of it is going on at the present time.

The existing maximum penalty was clearly inadequate for someone known to be dealing in quantities in the order of 2,400 ounces of morphine and 2,500 ounces of cocaine. (Similar reasons were given when the Controlled Drugs (Penalties) Act of 1985 increased the maximum penalty for trafficking in heroin and cocaine from 14 years to life imprisonment and when the Drug Trafficking Offences Act 1986 was introduced.)

The 1923 Act also extended the existing limited police powers of search. The 1920 Act had empowered the police to enter the premises and inspect the stocks and records of manufacturers, wholesale chemists, etc., but did not provide for them to obtain a search warrant for any other premises. There was also a need to bring within the law acts carried out in the UK with a view to illicit transactions abroad – further confirmation that this was primarily a measure against the international traffic.

One late amendment to the Bill, which conflicts with Delevingne's hard-line image, has gone largely unnoticed. To meet the concerns of the pharmaceutical and medical professions about the penalties to which their members could now be liable, two safeguards were introduced. The first was that proceedings on indictment could only be instituted with the approval of either the Attorney-General or the Director of Public Prosecutions. The second was that a person convicted of a technical (e.g. record keeping) offence could not be sentenced to imprisonment without the option of a fine, nor could they be given a fine exceeding £50, if the Court was satisfied that the offence had resulted from 'inadvertence'.

## Doctors prescribing for addicts

It is the alleged attitude of the Home Office to doctors prescribing for addicts which goes to the heart of any analysis of the British system, and for which Delevingne has attracted the fiercest criticism. It is also where the most serious re-writing of history has occurred.

What is the basis for the charges that the Home Office disapproved of doctors who continued to prescribe for addicts who could not function without their drugs and was determined that abrupt, rather than gradual, withdrawal should be their only treatment option? If a fair and just verdict is to be returned, it is essential to look at the practical problems Delevingne was facing. Yet these have received scant attention. The fundamental question was whether the continuing prescribing of morphine or other drugs to addicts was accepted by the profession as legitimate medical treatment. If it was, Regulation 11 gave doctors complete clinical freedom to prescribe or supply such drugs as they considered necessary; if it was not, the Home Office, responsible for administering and enforcing the law, had to do something about those doctors who were supplying or prescribing drugs contrary to Parliament's intentions.

Prescribing for addicts presented a number of problems. The first of these was the question of the treatment of addiction by gradually diminishing doses. As explained to the Rolleston Committee in the Home Office memorandum at paragraph 5 there was uncertainty:

> ... whether it was in accordance with approved medical practice and the best medical opinion in the country for a medical practitioner to treat an addict with a view to a cure on a system of gradually diminishing doses, or whether the right course for him to take was to refuse to supply or prescribe the drug at all in such cases.

The Home Office approaches to the Minister of Health during November 1922 for advice on this question have been seen as the beginning of the negotiations leading to the appointment of the Rolleston Committee. But the question had been put to the Minister six months earlier, on 17 May 1922, when, at Delevingne's suggestion, a copy of a pamphlet published by the Canadian Department of Health was sent to the Minister with a covering letter asking for his 'observations upon the criticisms therein contained of the treatment of addiction by diminishing doses, a method which is known to be practised in this country', and for consideration of 'some pronouncement on the subject for the guidance of the medical profession'.[57] Delevingne commented, in his note on the pamphlet, that it made the 'strongest criticism of the system which the Home Office had come across'.

The reply from the Ministry, in a letter of 20 June 1922 (signed by T. Lindsay), was not very helpful:

> The Minister is advised that the question of the immediate withdrawal of the drug in the treatment of drug addicts is one upon which there is considerable diversity of medical opinion in this country. In these circumstances the Minister does not feel that at the present time he could usefully issue any pronouncement on the matter.

By November 1922 a number of cases had come to Home Office notice of doctors obtaining large quantities of drugs for their own use or prescribing large quantities for patients. Enquiries had revealed that in several instances the doctor or the patient had become 'a victim of the drug habit' which it was hoped to break by treatment with gradually diminishing doses. Although it was believed that this explanation was often only a pretext, it was difficult to secure the conviction of the doctor on a charge of obtaining, or assisting the patient to obtain, the drugs for purposes other than legitimate medical practice. In the circumstances, the Home Office again sought advice from the Ministry of Health, in a letter dated 2 November 1922,[58] suggesting that:

> It would be very desirable on general grounds that the question of the utility of the method of treatment by diminishing doses should be carefully investigated and an authoritative pronouncement made on the subject and generally on the treatment of drug addicts.

The letter added that, although it was understood 'there is divergence of opinion among medical practitioners in this country, official experience in New York, where the drug habit was very prevalent', was apparently against this method. It was also suggested that consideration should be given to asking the Royal College of Physicians 'to appoint a Committee to investigate and report on the question'.

## The Adams report

The Ministry of Health's response was to ask one of their medical staff, Dr E. W.

Adams, to look into the question Delevingne had posed. On 17 February 1923 Dr Adams reported his conclusions to Dr McCleary.[59] In the meantime, as is clear from a memorandum he wrote on 28 December 1922, Delevingne had discussed a number of individual cases with McCleary, as a result of which he decided that another difficulty should be formally raised with the Ministry, with a view to it being passed on 'to the RCP (Royal College of Physicians) for consideration'.

It is this memorandum, together with his response to Adams' report, which give the lie to the allegation that Delevingne was determined to follow an 'absolute line' and to disregard the disease concept of addiction. Pointing out that the Home Office had already sought advice on the question of treatment by diminishing doses, he commented:

> It was certainly not the intention when the Act and Regulations were passed to allow the drugs to be supplied to drug takers for the satisfaction of the craving which possesses them, and it is only in cases where there is something more than this that the action of doctors would be justified, i.e. where the drug is required for a definite therapeutic purpose.

The new difficulty involved the prescribing of drugs to 'persons who, according to the accounts given to us, have become so dependent on the drug (which in some cases they began by taking for the relief of some pain), that they cannot now give it up without suffering greatly and possibly without a complete breakdown of health'. These persons were to be described later in the Home Office memorandum to the Rolleston Committee, at paragraph 6, as cases:

> ... of such long standing that the addict appeared to be beyond the possibility of cure, and in which it was claimed or suggested by the addict or his medical adviser that the deprivation of the drug or the diminution in the normal supply rendered him incapable of continuing his normal life and occupation, or even reduced him to the condition of a physical wreck, or in some cases endangered the addict's life itself.

Details of a number of such cases, including that of Thomas Henderson,[60] in which it appeared the drug was 'being prescribed by the doctors in order to enable them to gratify their addiction and without any design or hope of effecting a cure', were accordingly sent to the Ministry of Health on 19 January 1923. This was followed on 23 February by further examples, including those of some prescribers who were only too obviously making no attempt to cure or treat their addict patients and were supplying drugs virtually on demand. The covering letter also drew the Ministry's attention to new South African regulations prohibiting a doctor from prescribing any habit-forming drug for other than 'a medicinal purpose', which was defined as 'treatment of a disease or some other definite curative or therapeutic purpose, but does not include the satisfaction or relief of a habit or craving for the drug used or for any other habit-forming drug' and asked for the Ministry's views 'as to the powers and duties of medical practitioners in such cases'.

No reply to this letter had been received by 5 March 1923 when McCleary sent Delevingne, informally, a copy of Adams' report. It was Adams' view, taking into account American practice, that 'it is impossible (except perhaps in the case of co-caine) suddenly to cut off the addict from his drug unless he is placed in a suitable Institution and carefully watched, nursed and treated'.[61] McCleary fully endorsed Adams' conclusions but, when it came to sending Delevingne a copy formally, it was felt at higher administrative levels in the Ministry of Health that McCleary's proposed covering letter contained 'a more definite expression of opinion than the extent of the (Adams) investigation altogether warrants'. Consequently, Delevingne was told, on 16 March, that:

> It will doubtless be agreed that the report indicates that the method of sudden with-drawal cannot usually be adopted except as part of institutional treatment, and would therefore only be practicable in a relatively small number of cases in this country in view of the limited institutional accommodation available.

The Home Office readily accepted the conclusions in Adams' report and acted in accordance with it in dealing with the cases which arose thereafter, as paragraph 5 of the memorandum to the Rolleston Committee makes clear: 'Where the sup-plies to the addicts under medical treatment showed a gradual diminution in amount the Home Office has not taken exception'.

But there were other important conclusions in the Adams report, which an 'absolutist' might have been expected to contest. Adams had no doubt that:

> ... drug addiction can only be regarded as a disease – as a pathological state calling ur-gently for treatment and relief. The best opinion is unanimous on this point. The only exception, perhaps, is in certain rare criminal cases where the drugs are taken from purely vicious motives. But criminal cases are matters for the policeman rather than the physician, and even here, there is the pathological element. If it be admitted, as it now universally is, that drug addiction is a disease, and, if, as will be further shown, this ad-diction, for its treatment, requires a use of the drugs coming within the purview of the D.D. Act, then it is just as legitimate to use morphia in this class of case as it is to use it for the relief or cure of any other disease. Both uses come within the legitimate em-ployment of the drugs in question.

Delevingne's response to the Adams report was to write to McCleary, on 9 March 1923, the letter which Berridge has used to support her contention that the Home

Office put pressure on the Ministry of Health 'in part in the hope of obtaining medical support for an absolute line, a medical declaration that abrupt withdrawal was possible and maintenance prescribing improper'.[62] The full text of Delevingne's letter is set out below,[63] with the words quoted by Berridge shown in italics.

> Many thanks for Adams's memorandum. It seems to clear up the question of the validity of the treatment of morphine addiction by the method of diminishing doses. For administrative purposes, however, I think we want something more, viz (1) *an authoritative statement which we could use in dealing with practitioners, and to which we could refer the courts, that regular prescription of the drugs on the grounds that without them the patients would suffer or even collapse*, without any attempt to treat the patient for the purpose of breaking the habit, *is not legitimate and cannot be recognized as medical practice*; (2) publication both of that statement and of the conclusion in Adams' memorandum with the authority of the medical profession, whether represented by the Ministry of Health or such a body as the Royal College of Physicians, behind it; (3) would it be possible to amplify the method of British treatment as described by Adams on page 5 of his memorandum and also to bring out more strongly that the morphine addict must place himself in the hands of and remain under the close and constant supervision of a qualified medical practitioner until the cure is effected?

Delevingne ended this letter with the suggestion that McCleary and Adams discuss these questions with him. There was clearly a swift response from McCleary because on 12 March 1923 Delevingne again wrote to him setting out his understanding of what had been agreed in 'our subsequent conversation'. This was that, apart from sending the Home Office, officially, a copy of the Adams report, the Ministry of Health would write further on the question of 'obtaining an authoritative statement as to the conditions under which morphine might be supplied or, prescribed for a morphine addict by a medical practitioner' (answering the Home Office letter of 19 January 1923). The Ministry's reply would also cover the possibility of having:

> ... it laid down that a doctor is only justified in supplying morphine or prescribing morphine for a morphine addict if the addict has placed himself in the doctor's hands for the purpose of medical treatment with a view to a cure, and the doctor is in fact treating him for this purpose [and of] giving some definite guidance to practitioners as to the general lines of treatment in such a case.

These letters are surely totally incompatible with the image of Delevingne as someone implacably opposed to the continuing supply of drugs to any addict, who was determined to stop the giving of regular doses to addicts 'who could not otherwise function', and who saw addiction 'as essentially a short-term issue, the only problem being to eliminate all existing addicts and their sources of supplies'.[64]

As support for the statement that Delevingne faced 'intense professional opposition', Berridge [65] has quoted extracts from a letter, published in *The Times* newspaper on 21 March 1923, by Professor W. E. Dixon, an eminent Cambridge pharmacologist and later a member of the Rolleston Committee. This letter appears to present a serious challenge to the attempted 'intrusion of government policy into the area of the doctor/patient relationship' but when the letter is placed in its true context a totally different picture emerges. The following is the paragraph to which Berridge refers, with the words she quotes shown in italics:

Our own somewhat less drastic law came into force in September 1921 and it is too early as yet to see its effect; but *we do not seem to have learned anything from the experience of our American brethren*, since in the amending Bill to the Dangerous Drugs Act now in Committee stage of the House, the medical profession is subjected to a number of pin-pricks. *Cannot our legislators understand that our only hope of stamping out the drug addict is through the doctors, that legislation over the doctors' heads is likely to prove our undoing and that we can no more stamp out addiction by prohibition than we can stamp out insanity?* Yet in the amending Bill practitioners not in actual practice are, in effect, forbidden to purchase narcotic drugs. Every practitioner is in practice but in this case the 'actual' is likely to be interpreted as 'for gain.' Registration under the Medical Act has up to now given certain rights; but registered doctors are now to be divided into two groups and from one these rights are to be taken away. The doctor is no longer allowed to prescribe for himself and is to be subjected to horrible penalties for any infringements. There can be little doubt that the passage of the amending Bill as it stands will do particular harm; it will cause intense resentment in the medical profession.

The bill to which Dixon referred was the Dangerous Drugs and Poisons (Amendment) Bill 1923, which had little to do with his real targets, self-prescribing and the widely misinterpreted phrase 'in actual practice'. It had even less to do with the exercise of a doctor's clinical freedom to treat patients as he thought fit. Dixon's letter is illuminating for other reasons. His final sentence gives the game away as far as the medical profession's real objections to the new controls were concerned; it provides further confirmation that the criticism of what Delevingne was trying to achieve amounted to little more than resentment at the ending of their 'self-regulating autonomy'.

Following the acceptance by the Home Office of the main conclusion of Adams' report, the initiative now passed to the Ministry of Health to offer some advice on the other practical problems which Delevingne had raised. McCleary's opinion, expressed in a long minute to Smith Whitaker on 13 March 1923,[66] was that a doctor could not be adversely criticised for continuing to prescribe to an addict if their relationship was that of doctor and patient, but the doctor was 'deserving of censure' if he prescribed merely to enable the addict to obtain the drug for the satisfaction of his craving. In such a case the doctor 'did not act in a medical capacity at all but misused his position as a medical practitioner to order morphia for a non-medical purpose'.

Adams had taken a similar position in his memorandum of 17 February 1923 to McCleary:[67]

> The aim of the (1920 Dangerous Drugs) Act and Regulations is to suppress all illicit dealings in the drugs of which they take cognisance without placing any hindrances in the way of the use of these drugs for the treatment, relief and cure of disease. Certainly then the mere satisfying of the craving of a drug addict, without further object, whether this is attained by the provision of the drugs by the addict himself or through an intermediary, comes under the head of illicit dealing. That the intermediary is the habitué's own doctor makes no difference. If it did make a difference, then the Act could only be regarded as a measure designed to enable the addict to obtain his drugs legally and easily, which is absurd.

Reassuring though it must have been to know that there was general agreement between the two departments as to what constituted legitimate medical practice, the Home Office was still faced with the problem of having to deal with such prescribers, of whom Dr S. G. Connor, practising in Soho, was then the prime example. His activities were summarised for the benefit of the Rolleston Committee as Case 1 in Appendix 1 in the Home Office memorandum prepared for the Committee. (Delevingne had suggested that Connor should be invited to give evidence to the Committee but this was not followed up.)

### The Connor case

Connor had first come to attention in May 1919 when it was found he had been giving prescriptions for cocaine to 'men more or less in the underworld', and that he was also obtaining cocaine for his medical practice, claiming he was using it as an anaesthetic in treating cases of venereal disease. In September 1922 further regular prescriptions were reported, again to 'men and women of the underworld' and it was estimated by a West End chemist that Connor had 'three or four hundred patients of this class'. When seen by a Ministry of Health Regional Medical Officer in May 1923 he admitted prescribing cocaine to addicts purely for the satisfaction of their addiction and when told this was improper, expressed his thanks and gave a written undertaking to prescribe in future only 'for such cases as I can treat'. The next month he was called to give evidence in a case involving three persons found drugged in a West End flat, and he admitted knowing them as patients. Two other instances of Connor's 'treatment', were quoted in the summary; one involved a woman supposed to be under the care of doctors in Glasgow for whom he was regularly sending prescriptions for morphine to a London chemist for on-ward despatch to Glasgow; and the other involved a woman living in Surrey for whom he was similarly prescribing morphine although she was supposed to be under the sole treatment of a doctor in Hove.

There were two possible options open to the Home Office: either to institute proceedings against Connor for an offence against the Regulations, or to refer him to the General Medical Council. However, when the case was referred for a Legal Opinion, Counsel advised that on the evidence available, it would be impossible to bring any charge against Connor, on the grounds 'that the Regulations admit the right of a medical man to prescribe dangerous as well as other drugs, and do not in any way limit that right'. Reference to the General Medical Council presented a similar difficulty as the Council's proceedings were akin to those in a court of law and required the same standards of proof. Also, the General Medical Council could not take action against a doctor merely because it disapproved of his partic-ular method of treatment, and it would be open to him to claim that he was exer-cising his clinical judgement in treating his patients and the Council had no authority to interfere.

Connor did eventually appear before the Council's Disciplinary Committee in 1926, after he had been convicted of offences under the 1920 Act, and he was placed on probation for a year.[68] But even here Berridge's view of a 'Home Office versus medical profession' battle intrudes, when she describes the penalty imposed on Connor by the General Medical Council as confirmation that 'professional forces were not prepared to abandon addiction without a struggle'. This is to portray Connor as someone who was 'simply giving drugs to patients who could not func-tion without them', instead of what he really was, an early example of the long line of 'script doctors' who were to cause such problems in later years.

## The discussions leading to the appointment of the Rolleston Committee[69]

But if there was support in the Ministry of Health for Delevingne's views, and sympathy with his difficulties, particularly about prescribers such as Connor, there were no immediate solutions on offer. Smith Whitaker and McCleary also had a difficulty; Delevingne had come to them for advice, but it was not for the Ministry to provide the authoritative medical statements he thought would solve his problem. These involved clinical questions which they were in no position to answer and on which, in any event, medical opinion was divided. Why, then, has Delevingne been made the scapegoat for the failings of the medical profession, and why has responsibility for the 'lengthy and protracted' negotiations before the Rolleston Committee was appointed not been laid where it rightly belongs – at the Ministry of Health's door?

Following Delevingne's letter of 12 March 1923 setting out his expectation that the Ministry of Health would write further on 'an authoritative statement' on the prescribing of morphine to an addict, Smith Whitaker was not again in touch until 5 July, and then apparently only as a result of a telephone enquiry to Mc-Cleary, asking about the current state of play. Smith Whitaker replied:

> I am afraid I have been the cause of the delay, seeing great difficulties in the way of deal-ing with the matter on the particular lines suggested and not finding it easy to suggest, as one would like to do, some other way of meeting your requirements. P.S. I may ask for a talk before a written reply as I wish to test my notions by discussion with one or two help-ful people before taking up your time.

These 'helpful people' included Sir Humphrey Rolleston, in his capacity as President of the Royal College of Physicians, and Dr R. W. Branthwaite, later to be a member of the Rolleston Committee. At a meeting with Delevingne on 8 August, Smith Whitaker expressed the view that it would be impracticable to issue any for-mulae by which the prescribing of drugs to addicts could be regulated. Nor could the Royal College of Physicians usefully consider the problem or issue recommen-dations. He therefore suggested that 'after the leave season', a committee should be established to go into the whole question and consider what suggestions could be made for the guidance of the profession.

Smith Whitaker appeared to become less enthusiastic about the appointment of a special committee. When he sent Delevingne, on 9 November, a copy of the Regional Medical Officer's report on enquiries into the prescribing practices of two doctors, he also enclosed a copy of the detailed 'official instructions' (which unfortunately do not appear to have survived) given to the Regional Medical Of-ficer before he made his visit. Smith Whitaker explained that giving advance instructions:

> … constituted an attempt to utilise the case for our assistance in elucidating certain questions of principle affecting the circumstances in which a doctor may, or may not, properly order or supply morphine.

While seeking Delevingne's comments on this approach, he was himself of the view that:

> We shall all arrive more safely, in this way, at the correct answers to the very difficult questions you put to us early this year, than by an attempt to obtain ex cathedra pro-nouncements from high medical authorities.

Moreover, there was general agreement among a number of eminent doctors, including Sir William Willcox, Dr Branthwaite and Dr Dale of the Medical Research Council, that it would be impossible, in the present state of medical opinion, to obtain a pronouncement from any body of medical men of high qualification to the effect that in no circumstances could morphine properly be ordered for a morphine addict who was not suffering from any other disease.

In a reply dated 19 November 1923 Delevingne thought the instructions which had been given to the Regional Medical Officer 'admirable', although they related to the special circumstances of a doctor prescribing for a stranger who came to him casually. He assumed the instructions would be modified for the more difficult cases he and Smith Whitaker had discussed and would make it clear that a doctor should not prescribe for any patient whom he knew to be an addict unless the patient was prepared to place himself in the doctor's hands for a course of treatment with a view to a cure. Delevingne also asked how Smith Whitaker proposed to deal with the case, which he had apparently mentioned in discussion, of the addict whose mental and physical powers could not function properly without a periodical dose of morphine. However, following up all the cases coming to notice from enquiries based on these instructions, while extremely useful, did not help the Home Office deal practically with dubious prescribers, nor did it help those genuine practitioners who were in doubt about how to respond to addict patients. This was why Delevingne still favoured 'an authoritative announcement by a representative committee'.

Whether this reply changed Smith Whitaker's mind is not clear but a note in Delevingne's hand, on the file copy of the letter of 19 November, records that he had discussed the matter with Smith Whitaker and McCleary on 28 November 1923 when it had been agreed that a committee would be appointed, either by the Home Office or the Ministry of Health. Smith Whitaker had produced some draft terms of reference, which seemed 'adequate' and would now consult the Chief Medical Officer, Sir George Newman.

It was not until 14 May 1924 that Smith Whitaker again wrote to the Home Office, apologising for the matter having been 'so much delayed'. Newman was 'much opposed to some of the lines originally suggested for dealing with the difficulty of the supply of morphine to morphine addicts'. Presumably his opposition was to the proposal to proceed by 'case law', but he liked the idea of a reference to a committee. If Delevingne agreed, which of course he had done with Smith Whitaker six months earlier, Newman would recommend that a committee be established. The first signs of Delevingne's impatience emerged in the minute on 20 May in which he sought Sir John Anderson's agreement:

The terms of reference are not quite as wide as I should have liked – but they are sufficient to achieve our main object, which is to obtain an authoritative statement as to the circumstances in which, and the conditions under which morphine should be supplied, if at all, to addicts – and as it has taken so long (more than a year) to bring the Ministry of Health to this point, we had better accept quickly what they offer and be thankful.

The following day Delevingne wrote to Smith Whitaker confirming Home Office agreement to the establishment of a committee, and acceptance, with one or two minor textual amendments, of the proposed terms of reference. In this letter he proposed that the committee should also be asked to take heroin addiction into consideration but he did not mention cocaine, as Perrins had suggested to him. (Perrins had also favoured an investigation into the causes and nature of addiction.) On 29 July 1924, having heard nothing more from Smith Whitaker, Delevingne wrote to L. G. Brock, an Assistant Under-Secretary of State at the Ministry of Health, asking if he could do something 'to expedite the matter and if possible get a decision as to the appointment of the Committee before the (parliamentary) Recess'. Brock replied, on 31 July, that he had not yet received Smith Whitaker's proposals but was expecting to do so within a couple of days. The Departmental Committee on Morphine and Heroin Addiction was formally appointed by the Minister of Health, John Wheatley, on 30 September 1924, over two years since Delevingne has first sought expert medical advice from the Ministry.

If this is how the surviving papers show the Rolleston Committee came into being, others have seen its origins in a different light. To Berridge,[70] Delevingne was determined to follow 'a policy aimed at penalising addicts and doctors alike' and to stop maintenance prescribing. She interprets his straightforward requests to the Ministry of Health to whom he naturally turned for an 'authoritative pronouncement made on the subject (treatment by diminishing doses) and generally on the treatment of drug addicts' as arising from his 'reluctant recognition' that it was 'impossible to exclude doctors from the structure of control and from the formulation of policy' with the Ministry of Health acting as 'an important mediator of the professional view' and it was not really advice he was seeking, but 'validation' of his already determined policy.

It was not the Home Office which persuaded the Ministry of Health to set up the Rolleston Committee.[71] It was, in fact, Smith Whitaker's idea, a year after the rejection of Delevingne's suggestion that the Royal College of Physicians be asked to appoint a committee to examine the problem. And it is a little difficult to accept polite enquiries about the current state of play, after a delay of a year, as 'pressure' being put on the Ministry of Health.

At least one other commentator has seen the establishment of the Rolleston Committee rather differently from Berridge. Parssinen[72] notes that its purpose was primarily to find an answer to 'a small but persistent problem' of doctors who prescribed large amounts of narcotic drugs for addicts without in any way trying to 'cure' them, and of doctor-addicts who prescribed for themselves. Parssinen was fully seized of the practical problems with which Delevingne was dealing: namely, the inability to deprive doctors of their rights to obtain or supply drugs unless they could be convicted of an offence under the Dangerous Drugs Act and, because of the lack of any clear definition of 'medical treatment', the virtual impossibility of mounting a successful prosecution. However, Parssinen has also seen the appointment of the Committee as 'a small defeat for Delevingne in the guerrilla wars of bureaucracy'. But Parssinen at least concedes that although Delevingne may have been unable to secure the definitive medico-legal opinion he sought, his 'attempts to influence the Committee members were limited to laying the problems before them and steering them away from controversial and expensive solutions'. These 'solutions' included the extension of the Inebriates' Act to embrace addicts, and legislation for their involuntary incarceration.

## The Rolleston Report: the authoritative statement of the treatment of addiction

The Rolleston Committee's main conclusion,[73] well known and generally accepted as laying the foundations of the British system, was:

> There are two groups of persons suffering from addiction to whom the administration of morphine and heroin may be regarded as legitimate medical treatment, namely:
>
> (a) Those who are undergoing treatment for cure of addiction by the gradual withdrawal method;
>
> (b) Persons for whom, after every effort has been made for the cure of the addiction, the drug cannot be completely withdrawn, either because:
>
> (i) Complete withdrawal produces serious symptoms which cannot be satisfactorily treated under the ordinary conditions of private practice; or where
>
> (ii) a patient, who while capable of leading a useful and fairly normal life so long as he takes a certain non-progressive quantity, usually small, of the drug of addiction, ceases to be able to do so when the regular allowance is withdrawn.

This is, of course, the authoritative statement Delevingne had been seeking. It is also significant, in view of his alleged anti-medical bias, that it was not accompanied in the Committee's Report by any criticism of the way in which the Home Office had acted in the preceding years.

Apart from the extension of record-keeping to non-dispensing practitioners, there were three other important recommendations in the Rolleston Report, one of which is not usually mentioned in commentaries on the work of this important Committee. (The other recommendations – the establishment of a medical tribunal to consider cases of dubious prescribing and the closure of a loophole in the Regulations exploited by Dr Connor – are discussed later.) In the Home Office memorandum of evidence Delevingne had drawn the Committee's attention to the fact that the Regulations to the 1920 Dangerous Drugs Act did not expressly provide that a prescription given by a duly qualified medical practitioner should be given only for *bona fide* medical purposes, as was clearly the intention of Parliament. The Committee took the point and in paragraph 76 of its Report recommended that the Regulations should explicitly provide that 'a prescription for Dangerous Drugs shall not be given except, *bona fide*, for medical purposes.' This proposal was given effect in the Dangerous Drugs Regulations, 1926 (S.I.996).

Delevingne was perfectly content with the Rolleston Committee's report and does not appear to have regarded it as 'a defeat'. In a minute to Sir John Anderson on 22 February 1926 he welcomed it as 'an admirable and important report'. Not only would it 'furnish a standard of professional conduct to which the practitioner in treating such cases, can be expected to conform' but the recommendations would strengthen the administration of the Dangerous Drugs Acts, particularly in respect of medical practitioners who 'cannot safely be trusted with the possession and use of the drugs or the treatment of persons addicted to the drugs'.

There is nothing in the papers describing the events which led to the appointment of the Rolleston committee which supports an implication that Delevingne had some hidden agenda. Throughout he was entirely consistent; he needed a clear interpretation of what constituted legitimate medical practice and, as his response to Adam's review of the literature demonstrated, was quite content once he had received the authoritative advice he sought. What, perhaps, he failed to appreciate was that the problem could not be resolved simply by the drawing up of a set of rules, against which an individual prescriber's conduct could be judged, or that there was no medical body with the necessary authority to make rules which would be binding on medical practitioners.[74]

# 2

# Monitoring the British system

The Rolleston Committee may have gone a long way towards resolving some of Sir Malcolm Delevingne's difficulties but how was the Home Office, responsible for administering the 1920 Dangerous Drugs Act and the 1921 Regulations, to ensure that its guidance would be followed and what was to be the response when it was not? Clearly, it was important that the detailed advice and guidance should be brought to the attention of doctors generally. Both *The Lancet* and the *British Medical Journal* on 27 February 1926[1] published extracts from the Committee's Report, with the latter commenting:

> The whole report is a document of great medical interest and should be read by all practitioners whose work brings them in contact with these distressing cases of drug addiction. It has also sociological aspects which deserve close study.

But not every practising doctor was an avid reader of the medical press, far less of such specialist reports. It was equally important that the arrangements for monitoring the medical use of dangerous drugs should speedily identify those cases where some form of intervention appeared necessary.

## Home Office Memorandum DD 101

In March 1929 extracts from the Rolleston Report, paragraphs 50–60, dealing with the precautions to be observed in the administration of morphine and heroin both in the treatment of addicts and in ordinary medical practice, were reprinted in a new (3rd) edition of the 'Memorandum as to the Duties of Doctors and Dentists', numbered DD 101. This short memorandum had first been produced in 1921 by the Home Office, in consultation with the Ministry of Health, to explain to doctors and dentists the main requirements of the 1920 Dangerous Drugs Act. The first edition had been reprinted in the Supplement to the *British Medical Journal* on 27 August 1921 with a second edition, in July 1923, going to *The Times*, the *Morning Star* and *Manchester Guardian* newspapers, in addition to the medical and dental press. Between 1921 and 1961 nine editions of DD 101 were published and distributed to doctors, usually by Regional Medical Officers in the course of their routine visits. However, in 1961 the Interdepartmental Committee on Drug Addiction, in its first report,[2] considered the 'essential features could be presented in a more readable form', which effectively saw its demise.

Although the earlier editions of DD 101 had explained that a doctor's authority to use dangerous drugs was limited to 'ministering to the strictly medical … needs of his patients', it is the 4th edition, published in May 1938, which is particularly important in the context of the 'British system'. This included, for the first time, the statement that 'the continued supply of drugs to a patient if solely for the gratification of addiction is not regarded as medical need'. Why, and by whom, this additional clarification was felt necessary is not clear but it appeared in the draft of the memorandum, sent to the Ministry of Health for comments, which suggests it originated in the Home Office. It is, however, possible that the seed may have been sown by R. H. Crooke of the Ministry of Health some years earlier when, in a comment on Delevingne's draft amendment to Regulation 5 of the 1920 Act to give effect to the Rolleston Committee's recommendation that it should be made quite clear a prescription for dangerous drugs should be given only for *bona fide* medical purposes, he wrote:[3]

> I should like to add that medical treatment does not include gratification (vide South African legislation) but I suppose we cannot go as far as that, as the Rolleston Report makes it clear that cases exist when it may be legitimate to prescribe continuously for an addict in non-diminishing doses.

But whatever the origin, it has to be remembered that neither this 1938 'clarification', nor the editions of DD 101 in which it appeared, ever had any statutory authority. This is important because the failure to appreciate that guidance in an administrative memorandum does not have the force of law is responsible for some of the misunderstanding of the British system. More than one American commentator has fallen into the trap of describing DD 101 as the 'regulations' upon which our post-Rolleston approach was founded.[4]

The establishment of effective monitoring arrangements to ascertain whether both the spirit and the letter of the law were being observed was less straightforward. Not only was it necessary to ensure that all patients receiving regular or large supplies of drugs were readily identified, there had also to be some means, acceptable to the medical profession, of enquiring into the reasons for those supplies. Patients who needed drugs because they were suffering from some painful organic disease or injury were obviously of little further interest. But, if the patient was addicted, was the supplying or prescribing doctor in complete control of the case and following the principles set out by the Rolleston Committee? Furthermore, if the addict was a doctor, was the doctor prepared to stop obtaining drugs on their own authority and agree to place themself under a colleague's care? For this monitoring, the Home Office has relied primarily on three agencies: its own Drugs Inspectorate; the police; and the Regional Medical Officer service of the Ministry (now Department) of Health.

## The Home Office Drugs Inspectorate

In one of the few published references to the origins of the Inspectorate, Smart[5] said 'an Inspectorate to check on prescribing practices of doctors and to issue licences for the prescribing of scheduled drugs was established' after the publication of the second report of the Interdepartmental Committee on Drug Addiction in 1965.[6] She was wrong by almost 50 years.

The origins of the Drugs Inspectorate are to be found in 1916 when, in December of that year, a temporary administrative assistant in the Home Office, A. J. Anderson, was authorised by the Secretary of State to inspect the records with regard to cocaine which pharmacists were required to keep under DORA 40B. The reason for a civil servant being given authority to inspect records was the belief that from time to time it might be necessary to make special enquiries, probably involving medical practitioners, for which it would be better not to employ the police. The Ministry of Health was not created until 1919 so that there was no appropriate medical agency at the time to make such enquiries.

The Dangerous Drugs Act 1920 came into force in September of that year. It was agreed in July 1921 with the Ministry of Health, that Anderson and Frank Thornton (who had transferred to the Home Office from the Board of Trade where he had been dealing with the issue of export licences for cocaine and opium under DORA 40B) would be responsible for the inspections required under the Act. There do not appear to be any surviving papers setting out their job description but, in a memorandum of 18 June 1922, prepared in connection with a claim for subsistence allowances, Anderson[7] wrote:

> The work of the Inspectors under the Dangerous Drugs Act will not be confined to visits to factories and commercial undertakings. It will be necessary when making inspections in the provinces to interview Chief Constables and police officers of high rank with regard to that part of the inspection under the Acts carried out by them, to call on Clerks of County Councils with reference to the inspection by certifying authorities of registers of purchases kept by midwives, to see from time to time other officials, such as Customs officials, and to visit hospitals and laboratories and places of research or instruction attached to Universities, University Colleges, Medical Schools and similar institutions.

A year earlier, in June 1921, it was thought that the work arising from the new dangerous drugs legislation would be heavy only in the initial stages, as a Treasury official commented:

> There is little question I suppose that some of this work will continue, but surely its

volume will diminish when the drug craze, or at any rate the public outcry against it, becomes less violent.

In December 1926 Sir Malcolm Delevingne submitted proposals to the Treasury to modify the inspection arrangements in the light of the six years' experience in the operation of the 1920 Dangerous Drugs Act, and the changes that would be necessary with the coming into operation of the 1925 Geneva Convention (in September 1928).[8] The Convention required all persons engaged in the licit trade in narcotics to be licensed and to keep records of all transactions, and all imports and exports of the drugs to receive the approval of the government of both the importing and exporting countries. It further required that a Permanent Central Opium Board be created to review the course of international trade and to which signatories of the Convention were required to submit detailed statistics of their production, sales, imports and exports of narcotics. The Convention also extended international controls over coco leaves and Indian hemp (cannabis).

Sir Malcolm described the duties of the Inspectors as: inspection of persons licensed under Regulations to the 1920 Act; advising on the grant of licences; the issue of export licences; the examination and checking of the (statistical) returns collected annually for the information of the League of Nations; miscellaneous work in connection with the administration of the Act; in special cases, inspection of doctors' records (in this Medical Officers of the Ministry of Health would give assistance) and of chemists' records (which would normally be inspected by the police).

By May 1933 there was recognition at senior administrative level in the Home Office that the work of inspection called for expertise and continuity of experience, as shown by a memorandum[9] describing the intention to create the Drugs Branch and Inspectorate:

> Those of us who have acquired some knowledge of the problem of dangerous drugs are convinced that the work is essentially different from the many other subjects which are dealt with administratively in the Home Office and what we really need is a small group of experts ... We propose therefore that as from the beginning of next year the dangerous drugs work should be entrusted to a small group attached to a division but not forming part of the ordinary administrative system. The head of the group ... will be the chief advisor on the subject to the Home Office, and as required, to other departments and would be generally responsible for the efficient conduct of the business both in its national aspects and to a large extent in its international aspect.

In October 1934 Major W. H. Coles, who had joined the Home Office in 1924, was appointed the first Chief Inspector.

It is probable that the decision to create the Drugs Branch was also influenced by Article 15 of the 1931 International Convention for Limiting the Manufacture and Regulating the Distribution of Narcotic Drugs (the Limitation Convention) which required contracting parties to set up 'a separate administration' to oversee and implement the requirements of the various Conventions. In 1935 the control arrangements in the United Kingdom (UK) were reported to the League of Nations in the *Annual Report on the Traffic in Opium and other Dangerous Drugs*, which noted that 'a branch of the Home Office has been created for the specific purpose of dealing with dangerous drugs'. The report also included the confident assertion that:[10]

> ... all the channels through which dangerous drugs circulate legitimately are open to frequent inspection, and that the addict or would-be trafficker has but little chance of obtaining drugs from such sources without the facts of excessive or remarkable supplies speedily coming to light.

Unfortunately theory and practice do not always coincide and in reality there were few grounds for this optimism for two main reasons. First, given their other responsibilities, two Inspectors were unable to give more than sporadic attention to licensed wholesale suppliers. Second, and more important, the inspection of retail pharmacy records by the police, to whom the task had been entrusted in 1921, was at best haphazard and at worst non-existent. But why were the police given this responsibility, which in most other countries is discharged by specialist pharmacist inspectors?

## Inspection of pharmacy records by the police

In May 1917, following a review of the operation of DORA 40B, and at the request of the police, 'officers of police of a rank not below that of an inspector' were authorised to inspect 'all books and records' required to be kept.[11] But they were not asked, or expected, to use this power on a regular basis.

When the 1920 Dangerous Drugs Act Regulations came into force in 1921 the Home Office had only one Inspector, plus an assistant, to oversee the practical application of the new controls. The routine inspection of several thousand retail pharmacies was clearly beyond their capacity and Delevingne had little option but to seek an alternative solution. That he chose to call on the police, which he did by way of a circular letter to chief constables dated 20 August 1921, is perhaps a little surprising, given that the idea of using qualified pharmacists had been suggested by McCleary in a memorandum of 11 June 1919.[12]

In his letter to chief constables, Delevingne[13] explained that the police would be mainly concerned with 'the enforcement of the provisions in regard to supply and possession', but he asked that:

... special attention should be given to the observance of the Regulations which apply to the sales of the drugs to the general public ... chemists are required by Regulation 9 to keep records of their purchases and sales of the drugs, and to preserve the prescriptions which they have dispensed ... the records and prescriptions should be inspected by the police from time to time.

Not surprisingly the imposition of this new duty was not welcomed by the police but Delevingne firmly rejected their representations and made it clear that whatever the difficulties, arrangements had to be made for the records of all chemists to be systematically inspected.

But neither in 1917, nor in 1921, were the police asked specifically to provide the Home Office with details of anyone receiving large or unusual supplies of drugs, although they had been asked to report any cases in which they suspected the requirements of the Regulations were not being observed. This omission suggests that Delevingne was slow to recognise and address the fact that a key element in his control strategy was not functioning.

In April 1932 a meeting of chief constables drew attention to the four Acts, 15 sets of Regulations, Orders and Authorities and 23 Circulars about dangerous drugs that had been issued since 1920 and asked for a handbook to guide their officers through the 'maze'.[14] This suggestion was readily accepted, as such a handbook was said to have been 'in the air for a considerable time past', but in December 1932 the Central Conference of Chief Constables was told that although a draft had been prepared, further imminent changes in the legislation meant it would have to be held over. The Manual of Guidance was eventually distributed on 23 June 1939. It contained notes on offences, a copy of the current Dangerous Drugs Regulations, notes on reading prescriptions and, for the first time, provided the police with guidance on the information from pharmacy registers that should be forwarded to the Home Office for further enquiry.

When the work of the drugs inspectors was reviewed in 1932, in the light of Anderson's retirement, their primary duty became the supervision of the administration of the 1920 Act by the police. Inspectors were now to visit all police forces periodically, and to make certain that each force had an officer 'told off for dangerous drugs work'. The realisation that regular and effective inspections of retail pharmacy records provided the best means of bringing to notice those cases where further action was likely to be necessary was welcome, but persuading the police of this was very much an uphill battle (which was to continue for the next 50 years). Inspectors did what they could to stimulate police interest but their efforts were not visited with conspicuous success as many police forces took only a perfunctory interest in this duty.

The issue of the Manual of Guidance in 1939 did have some beneficial effect but it was not until the post-war years that raising the standard of police inspecting and reporting to an acceptable level again became a high priority. The main problem for the Inspectorate was overcoming two firmly entrenched beliefs of the police, that the inspection of retail pharmacies was an extraneous duty which had nothing to do with 'real' police work, and that as they were dealing with professional men, officers 'could easily be blinded with science'.

In 1963 the Metropolitan Police was persuaded to appoint four detective sergeants as full-time 'chemists officers', which meant that, for the first time, there was effective inspection of retail pharmacies in London. Up until then, dangerous drugs registers were said to be checked twice a year by a senior detective sergeant at each local police station.[15] But effective inspection was not the only benefit. The expertise which the 'chemists officers' rapidly acquired was passed on by way of lectures to police training courses and by the temporary attachment of officers from provincial forces to Scotland Yard. This led to a dramatic improvement throughout the country in the standard of inspecting and reporting. Other forces followed the Metropolitan Police example and by 1986 most had specialist 'chemists officers', usually attached to the force drug squad. This recognised the importance that pharmaceutical preparations diverted from legitimate sources have played, and continue to play, in the UK drug scene.

## Ministry of Health Regional Medical Officers

Once it was brought to the notice of the Drugs Inspectorate that a patient or a medical practitioner was receiving or obtaining large or regular supplies of drugs, it became necessary to determine whether the case was one of 'medical need' or of addiction. The enquiries were usually undertaken by Regional Medical Officers of the Ministry of Health, who, in 1922, had also been authorised to inspect the records required by the 1920 Dangerous Drugs Act and Regulations. The precise arrangement was set out by Smith Whitaker in a letter to Delevingne dated 22 August 1922,[16] in which he agreed that Regional Medical Officers would make enquiries of any doctor or institution particularly requested by the Home Office. They would also inspect the records of a sufficient number of doctors, and with enough frequency, 'to prevent general disregard of the Regulations'. However, it was always understood that Regional Medical Officers would not be asked to undertake any enquiry likely to impair their relationship with general practitioners – for example, if this might involve them in giving evidence in court against a fellow member of their profession. Such enquiries, usually of unco-operative doctor addicts, would be undertaken by Home Office inspectors.

The involvement of Regional Medical Officers in Home Office matters did not please Dr Cox of the British Medical Association. In a letter of 2 January 1923, he expressed his sorrow that inspections were being 'put on the Regional Medical Officers', who already had enough to do and for some of whom this might well prove to be 'the last straw'. But in a phrase with a familiar ring in the 1990s, he supposed 'it was inevitable in the present stage of the economy'. His main objection, however, was that it emphasised 'the official ... and detective side of their duties to the grave disadvantage of the far more important advisory side'. Many National Health Insurance practitioners were already very suspicious of the Regional Medical Officers and their appearance in the role of Inspectors for the Home Office would 'damn them effectively in the eyes of a considerable section of the profession'. Smith Whitaker was quick to let Delevingne know he did not share Cox's forebodings and there is no evidence in Home Office records that Regional Medical Officers encountered any difficulty in conducting their 'detective' enquiries.

In October 1938 the Home Office was informed by the Ministry of Health that, because of a special investigation, it would not be possible for any drug enquiries to be undertaken until the following March. When the position was reviewed, in August 1939, there were no Regional Medical Officers available even for special enquiries and a few months later the service was suspended for the duration of the war. The immediate result of this was an increased burden on Home Office inspectors: in 1939 the Inspectorate made a total of 38 visits to doctors, in the first five months of 1940 one inspector alone visited 63, most of whom had been purchasing drugs regularly or on a large scale. In September 1948, when the Home Office next approached the Ministry of Health, it was agreed that special enquiries by Regional Medical Officers could be made, although routine visits to doctors had not yet been resumed.

By 1952 Regional Medical Officers were seldom involved in drug enquiries, as the Inspectorate had adopted the practice of writing to doctors, in confidence, when pharmacy records showed they had been prescribing dangerous drugs to a patient for a few months. The letter sought the doctor's opinion on whether the case was one of addiction or genuine medical need. This procedure prompted no complaints from the profession and only very rarely did prescribers fail to respond. Even when there was an initial refusal, a follow-up letter explaining the purpose of the enquiry in a little more detail and assuring the doctor that the enquiry was not intended to interfere in any way with the patient's treatment, usually produced the desired information. However, around 1955 this effective, and economical, practice was terminated. It had come to the notice of an Assistant Under-Secretary of State, Sir Austin Strutt, who did not think the Home Office should be approaching doctors in this way. As a result, Regional Medical Officers again became involved and by 1964 were making about 1,500 enquiries annually, a reflection also of the improvement in police examination of pharmacy records.

Neither Home Office Inspectors nor Regional Medical Officers have ever had any authority either to compel doctors to disclose why they were prescribing drugs to a particular patient or to interfere with the way in which they exercised their professional discretion and judgement. The purpose of the enquiry was simply to establish the reason why the patient needed 'dangerous drugs'. If the drugs were being prescribed for the relief of some physically painful condition, that was usually the end of the matter; if the patient was an addict the dosage was kept under review and, if there appeared to have been a significant change, the Regional Medical Officer might be asked to pay the prescriber a further visit.

## Monitoring the prevalence of addiction: the Addicts Index

Changes in the prevalence of addiction are obviously important measures of the effectiveness of the arrangements for monitoring the availability of dangerous drugs. In 1926 the Rolleston Committee considered the evidence from a range of medical witnesses: 'all tended in the same direction … that, in this country, addiction to morphine or heroin is rare' and 'There is also a general concurrence of testimony to the effect that addiction has diminished in recent years'.[17] There was no estimate of the number of addicts in the Home Office memorandum to the Committee.

In February 1931, at the 14th meeting the League Advisory Committee, Sir Malcolm Delevingne referred to a 'register kept at the Home Office (which) showed that only 245 addicts were known to the Government'.[18] This 'register' was probably no more than a list of the personal files kept by the Home Office since the 1920s of addicts coming to notice following visits by Regional Medical Officers to doctors when police inspections of pharmacists' records showed they were prescribing dangerous drugs, as well as of addicts who were discovered by the Drugs Inspectorate.

It was not until 1934 that a central collective record, or index, of addicts known to the Home Office appears to have been kept. It is probable that the impetus was a request from the Opium Advisory Committee of the League of Nations in 1930 to the countries party to the international drug control treaties to include statistics about drug addiction in their annual reports. The Home Office was able to estimate an addict population of 300 in 1934 which was revised to 700 in the following year. It was not until 1937 that the League made it a formal requirement for countries to submit annual statistics of the number of known addicts.

The Drugs Inspectorate was the custodian and principal user of this original Addicts Index. The information recorded in it played a vital part in our efforts to monitor the legitimate use of dangerous drugs in the days when there was no illicit traffic in imported opiates and almost all addicts obtained their supplies from doctors' prescriptions for themselves or someone else. This Index was also the source of the annual addict statistics which, together with the drug offence statistics, were produced by the Inspectorate until 1968 when the responsibility passed to the Home Office Statistical Branch.

The suggestion that the Index had always been partly constructed on the basis of voluntary reporting by doctors of their addict patients to the Inspectorate is misleading.[19] From the beginning, the bulk of the information in the Index came from the police inspections of pharmacists' records and it was not until the dramatic increase in heroin addiction in the early 1960s that reports from doctors made any significant contribution. Even then, only a few of the prescribers told the Inspectorate about their new addict patients before we had already noted their prescriptions. Without exception the prescribers, when approached, were willing to provide some basic descriptive information about their patients.

Despite their obvious imperfections, the arrangements for monitoring the prescribing of dangerous drugs provided a means of building up a reasonably accurate picture of narcotic drug addiction in the UK in the post-Rolleston era. As T. C. Green, then in charge of the Home Office administrative division to which the Inspectorate was attached, explained in a lecture in 1960:[20]

> ... it is true that our sources of information in this country are not as good as those available to the authorities in North America, but we believe that, while it may take us a little longer to find out that a person has become addicted, we do in the long run come to know about the great majority of addicts.

Green's suggestion that North American methods of detecting addicts were better than ours was based on a visit he had recently made to Canada where there was a comprehensive, but very manpower intensive, system for recording and examining all legitimate movements of narcotics.

Until the 1950s, when the character of drug misuse in the UK began to change significantly, it really had not mattered that 'in the long run' could sometimes be as long as 25 years and that some addicts, for the most part therapeutic in origin, were slipping through the net. During the period between the wars, and in the immediate post-second world war years, the numbers of known non-therapeutic addicts, as well as 'professional' addicts (doctors and others with ready access to narcotics – such as pharmacists and nurses) was small.[21]

Another key indicator of the extent of drug misuse, which Green did not mention, was press interest. By 1930, after the excitements of the 1920s, drugs had 'virtually disappeared from the newspapers, then from novels and films, and finally from the public consciousness'.[22] Press reports on dangerous drugs remained negligible until the appearance of cannabis in the late 1940s.

## Dealing with doctor addicts and 'script doctors'

Doctor addicts and 'script doctors', the term used by the Drugs Inspectorate for the generous prescriber, were not always identified by the routine inspections of pharmacy records by the police. Frequently the prescribing behaviour of a doctor addict aroused the suspicions of a concerned pharmacist and many cases were brought to light when the pharmacist suggested to the local police that it was time to inspect his Dangerous Drugs Register. Similarly, the script doctor successors to Dr S. G. Connor (whose prescribing had been described anonymously in the Home Office memorandum to the Rolleston Committee) rarely operated for long before their names became known to the Inspectorate. This was especially true in the 1960s and 1970s, as the Inspectorate's 'early warning system' developed, and we heard from various sources that a new prescriber had appeared. On one occasion an addict telephoned and asked the Inspectorate to do something about a new prescriber, who was taking on so many patients who were not addicted, that the addict was concerned the doctor was 'going to spoil things for we real junkies'.

## Medical tribunals

Having identified problem doctors, how did the Home Office then deal with them? In addition to clarifying what constituted legitimate medical practice in relation to the treatment of addicts, the Rolleston Committee had provided Delevingne with a practical solution to his other two main problems: the doctor addict and the prescriber who was making no attempt to treat his addict patient. The Committee proposed the establishment of a tribunal of three doctors and a legal assessor to judge the medical issues involved in such cases and on whose recommendation the Home Secretary would be able, under Regulation 12 of the 1920 Dangerous Drugs Act, to withdraw from the doctor concerned his authority to possess and supply dangerous drugs.[23]

Berridge has suggested that the original idea for medical tribunals came from the British Medical Association.[24] The minutes of the Rolleston Committee's meetings do not support this view.[25] At the 6th Meeting it was decided to invite Dr Cox, the secretary of the British Medical Association, to attend 'when the Committee were in a position to put before him any administrative measures which might seem to be expedient'. This did not occur until after the 17th Meeting on 8 June 1925, by which time, as the minutes show, the Committee unanimously favoured the establishment of a tribunal independent of the Home Office and any other government department. The tribunal was to deal with:

(a) doctors from whom it was proposed to withdraw their authorisation to be in possession of, to supply and to prescribe dangerous drugs, on the grounds they were addicted;

(b) doctors who committed offences under the Dangerous Drugs Act, where the Home Office desired to withdraw their authorisations 'as an alternative to proceeding in the Courts';

(c) doctors who habitually ordered drugs for patients in circumstances which suggested that the drugs were not being ordered for *bona fide* medical purposes, or where they were being ordered with marked laxity and carelessness, where the Home Office considered the authorisations should be withdrawn.

By its 6th Meeting the Committee had already heard the views of the Director of Public Prosecutions, Sir Archibald Bodkin, who first suggested a possible solution to the problem of doctors who contravened the spirit, if not the letter, of the Dangerous Drugs Act and Regulations. Sir Archibald explained that, as the 1921 Regulations placed no limit on the quantity of drugs a doctor might obtain for use in his medical practice, the difficulty of obtaining legal proof that he was ordering dangerous drugs 'in excess of his *bona fide* professional requirements' would be 'almost insuperable'. Instead, a less drastic course might be to deal with such a case as 'an abuse of authority or breach of trust' under Regulation 12, which allowed the Secretary of State to withdraw the authorisation of anyone who 'cannot properly be allowed to … supply or be in possession' of the drugs. However, as this power could be exercised only after a conviction for an offence against the Dangerous Drugs Act, an amendment of the Regulations would be necessary if this suggestion were to be followed. Sir Archibald believed 'such a power might well have a very deterrent effect, even if only put into force occasionally', but he thought it might be advisable 'to provide some kind of tribunal to whom appeal might be made by a doctor whose authority it is proposed to withdraw'.

Although it was the doctor addict rather than the careless prescriber Sir Archibald had in his sights, the Committee obviously saw his suggestion as also offering a possible solution to the problem presented by the indiscriminate prescribers whose activities had been brought to its attention. But if there was any detailed discussion of the proposal, as seems probable, it is not recorded in the minutes. A memorandum setting out the Committee's proposals was prepared and sent to the British Medical Association (BMA) seeking their views. Dr Cox and other BMA representatives attended the meeting on 11 July 1925 and the agreed record of their evidence shows that they 'supported' the proposal that a medical tribunal should be established to deal with doctors whose authorisation to supply and possess drugs it was proposed to withdraw on the grounds set out in the Committee's memorandum. If withdrawal of authorisation was recommended by a tribunal constituted in the manner proposed, the BMA believed it would be preferable to proceedings in a court or before the General Medical Council.[26]

However, the BMA was not in favour of the Committee's further recommendation that the Home Secretary's power under Regulation 12 should be extended to cover the right to prescribe dangerous drugs. The basis of their objection was that, if exercised, this additional power would preclude a doctor from carrying on his practice and it was therefore a step which should only be taken after reference to the General Medical Council. While the BMA's concern for the patients of a doctor addict who was practising alone or in some remote rural area, was understandable the Committee saw the proposal as offering an unacceptable loophole:[27]

> … the object of the withdrawal, as regards protection of the community, would obviously not be achieved if he were still permitted to prescribe, and so enable supplies to be obtained in cases in which they were not medically needed.

Leaving aside the question of the inevitable delay while the Council reached a conclusion, and whether its view would be binding on the Secretary of State, under the BMA's proposal, doctor addicts would have still been able to obtain their drugs by the simple expedient of writing prescriptions in their own or their patients' names. A script doctor would also have been able to continue to prescribe while the Council was deliberating.

That the Rolleston Committee were right to reject the BMA's proposal was demonstrated almost immediately after their report was published, in February 1926. Dr S. G. Connor was convicted in March 1926 of failing to enter details of purchases of morphine in a register, and failing to specify the patient's address on a prescription. He was sentenced to two months' imprisonment and a £50 fine on each of his three record-keeping offences as reported in *The Times* newspaper on 30 March 1926. Although the subject of a Withdrawal Notice in the *London Gazette* of 23 April 1926, Connor continued to issue prescriptions for his flock of addict patients. Furthermore, as the Regulations to implement the Committee's recommendations had not yet been finalised, the Home Office, after consultation with the Director of Public Prosecutions, referred the facts to the General Medical Council. The Council found that the charges of indiscriminate prescribing for addicts had not been proved to their satisfaction and decided that the very fact that he had been convicted of a record-keeping offence was severe enough punishment and placed him on probation for a year.

But having provided, in the 1926 Dangerous Drugs Regulations, the statutory basis for the establishment of the tribunal, and arranged for the nomination of tribunal members by the General Medical Council and other bodies, the Home Office, for the next 25 years, chose not to use the machinery either for doctor addicts or script doctors. This is both surprising and puzzling, as Delevingne had told the Rolleston Committee that the case of the doctor addicted to drugs was 'perhaps the most difficult with which the Home Office has to deal' and he had been equally troubled by the activities of doctors like Connor.

There is no ready explanation for why, after asking for assistance from the Rolleston Committee, the Home Office then seemingly rejected the solution proffered. The answer cannot lie entirely in the small number of cases considered to be suitable for reference to a tribunal, as suggested by the Interdepartmental

Committee on Drug Addiction in 1961 when recommending 'that such special tribunals should not be set up in this country'.[28]

## Withdrawal of a doctor's authority to prescribe dangerous drugs

If there was a reluctance to use the tribunal option, how did the Home Office deal with the doctor addict? The pre-1924 approach had been set out clearly in paragraph 8 of the Home Office memorandum to the Rolleston Committee:[29]

> When a case of this kind comes to the notice of the Home Office arrangements are made for the practitioner to be seen by one of the Medical Officers of the Ministry of Health or Scottish Board of Health, and in a number of cases the Department has succeeded, with the help of the Medical Officer, in inducing the addict either to go into an institution or to place himself unreservedly in the hands of a brother practitioner for treatment. It has been pointed out to such practitioners that they are not authorised by the Regulations to obtain drugs for the purpose of indulging in a drug habit, and that in doing so they are committing an offence against the Acts for which they are liable to a severe penalty. In one or two clear cases where the offence continued the Home Office has been successful in securing a conviction, but such cases are usually difficult to deal with and the Home Office would welcome any recommendations from the Committee on the point.

It was when this approach failed and it became necessary to consider withdrawing the doctor addict's authority to possess and supply dangerous drugs under Regulation 12 that difficulties arose. The Rolleston Committee fully endorsed Withdrawal of Authority as being 'specially valuable in the interest of the practitioner himself',[30] but as Sir Archibald Bodkin had reminded them, this could not be done until the doctor had been convicted of an offence against the Dangerous Drugs Act. Unfortunately, from the doctors' point of view, prosecution exposed them to the risk that the court would impose a severe penalty which was 'in the majority of cases neither necessary nor desired'.[31]

The reference in Delevingne's memorandum to 'one or two' successful convictions is a little misleading, as it is quite clear that by 1924 the Secretary of State was regularly using his Regulation 12 powers. By the time the Rolleston Committee was appointed in September 1924 nine Withdrawal Notices had been issued. These Notices do not give the reasons for the Secretary of State's action, and the original case papers have long since been destroyed, but it is more than likely that all the Notices related to doctor addicts or addicts employed in other professions, such as pharmacists and veterinary surgeons, with ready access to dangerous drugs. It is also highly probable that the Notices followed successful prosecutions for technical offences, such as the failure to maintain proper records. With the memory of the furore created by his unsuccessful attempt in 1922 to make it a statutory offence for doctors to prescribe dangerous drugs for themselves, and the opinion of the Director of Public Prosecutions that the chances of mounting a successful prosecution on the basis of the Home Office interpretation of the limits of a doctor's authority to prescribe were negligible, it seems doubtful that Delevingne would have risked further failure in the courts.

Prosecution was always seen as the last resort, to be used when all other options had failed, or in a few instances where it was obvious from the outset that the doctor addict was not prepared to co-operate. In the majority of cases, once it had been established that a doctor was obtaining drugs to sustain his or her own addiction, it was unnecessary to contemplate such drastic action, as most doctor addicts, having admitted their addiction, although invariably over-confident that they could 'give it up tomorrow', were only too willing to seek independent medical help.

But, in my experience, confirming that the drugs doctors were obtaining were for their own, and not their patients', use was often difficult and sometimes impossible. Many and varied were the explanations offered by doctor addicts over the years for their regular purchases of drugs. Two of the most original came from an eminent physician and a Harley Street bacteriologist, both of whom were obtaining appreciable amounts of heroin. The physician claimed he was treating cancer patients with the juice of strawberries into which he had previously injected heroin, although in those far-off days when freezers and frozen foods were virtually unknown, he could not explain what happened to his patients when strawberries were out of season. The bacteriologist was supposedly using solutions of heroin as culture media. Having failed, as had others before me, to confirm our suspicions, I was somewhat taken aback to be told by Frank Thornton, then Chief Inspector, who knew the physician through a shared interest in motor racing at Brooklands, that 'everyone knows he's been addicted for years'.

There were no time constraints on the Secretary of State's exercise of his Regulation 12 powers and once convicted, the doctor's authority could be withdrawn at once, or at any time in the future. Similarly, it could be restored temporarily or permanently at any time; if restored temporarily (by 'suspension' of the *London Gazette* Notice) it could again be removed if the doctor relapsed into addiction, without the need for a further conviction.

In 1957 a review of the operation of the Withdrawal provisions showed that in the majority of cases, doctors' authorities had been withdrawn immediately after conviction but in a small number there had been an interval of over a year before this happened. As a result, it was decided that a decision for or against withdrawal should be taken, as far as possible, within one year and, at most, within two years of the conviction. While this was undoubtedly an acceptable administrative arrangement, it created a number of practical problems, not least for doctor addicts, who, if they relapsed three years after a first conviction, could be prosecuted again. This exposed them to the risk of a heavier penalty and the possibility that the General Medical Council would take a more serious view of a second conviction. From the Inspectorate's point of view it meant that if a doctor had not learned from an earlier experience it would be virtually impossible to obtain the evidence upon which to base a second successful prosecution.

The prosecution of doctor addicts for record-keeping offences presented other problems. The most important was the possibility that, after the 1948 Criminal Justice Act, the court, while convicting the doctor, might nevertheless impose a penalty which did not allow the Secretary of State to withdraw the doctor's authority. Under the terms of Section 12 (2) of this Act, the conviction of any offender who was placed on probation or given an absolute or conditional discharge, was to be 'disregarded for the purposes of any enactment which imposes any disqualification or disability upon convicted persons, or authorises or requires the imposition of any such disqualification or disability'. Conditional discharges and probation were likely penalties as, apart from regarding record-keeping offences as 'technical', the court tended to take into account the fact that the doctor would later have to appear before the General Medical Council. Yet if a court convicted and fined the doctor as little as £1 this was a penalty which allowed statutory disqualifications. Unfortunately, magistrates were rarely aware of this and as a result it was occasionally necessary, with a particularly unco-operative doctor addict, to bring a second prosecution which could attract a more severe penalty.

There was a further problem. Most of the early doctor addicts were convicted of failing to keep a register and/or of failing to enter the required details of purchases or supplies of drugs. These were straightforward 'black and white' offences, which it was difficult for the doctor to contest. But over the years, and especially as a result of changes in medical practice following the introduction of the National Health Service in 1948, there was a gradual change in doctor addicts' *modus operandi*. This saw them diverting to their own use, drugs which they had prescribed on NHS prescription forms to patients who would usually be too ill or infirm to testify in court that they had not received the drugs ostensibly prescribed for them, so that it was a difficult offence to prove. In 1947 the Divisional Court confirmed that a doctor who obtained drugs in this way was committing an offence against the Dangerous Drugs Act.[32]

There also remained the difficulty in such cases of persuading the police to charge the doctor with this offence because, from their viewpoint, a charge of obtaining drugs by deception or false pretences had an important advantage because it counted as 'cleared up' in their crime statistics, whereas a conviction for an offence against the Dangerous Drugs Act did not. Unfortunately it was only the latter conviction which allowed the Secretary of State to withdraw the doctor's authority.

**Undertakings**

As an alternative to prosecution, doctor addicts would often be first asked by the Inspectorate to give a formal Undertaking, which had no legal status, that in future they would not obtain any dangerous drugs on their own authority, they would not take possession of any drugs they prescribed for patients, and any drugs required for their own consumption would be prescribed for them by another named practitioner. Undertakings were usually considered when it was felt that prosecution of a doctor addict was not justified – for example, if the doctor readily agreed to seek help or when the evidence upon which to base proceedings was inadequate or, as in the case of the Drs Boddy, inconclusive.

There were variations of the basic conditions. For example, in rare instances the Undertaking might allow doctors in single-handed rural practices to obtain supplies in an emergency, provided they then reported the circumstances to the Home Office. Occasionally a recently convicted doctor could be offered the opportunity of giving an Undertaking as an alternative to Withdrawal of Authority to prescribe dangerous drugs. The Undertaking procedure, first used in 1922, shows the Home Office concern for the doctor's welfare and rehabilitation, contradicting the belief that it was more interested in punishing the wayward doctor addict.

Home Office policy for dealing with doctor addicts was reviewed in 1953 in consultation with the Ministry of Health. This was apparently prompted by the interest being shown by the UN Narcotics Commission in treatment and care issues. As our representative on the Commission, J. H. Walker, was 'uncomfortably aware' that in the UK we relied on general impressions, he asked for our current practices and policy to be examined.

The review reaffirmed the Undertaking procedure. The general conclusion, as Walker commented in March 1954 to Hossick, Chief of the Division of Narcotic Control in Ottawa, was that no evidence had been thrown up to suggest that the policy was wrong or misguided in any particular respect.[33] Despite having no legal force, the procedure was considered to offer advantages for both the Home Office and the doctor addict. For the former, the extent to which a doctor had or had not honoured an Undertaking provided useful information when decisions had to be reached on whether the doctor's authority to prescribe should be withdrawn or restored. For the doctor, its existence could in some instances, be a strong deterrent to a relapse into addiction, as I was told in 1968 by a doctor nominated for a heroin prescribing licence, who had given, and strictly observed, an Undertaking given some 20 years earlier. On the other hand, it could have little effect, as in the case of the doctor who came to the Home Office to see Frank Thornton, signed two copies of an Undertaking and, before returning to Scotland, obtained four supplies of morphine from London pharmacies on 'signed orders' written on the back of his copy.

### The Bonnyman case

But just as many lay addicts cannot be induced to accept professional help, so the Withdrawal of doctor addicts' authority to prescribe dangerous drugs did not always guarantee they would accept the seriousness of their position and place themselves under treatment. This, and a number of the points made above, are well illustrated in the case of Dr Bonnyman, undoubtedly the worst case of professional addiction in Home Office records. Again, the personal files have not survived but much of the story can be put together from press reports and what I recall being told about it by Frank Thornton.

Alexander Gordon Bonnyman first came to Home Office notice in 1931 when his large purchases of morphine attracted attention. In May 1932 he was prosecuted for 'register offences' and admitted his addiction but, as the court merely bound him over to receive treatment in a nursing home, it was not possible for the Home Secretary to withdraw his authority to possess and supply dangerous drugs. In August 1934 he was again prosecuted for similar offences. On this occasion he was fined £10 and his authority to prescribe was promptly withdrawn. He then resorted to obtaining morphine by forged prescriptions which his wife presented at pharmacies. When Bonnyman himself attempted to do so he was prosecuted and sentenced to eight months' imprisonment for unlawful possession of morphine.

In 1940 Bonnyman applied for the restoration of his authority to prescribe dangerous drugs and, after taking appropriate medical advice, the Home Secretary agreed that the Withdrawal order should be suspended. That this was an unwise decision soon became apparent as further purchases of morphine by Bonnyman were reported. He was first given the option of signing an Undertaking, which he promptly broke and the Suspension Order was therefore cancelled. He then acted as locum for other doctors in various parts of the country, often forging their names on prescriptions. He also obtained morphine in the form of uncontrolled preparations containing less than 0.2% morphine which he and his wife then concentrated before injecting.

In April 1941 the Bonnymans' house in London was damaged in an air raid and Mrs Bonnyman was found in a very dirty and neglected condition. She was moved to a neighbour's house where Dr Bonnyman called frequently to give her injections, which he said were for treating anaemia. She was eventually admitted to hospital where she died. At the time of her death Mrs Bonnyman weighed 52 pounds with the cause of death recorded as heart failure from bronchial pneumonia, due to undernourishment and chronic morphine poisoning.

Bonnyman was charged with her manslaughter by negligence and appeared at the Central Criminal Court on 27/28 April 1942. His defence was that he had tried to break his wife's morphine addiction but she would not allow him to give her any attention whatsoever. He was found guilty and sentenced to 12 months' imprisonment, which he unsuccessfully appealed. His name was subsequently erased from the Medical Register.[34] Twenty years later he successfully applied to the General Medical Council for restoration to the Register and his authority to possess and supply dangerous drugs was also restored. He gave rise to no further concern.

## Doctor addicts and General Medical Council health procedures

Nowadays, in contrast to the many years when doctor addicts and others of the 'professional classes' (nurses, pharmacists etc.) accounted for around 20% of the known addict population, doctor addicts present few problems for the Drugs Inspectorate. This is not because doctors no longer misuse drugs but because in 1980 the General Medical Council introduced procedures for rehabilitating doctors whose fitness to practise was seriously impaired by a physical or mental condition, including alcoholism and drug addiction.[35] Under these procedures, which can be set in motion by 'concerned colleagues … hospitals or health authorities, the police, pharmacists, patients and others', the Council, in addition to requiring doctors to accept medical supervision, can impose conditions upon their registration for up to three years, or suspend it for up to 12 months. As the conditions can include restrictions on doctors' professional practice, for example, in relation to the prescribing of certain drugs, these 'health procedures' can achieve the same result as a Withdrawal of Authority order.

## Dealing with 'script' doctors

Prosecution for record-keeping offences was the usual Home Office response to unco-operative doctor addicts and was also the preferred means for dealing with 'script' doctors. But this solution was only available for doctors who both prescribed and dispensed dangerous drugs. Script doctors who merely prescribed the drugs were in no danger of prosecution. The only course open would have been to refer the details of their prescribing to a medical tribunal, as the Rolleston Committee had recommended; but that procedure was never invoked.

Although it is not now possible to be certain about the chronology, probably the first of the script doctors to emerge after Connor was Dr Albert Edwin Tait, whose purchases of morphine had first attracted attention in 1927. When seen by a Regional Medical Officer he refused to name the patient he was supplying. At the time he was practising from poorly furnished premises above a shop in the Harrow Road but his move to the West End of London a few years later was accompanied by a corresponding improvement in his economic circumstances. By then he had acquired about a dozen addict patients, for some of whom he had prescribed morphine immediately on their release from prison.

Some of Tait's patients were members of a small group who frequented certain well-known night clubs in the West End of London and who sniffed heroin at 'snuff parties'. The heroin usually came from France, often sent by post but also obtained by various members of the group known to make frequent visits to Paris. One of these was Gerald O'Brien, a well-known West End figure who, according to Frank Thornton, was the originator of the 'bottle party', a scheme to circumvent the licensing laws. On 1 July 1937 O'Brien arrived at Newhaven on the ferry from Dieppe and was found by Customs officers to be in possession of 96 grains (5.7 grams) of heroin. He was subsequently sentenced to six months' imprisonment and the Prison Medical Officer confirmed that O'Brien had been sniffing heroin for some months and was addicted.

Gradually, other members of this closely knit circle began to find 'sympathetic' doctors willing to 'treat' them with generous prescriptions. While the exact size of the group was never known, it is doubtful if it exceeded 20–25 and its members were, on average, slightly older than the heroin addicts of the post-war years. They were also, as recently confirmed for me by a doctor who had treated some of them, of 'a higher social class', although several were employed as dance hostesses in the West End clubs. One of them was still receiving regular prescriptions for morphine in 1994.

Cannabis also circulated within this circle. Len Dyke, who was to transfer from the Metropolitan Police to the Drugs Inspectorate in 1941 and become Chief Inspector in 1956, had been responsible for the conviction of Bella Gold (reported in *The Times* newspaper of 11 October 1937) and Freda Roberts (reported in *The Times* newspaper of 13 October 1938) for possessing small quantities of cannabis. Both were addicted to heroin and were patients of Dr Tait, who paid the fine imposed on Roberts. Dyke knew Roberts well and described her as 'the toast of the West End'. She was living with O'Brien at the time of his arrest and was subsequently married for a brief period to the singer Al Bowlly. Some 20 years later she was to come to notice as a patient of Lady Frankau.

In the mid-1930s another small group of heroin addicts in Chelsea had gathered round Brenda Dean Paul who has been described as 'the first non-posthumous celebrity addict in Britain'.[36] She was the most well-known London addict of the time and her personal file at the Home Office ran to 97 sub-numbers. Her not infrequent court appearances were usually reported by *The Times*, perhaps because her father, Sir Aubrey, was the 5th baronet. Except for brief periods when she claimed to have been cured, as described in the *Sunday Dispatch* newspaper of 29 April 1951, she received regular prescriptions for morphine and cocaine until her death in 1958. At that time, her cocaine supply averaged 70 grains (4,200mgms) daily, although it was not unknown for her to 'share' some of this with other addicts.

The Chelsea group contributed to the 'most significant admissions' to Spelthorne St Mary, where the Sisters of the Community of St Mary the Virgin had been treating female alcoholics and drug addicts since 1879.[37] Such contacts as there were between the pre-war groups of London heroin addicts probably arose through their meeting at various doctors' surgeries and at the two 24-hour pharmacies, Boots in Piccadilly Circus and John Bell and Croyden in Wigmore Street, where most of their prescriptions were dispensed.

In February 1939 Tait was interviewed by Frank Thornton and charged with offences of failing to record purchases of dangerous drugs. He subsequently pleaded guilty and was fined £20, as reported in *The Times* newspaper of 27 May 1939. This conviction enabled the Home Secretary to withdraw Tait's authority to possess and supply dangerous drugs, and to direct that he should no longer be able to prescribe them, as published in the *London Gazette* of 2 June 1939.

A successful prosecution for a record-keeping offence also provided the answer to the generous prescribing of Dr Joseph Hirschman, who, over a short space of time in 1935, had acquired a small number of morphine addicts as patients, all of whom lived considerable distances from his practice in Maida Vale. Len Dyke, then still with the Metropolitan Police, had interviewed him and described him as 'one of the worst script doctors known to us'. Hirschman was convicted and fined on 25 February 1936. A Withdrawal of Authority Notice was published in the *London Gazette* on 6 March 1936; the short interval since his conviction was a clear indication of the seriousness with which his prescribing was viewed in the Home Office. The real reason for the proceedings did not escape the *Morning Advertiser* newspaper, which reported on 26 February 1936 that:

> ... the importance of the prosecution was that the doctor was known to be treating a number of drug addicts and it was clear from the information in the possession of the authorities that he was not dealing with these addicts as he should. The prosecution had prescriptions to show that the doctor, rather than reduce the dose of drugs, had been in a number of cases increasing the dose in a short space of a few months, one grain being increased to seven or ten grains.

Whether Tait's prescribing was ever considered for reference to a tribunal is not known, but in Hirschman's case, for reasons which will now never be explained, someone in the Home Office considered that the tribunal machinery 'would be of little avail in the case of a man of his stamp'. Preference for the quicker, more familiar and straightforward alternative of criminal proceedings is understandable, but given that the Rolleston Committee, at the Home Office's behest, had recommended the procedure[38] specifically for prescribers of 'this stamp', this statement is truly astonishing. Unfortunately, this was not the only indication that Home Office administrators had already set their faces against actually operating the tribunal machinery, although they were apparently prepared for its existence to be used as a threat against those doctors who were supplying persons at a distance or to unknown persons, or against doctors who were prescribing too liberally but on a minor scale. In 1935 it had been decided that, instead of prosecuting such doctors, they were better dealt with by a warning letter referring to the possibility of tribunal proceedings, followed by 'advice'.

Another example of the reluctance to use the tribunal option is provided by the case of Dr Gerald Quinlan, who was another major script doctor of the immediate pre-war years. Although few details now survive, Quinlan's prescribing for several of the West End addicts was described as 'lavish' but he was careful not to offer an opportunity for a 'technical' prosecution. Instead of using the tribunal machinery, the Home Office decided in 1941 that an approach should be made to the General Medical Council to see if the Council would be prepared to deal with Quinlan on the grounds of unprofessional conduct. The Council's response was given in a letter from the Registrar, Mr Heseltine, on 15 August 1941:

> ... while the Council would prefer to act on a conviction under the Dangerous Drugs Acts they would also be prepared to consider information and evidence from the Home Office which might support a charge of infamous conduct in a professional respect against the practitioner on the grounds that he had sold large quantities of dangerous drugs to patients under all or any of the following conditions namely, (1) at exorbitant prices, (2) at frequent intervals, (3) otherwise than as medicines in the course of treatment of them, and that, knowing they were addicted to the use of such drugs he continued to supply them with such drugs to their moral and physical detriment.

On the basis of this letter and further unofficial encouragement from Heseltine, a detailed summary of Quinlan's activities was prepared and submitted to the Council in time for a meeting of the Penal Cases Committee in April 1942. In accordance with the Council's procedure Quinlan was asked for his observations on the allegations. When these had been received and considered, the President, after consulting the Home Office, decided with some reluctance that he should be required to appear before the Disciplinary Committee.

The Home Office witnesses were asked to attend on 4 June 1942 but the hearing was postponed until 8 June, when the President informed Frank Thornton that he had decided to adjourn the case until the next session in November. Confirmation that the Council was not happy at being involved was provided by the President's further comment that it had been intimated to him that this was a case in which the Home Office should exercise the power under the Regulations to refer it to a tribunal and not employ the time of the General Medical Council. In September, when Quinlan's file was reviewed, it was found, not surprisingly, that he had reduced the number of his addict patients and, in some instances, the quantities he was prescribing. This obviously weakened the Home Office case, which Quinlan well realised, as shown by his remark to Len Dyke at a chance meeting, that 'I have a good defence, and these last few months I have made good progress with this crowd and gained experience in handling them'. The Council was accordingly told that the Home Office would not be unduly disturbed if the case was dropped, and this was done.

The Home Office's lack of enthusiasm for using the tribunal procedure was further demonstrated in 1948, in response to enquiries from the General Medical Council and the British Medical Association in 1944 and 1945 about the current status of the appointed tribunals. The two medical bodies had asked whether there were likely to be any tribunal references in the near future. They were told there were none and that there seemed little purpose either in replacing those original tribunal members, who had first been appointed in March 1927 and who had retired or died, or in re-appointing others. They were also told that doctors who misused drugs almost invariably committed offences which could be dealt with by the courts, a clear indication of the Home Office preference for using the criminal law. This reply appears to have been based on a review in 1944 of the practice of using the courts for dealing with doctor addicts. The Ministry of Health felt that doctors would rather be prosecuted for technical record-keeping offences than have the real reasons for their drug purchases disclosed before a tribunal. This was in direct contrast to the view of the Rolleston Committee, which had proposed the establishment of the tribunal machinery because 'consideration must be given to the public odium of a criminal trial and conviction which is specially felt when the prosecution takes place in the district in which the doctor practises'.[39]

What is revealing about the very belated reply from the Home Office is the hint it gives of the underlying complacency and short-sightedness which were to be a feature of our response to drug misuse over the next 20 years. Because most of the doctor addicts since 1926 (as well as script doctors like Connor, Hirschman and Tait) had carelessly provided opportunities to secure 'technical' convictions, and despite the unsatisfactory Quinlan episode, there was clearly an assumption in the Home Office that this was not a serious problem and that any future cases could be similarly resolved through the courts. There was quite clearly no appreciation of the damage which could be caused by just one script doctor, if his or her generous prescribing was not speedily terminated.

### The Ripka case

In 1948, when the General Medical Council and the British Medical Association were in effect being told the tribunal machinery was redundant, there was increasing concern in the Inspectorate about the prescribing of Dr M. D. Ripka of Gower Street, London W1. By 1952 this concern had reached the stage where the Home Office was dusting off the tribunal rules of procedure and asking the medical authorities to nominate members to serve on a tribunal.

Ripka had first come to notice in 1935, two years after qualifying. But it was his involvement after the war with many of the well-known West End addicts that focused attention on his practice. He was always very 'co-operative', writing to let the

Inspectorate know about each new addict patient or to explain why it had been necessary to increase a patient's dosage. Letters about new patients almost invariably contained a statement that he had not prescribed until the patient had shown withdrawal symptoms, while the most frequent reason given for an increase in dosage was that he was 'too soft-hearted'.

It was quite clear that Ripka's co-operation would never extend to the voluntary curtailment of his prescribing, and that there was no likelihood of court proceedings or a successful reference to the General Medical Council. Therefore, the Home Office Legal Adviser was consulted and in February 1951 he confirmed that in his opinion there was sufficient evidence to place before a tribunal. It was therefore decided that, for the first time, the machinery which the Rolleston Committee had thoughtfully provided would be used, but there followed a series of events which were to frustrate this intention.

Requests to the General Medical Council and the British Medical Association to nominate members to serve on an imminent tribunal gave urgency to a review of the Rules of Procedure then in hand. It had been planned to include the revised Rules in the consolidated Dangerous Drugs Regulations, under the Dangerous Drugs Act 1951 (currently under preparation), but because it took longer than expected for the various procedural arrangements and the admissibility of evidence to be agreed, this could not be done. As the Regulations could not be delayed, it was decided to introduce the tribunal provisions separately at a later date and the firm intention to reinstate the tribunal machinery was announced by the then Home Secretary, Sir David Maxwell Fyfe, in a Written Answer in the House of Commons on 3 April 1952.[40] However, this plan fell foul of the appointment of the Franks Committee on Administrative Tribunals and Enquiries in 1953 and had to be postponed until the Report of the Committee was published in 1957. In the meantime, the new Regulations had been promulgated in 1953. The Franks Committee merely recommended the creation of a Council to keep under review, and report on, the constitution and working of tribunals. By then yet another obstacle had been placed in the path of the restoration of the medical tribunals when, on 3 June 1958, the Minister of Health appointed the Interdepartmental Committee on Drug Addiction to review the advice given by the Rolleston Committee some 30 years earlier.

In the meantime, the immediate problem of Ripka's prescribing had resolved itself, following his appearance at Clerkenwell Magistrate's Court on 11 February 1953. As reported in the *Daily Telegraph* and *Daily Express* newspapers of 12 February 1953, Ripka pleaded guilty to aiding and abetting one of his addict patients, Angela Wyndham-Wilson, in the unlawful possession of heroin. Ripka, who claimed he did not know it was an offence to send drugs abroad, had been giving Wyndham-Wilson prescriptions for heroin intended for a former patient of his who was then living in Malta. Wyndham-Wilson had the prescriptions dispensed and posted the drugs to the man in Malta. Ripka was fined £150 on each of two charges, but by accepting his guilty plea and not proceeding with a substantive Dangerous Drugs Act charge, the prosecution had inadvertently deprived the Secretary of State of his power to withdraw Ripka's authority to possess, supply and prescribe drugs.

Ripka told the court he would not accept addicts as patients in the future. This was a welcome and timely announcement because he had recently accepted for 'treatment' Barry Ellis (a close friend of Wyndham-Wilson), who, over the next few years, was to acquire a similar status among the young post-war heroin addicts to that of Brenda Dean Paul among the 1930s group.[41] In only two weeks, Ripka had increased Ellis's heroin supply from two grains (120mgms) to just over 11 (660mgms) a day. There is little doubt that had Ripka not decided to 'retire', many more of the newly emerging addicts would have found their way to Gower Street. It was 14 years after Ripka first came to notice as a generous prescriber before he could be prosecuted.

## The post-war growth of heroin misuse

After the war the first noticeable change in drug misuse was an increase in the use of cannabis which began to spread beyond those parts of the country where there was a large, newly arrived West Indian population. Confirmation of this came in April 1950 when, following the seizure of a quantity of cannabis from a ship's steward at Southampton, the Metropolitan Police subsequently raided Club Eleven, a private dance club in the West End of London, and found 10 people in possession of the drug. The United Kingdom Annual Report to the United Nations for 1950 commented that, 'contrary to the normal experience in the country in cases involving hemp, only one was a coloured man'. (Club Eleven has a special place in the history of British modern jazz.[42] An account of the West End jazz and drug scene in the 1950s was provided by Raymond Thorpe who was involved in both.[43])

One of the results of this hitherto unprecedented police activity was to make cannabis less readily available. Unfortunately this scarcity coincided with, or perhaps was the reason for, the appearance in the West End, in the spring of 1951, of Kevin Patrick Saunders, or 'Mark', who had stolen a large amount of heroin, cocaine and morphine from All Saints Hospital, Chatham, where he was a porter. Some cocaine had been found during the Club Eleven raid (when Ronnie Scott, the jazz musician, was arrested for possession of it) but heroin had not previously featured prominently in the immediate post-war West End drug scene. Yet by the time of his arrest in September 1951, 'Mark' had been able to dispose of almost all the heroin and cocaine he had stolen by hawking the drugs around the London jazz clubs and coffee bars.[44] We were later told by some of his clients that they had taken to heroin because of the shortage of cannabis.

Of those to whom Mark was known to have supplied drugs, only two had previously come to notice as addicts. One was Barry Ellis, the other Angela Wyndham-Wilson who was involved in the Ripka case in 1953. It is a little surprising that following Mark's arrest there was no immediate rush by his customers to find legitimate medical suppliers of heroin, with only one surfacing in 1951. Most of his other customers, and a number of their close associates, subsequently approached doctors, and by September 1964 a total of 64 addicts were identified who were known to have, or strongly suspected of having, links with Mark and/or his original customers.[45] These formed the nucleus of a heroin addict population which was to expand gradually but inexorably over the next few years.

Apart from their understandable reluctance to become known to the authorities as a result of their names appearing on prescriptions, the most obvious explanation for the slow emergence of these new addicts was that there were adequate supplies of heroin circulating on the black market in the West End. If this was so, these supplies could only have come from the surplus quantities being prescribed for the few who had approached doctors. No important thefts from legitimate stocks occurred between 1951 and 1954 and there was no evidence of illicitly imported heroin, which in any case would have been in powder form and not in the hypodermic tablets then prescribed. In fact, the names of the main dealers at this time were well known but there was little the police could do about them, as any heroin found in their possession would have been lawfully obtained on prescription and the actual handover of drugs was not easy to detect.

Since the 1930s the small groups of London heroin addicts had been easy to monitor, as most of their prescriptions were dispensed at one or other of the two 24-hour pharmacies, where a prescription given one day, but dated for the next, could be dispensed at one minute past midnight. In the 1960s, frequent examination by the Drugs Inspectorate of the records at these pharmacies, and the invaluable co-operation of the staff, meant that new addicts, and more importantly, new prescribers, were quickly identified. But the congregation of addicts at only two pharmacies, while helpful to the Inspectorate, had serious drawbacks. It created a market place where addicts without prescriptions knew where drugs were always likely to be available. It also gave birth to the fiction of the 'long midnight queues' outside Boots in Piccadilly Circus, which became an essential tourist attraction for transatlantic students of the 'British system'.

Another reason why there is a fair amount of information about the heroin addicts of the pre-war and immediate post-war years was that in both periods there were officers at New Scotland Yard who took a special interest in the problem. Before the war this was Detective Sergeant Len Dyke, and in the Club Eleven/Mark era, Detective Sergeant George Lyle. Lyle's detailed knowledge of London drug problems was amply demonstrated by the talk he gave to the Society for the Study of Addiction in January 1953.[46] On many of his forays into the West End, Dyke was accompanied by Frank Thornton, who was a member of some of the well-known clubs, although not everyone was convinced he had joined them, as he always claimed, to gather intelligence. There is no doubt, however, they knew the older group of addicts extremely well.

But the most effective monitoring arrangements are of little value if the warning signs they reveal are then ignored. It soon became apparent that there was one important difference between the young, new heroin addicts who began to appear in London in the 1950s and their pre-war counterparts. In the 1930s and 1940s, Drs Tait, Hirschman, Quinlan and Ripka proved to be worthy successors to Connor, but the drugs they provided, under the guise of 'treatment', tended to remain within the existing addict circle. Whereas these older addicts were, for the most part, content with what they could obtain from such doctors and to indulge in some borrowing and lending of drugs within the group, the new generation were far more inclined to seek larger doses than they required, for disposal to others in a growing commercial illicit market.

### Drs Maguire and Rourke

There was one talent which the new addicts shared with the pre-war group, an uncanny ability to discover 'sympathetic' doctors who asked few questions and whose prescriptions bore little relationship to the addicts' actual needs, amounting in many instances to little more than prescribing on demand. In the early 1950s there were never more than two or three of these doctors, rarely with more than two or three addict 'patients' at any one time, but their prescriptions clearly met the demands of the current market. There were only two major prescribers, both in London: Dr E. A. Maguire of Linden Gardens, W2, and Dr J. M. Rourke of Kensington Church Street, W8. Two minor figures were Dr K., whose first contact with addicts had apparently come through acting briefly as a locum for Maguire, and Dr S., who was 'persuaded' by the Inspectorate to withdraw from the treatment of addicts. There were a few more who, from time to time, supplemented their NHS income with fees for private prescriptions for heroin or received 'gifts' in return for NHS prescriptions. As the wife of one addict (not addicted herself) told us, it was not unusual for one of these, Dr H. I. Pinches of Earls Court, who had qualified in 1903, to telephone and enquire whether another prescription was required.

Dr S., practising in North London, was one of the first to prescribe cocaine. As he explained to the Inspectorate, he did this at the request of his one addict patient, who claimed it would help him cut down his heroin consumption. Predictably, no reduction in heroin dosage followed and the addict continued to receive both drugs in ever-increasing amounts, at times reaching an average daily supply of 15 grains (900mgms) of cocaine and 25 grains (1,500mgms) of heroin. Nor was it altogether surprising that with these lavish quantities, the addict, an unemployed Nigerian, was able to move from North London and live in semi-luxury in the West End of London.

Although Maguire had been involved intermittently since 1946 with the older addict group, it was his acceptance of Barry Ellis as a patient, in September 1951, which brought him into contact with the new wave of heroin addicts. Despite repeated assurances that he would prefer not to have addicts as patients, by September 1953 he had been involved at one time or another with seven of the new group, although in April 1955 he was prescribing for only two. One of these was Broderick Walker, another Nigerian addict, whose death in March 1955 was indirectly to lead to Maguire 'retiring' from the scene; he had always been careful to get rid of any addicts likely to be troublesome, and to bring him unwelcome attention. Walker's death exposed what was said to be his 'working arrangement' with Rourke, the other generous prescriber, and required Maguire to give evidence in the unsuccessful proceedings against Rourke. The main beneficiaries of this 'working arrangement' were the addicts, who were protected from prosecution for obtaining dual supplies as neither doctor would admit he was aware of the other's prescriptions, even when each had prescribed for the same addict on the same day.

Rourke had first came to the notice of the Inspectorate in August 1953 when he issued two prescriptions to an addict already receiving regular supplies of heroin from Maguire. Soon afterwards, he accepted, in quick succession, the two addicts who were then believed to be major illicit suppliers to the heroin circle, followed by three more who remained with him for short periods only. Supplies to his two regular patients were especially generous, in one case reaching 17 grains (1,020mgms) of heroin daily, frequently boosted by supplementary prescriptions which considerably increased this daily average. When Rourke was visited by a member of the Inspectorate while one of these patients was in hospital, he promised he would have nothing more to do with the other. Shortly after the addict who had been in hospital was discharged, Rourke was giving him prescriptions for an average of 8 grains (480mgms) of heroin a day. There were many other examples of Rourke's total irresponsibility. In March 1955 he gave a prescription for 8 grains of heroin to an addict on the day he was released from prison and who had been reported by the Prison Medical Officer to be in good health. Rourke also allowed his two regular patients to write their own prescriptions, which he was legally required only to sign and date. One of them later told me that he usually had a few of Rourke's signed blank NHS prescription forms in his possession and that he was paying the doctor £7–£10 a week despite being an NHS patient.

It was, however, Rourke's 'treatment' of Broderick Walker which was falsely to raise the Inspectorate's hopes that, in the absence of the tribunal machinery, there was nevertheless a way in which his activities could be curtailed. In September 1954 Rourke issued his first prescription for Walker, who, after failing to convince six other doctors that he was in fact addicted, had recently been accepted as an

NHS patient by Maguire. Rourke's prescription was endorsed 'pp. Dr Maguire', as were several others in the following weeks; yet apparently at no time did he contact Maguire. Between August 1954 and January 1955 Walker's name appeared on 35 prescriptions issued by Maguire and on 47 by Rourke, with some being issued by each doctor on the same day.

In a statement for the Coroner, following Walker's death, Rourke thought he 'may have told the NHS' that he was treating Walker but he had never received his record card nor any remuneration for his services. He said he had only seen Walker on about 12 occasions, although he had also given prescriptions to the woman he knew as Walker's wife. Whether Rourke knew she was also addicted is not clear but he continued to give her prescriptions for a short period after Walker's death. The facts were referred to the Director of Public Prosecutions and in due course Rourke was charged with being in the unauthorised possession of heroin, the basis of the charge being that he had aided and abetted Walker to be in unauthorised possession of heroin (because he was obtaining supplies concurrently from two doctors) and was therefore liable to be tried as a principal offender.

Dismissing the case against Rourke at Marylebone Magistrate's Court on 8 September 1955, Mr Geoffrey Raphael echoed the opinion given to Sir Malcolm Delevingne before the Rolleston Committee was appointed, that the Regulations did not limit a doctor's discretion to prescribe or supply drugs in accordance with his professional judgement. They were 'aimed not at doctors but at patients who, by dishonest concealment from doctors of what is going on, get a larger quantity of drugs than they ought'. As reported in *The Times* newspaper of 9 September 1955, Mr Raphael found that the prosecution had failed to establish that Rourke had aided and abetted Walker to obtain extra supplies of heroin. In his written Opinion, Mr Raphael concluded:[47]

> It may well be that the patient committed an offence here. It is not for me to decide one way or the other. But to my mind, it would make nonsense of these Regulations, which as I see it, are designed to give duly qualified medical practitioners absolute discretion as to the way they should treat their patients, and the quantity of drugs they should prescribe, if I were to hold that these facts amounted to an infringement of the Regulations by this defendant. There is nothing in these Regulations to which my attention has been directed, which limits the quantity of drugs that may be lawfully prescribed by a doctor.

Mr Raphael's decision, that there was no case to answer, was a fatal blow to the Inspectorate's hopes of dealing with Rourke. His suggestion that Rourke's conduct might be 'gravely improper' and a matter which might be considered by the General Medical Council was of little comfort or assistance. When, almost a year later, the facts were put before the Council it was confirmed that their position had not changed since 1942 (the Quinlan case) and, in their view, the matter should be dealt with under the special provisions of the Dangerous Drugs Regulations. This was, of course, a polite way of telling the Home Office to restore the tribunal provisions as soon as possible. Fortunately, despite being given the 'green light' by Mr Raphael's decision, Rourke seemed quite content to carry on with just one or two addict patients until he died in September 1960.

## Revival of medical tribunals

It was not until 1973, under the provisions of the Misuse of Drugs Act 1971, that tribunals were revived. Under sections 13, 14 and 15 of the Act, the Home Secretary is empowered to set up special tribunals to deal with doctors who are considered to have prescribed any controlled drug in 'an irresponsible manner'.[48] The arrangements were set out in the Misuse of Drugs Tribunals (England and Wales) Rules 1974, which came into operation on 1 March 1974.[49]

The credit for plugging this gaping hole in our control machinery must go to Baroness Barbara Wootton and her colleagues on the Amphetamines Sub-committee of the Advisory Committee on Drug Dependence in 1970. In their report, they noted that the currently available statutory sanctions for controlling 'reckless or irresponsible prescribing' of amphetamines could not be applied quickly enough to deal with the prescribing of two doctors who were responsible for 'the epidemic of injectable methylamphetamine in 1967/68'. (The two doctors were John Petro and Christopher Swan, although they were not named in the report.) The Committee therefore proposed that 'special medical tribunals as originally recommended in the Rolleston Report' should be set up to deal with over-prescribing, although their preference was for the powers of the General Medical Council to be extended to deal with the problem.[50] The Council declined to take on the role of disciplining 'irresponsible prescribers' because its then president, Lord Cohen, as quoted on 21 March 1970 in the *British Medical Journal*,[51] thought 'this Council is not required to act, as I may so put it, as a police authority for the medical profession'.

The restoration of the much-needed tribunal machinery was not without its problems. As the Misuse of Drugs Act 1971 offered no definition of 'irresponsible prescribing' the Drugs Inspectorate had to be guided by advice from the Home Office legal advisor, which was that a charge of irresponsibility was the most serious accusation that could be levelled against a doctor. In practice this meant that, although there was no shortage of candidates, the only doctors we could take before a tribunal were those whose prescribing was so grossly irresponsible and persistent that it could not be ignored. But in his advice, the legal advisor had overlooked, or chosen to ignore, the interpretations of 'irresponsible', which Ministers had given to Parliament during the passage of the Act. In the House of Lords on 14 January 1971, Lord Windlesham, Minister of State at the Home Office, commented that:[52]

> ... "irresponsible prescribing" covers such a wide variety of possible practices. These range from infamous conduct at one extreme to poorly judged, but *bona fide* intention at the other.

The legal advisor's opinion led to the introduction of cumbersome administrative procedures to add to those already set out in the legislation. Our apparent failure to make good use of the new powers in those early years attracted the justified criticism from the Advisory Council on the Misuse of Drugs that the 'narrow legalistic approach' adopted by the Home Office had resulted in only nine tribunals being held between 1974 and 1982.[53]

Nevertheless, the existence of the tribunal machinery was a help to the Inspectorate for those prescribers who did not fit the script doctor profile. Many were elderly single-handed practitioners, often under intense pressure from drug misusing patients, whose prescribing was 'poorly judged' rather than irresponsible and which was often substantially modified or terminated after a voluntary interview with an Inspector when they were told that they might be referred to a tribunal.

Bean[54] complained that the tribunals have no power 'to sentence according to levels necessary to deter others'. But would fines or imprisonment have any deterrent value for the doctors who found themselves in a situation from which it was impossible to escape? The first case dealt with by a tribunal, in 1974, involved such a doctor, an elderly woman in a single-handed practice in the King's Cross area of London who readily admitted that 'swamped by the flood of human sewage' she had prescribed dipipanone (Diconal) irresponsibly. For legal reasons, the tribunal's recommendation did not allow the Secretary of State to make the Direction prohibiting her from prescribing controlled drugs which would have afforded her protection from those pestering her. She ceased to prescribe Diconal but within a few months had become a heavy prescriber of barbiturates. Her total inability to resist the pressure being put upon her brought her before the General Medical Council which erased her name from the Medical Register in 1983. In another case, an elderly general practitioner explained, 'it was easier to write a prescription (for amphetamines) than get thumped'. Within weeks of the issue of a Direction against him, he was again prescribing amphetamines, which resulted in prosecution and subsequent reference to the Disciplinary Committee of the General Medical Council.

The tribunals have to resolve questions of professional medical judgement. The Misuse of Drugs Act 1971 allows any doctor to prescribe any controlled drug to an addict (except heroin, cocaine or dipipanone unless he or she is licensed to do so) in whatever form and quantity his or her professional judgement dictates so long as it does not appear to be 'irresponsible'. Prescribing controlled drugs privately or not following a course of treatment recommended by guidelines for the treatment of addicts issued from time to time by the Department of Health are not *prima facie* evidence of 'irresponsibility'. By the same token, the guidelines do not provide a benchmark of 'responsible' prescribing.[55]

Since 1970 the General Medical Council, despite its earlier misgivings, has been willing to regard 'as serious professional misconduct the prescription or supply of drugs of dependence other than in the course of *bona fide* treatment' and allows for disciplinary proceedings to be taken by its Professional Conduct Committee.[56] Proceedings may also be taken against doctors who have been convicted of a drug offence when the offence appears to have been committed to gratify the doctor's own addiction or that of someone else. The evidence considered by the Committee is usually produced by the Home Office Drugs Inspectorate and the rules of procedure are similar to those of the criminal court, with a right of appeal to the Judicial Committee of the Privy Council. When 'a doctor has been proved to have been convicted of a criminal offence, or judged to have been guilty of serious professional misconduct' the Committee must decide on one of five courses of action – including directing that the doctor's registration is conditional on compliance, for a period not exceeding five years, with any requirements as the Committee may impose or directing the erasure of the doctor's name from the Medical Register.[57] Between 1972 and 1984, 39 cases of 'improper' prescribing were considered by the Committee with the names of 18 doctors erased from the Medical Register.[58]

# 3

# The attempt to ban heroin in 1955

At the first meeting of the Rolleston Committee a proposal by a member, Professor W. E. Dixon, an eminent Cambridge pharmacologist, that heroin should be banned was rejected.[1] Some 30 years later, at the instigation of the international control agencies, another attempt was made to ban heroin. On 18 February 1955 the government announced that it did not intend to renew, on their expiry at the end of that year, the licences to manufacture heroin held by the United Kingdom's principal manufacturers, J. F. Macfarlan and T. and H. Smith of Edinburgh.[2] The practical effect of this decision, once all existing stocks of the drug had been used, would have been to make heroin no longer available for any therapeutic purpose, including the relief of the pain of terminal illness or in the treatment of addiction.

On 26 January 1956 the decision not to renew the licences was rescinded by statements made in both Houses of Parliament,[3] in the House of Commons by the Home Secretary, Major Gwilym Lloyd-George, and in the House of Lords by the Commonwealth Relations Secretary, Lord Home. This brought to an end the first serious dispute between the Home Office and the medical profession over dangerous drugs since Delevingne's abortive attempt in 1922 to prohibit doctors from prescribing narcotics to themselves. Although the government's January 1956 statement represented a 'victory' for the medical profession, it was less clear cut than the dispute of 1922 and neither side emerged from the affair with much credit.

At first the February 1955 announcement produced little reaction but once the full significance of what was being proposed was realised, an intensive campaign was mounted by the profession to persuade the government to reverse the decision. The basic facts of this story have already been told,[4] and Bartrip has described the British Medical Association's opposition to the proposal,[5] but what has not been explained in any detail is how the government ever found themselves so seriously at odds with the doctors.

## Earlier international attempts to ban heroin

### The 1920s

The campaign to prohibit the legitimate manufacture and use of heroin first surfaced in 1923 at a meeting of the Opium Advisory Committee of the League of Nations. Although the Portuguese delegate had raised the issue, Delevingne suspected the Americans were behind the move, as Dr Rupert Blue of the United States (US)

Public Health Service had also raised the question at a meeting of the sub-committee of the Mixed Opium and Health Committees of the League. That sub-committee adopted a resolution that, as heroin could be dispensed with in therapeutics, the possibility of entirely forbidding its manufacture should be considered. The British delegate at this meeting, Sir George Buchanan, a senior medical officer at the Ministry of Health, tried without much success to find the evidence upon which the assertions in the resolution were based. All he could discover was that the sub-committee had received a memorandum from Dr Knaffl-Lenz, a Viennese doctor whose experience and credentials were not disclosed. On 21 November 1923, in a private note to Delevingne enclosed with a copy of his official report of the meeting, Sir George made no secret of his personal view:[6]

> If heroin is abused in America, let the Americans, who like prohibition, forbid it, but why should countries where heroin is not abused be put to all the trouble for the benefit of the United States?

The Home Office response to the resolution was to seek, through the Ministry of Health, the opinion of the medical profession. While there was general agreement that there should be a limitation on the quantities manufactured, only the Dean of the Marischal College in Scotland supported total prohibition. The president of the General Medical Council, Sir Donald MacAlister, thought 'no practical end would be subserved, in relation to drug addiction, by the prohibition of its manufacture'; he also considered heroin to be slightly safer therapeutically than morphine. The Royal College of Physicians referred the question to two eminent members, Sir William Willcox and Sir William Hale-White, and unanimously accepted their view that many in the medical profession believed heroin had certain therapeutic properties not provided by any other drugs. (Willcox was shortly to be appointed to the Rolleston Committee where his view prevailed.) The British Medical Association also considered that heroin had 'a legitimate use in medicine and that such being the case the Association could not agree that its manufacture should be prohibited'.

On 15 October 1924, the League was informed that HM Government was unable to support the proposal because representative medical opinion in this country appeared to be definitely opposed to the prohibition of heroin, though it agreed on the desirability of any action being taken to limit the amount available to the minimum required for medical and scientific purposes. The United Kingdom (UK) was not alone in taking this position. The League's enquiries revealed that only six countries, including the US and Canada, were prepared to support prohibition, with 14 others willing only to impose some limitation on the quantities being manufactured.

The US banned heroin in 1924 following Hearings by the Ways and Means Committee of the House of Representatives in April 1924 on a bill, introduced by Republican Representative Stephen G. Porter, to prohibit the import of opium for the manufacture of heroin.[7] For over a decade, until his death in 1930, Porter was a dominant force in shaping both his own country's and international drug control policies and the successful passage of this bill was to have a considerable influence on the latter.[8] The linking of heroin with crime featured prominently during the Hearings and some of the views expressed are still heard today. For example, there was testimony that as heroin destroyed 'the sense of responsibility to the herd, heroin addicts will more quickly commit crime and with no sense of regret or responsibility for it'. The chief causes of addiction were described as 'the excessive production of narcotic drugs, the association with addicts, and persuasion by drug peddlers'.

Although not a member of the League of Nations, the US sent a delegation, led by Porter, to the Second Geneva Opium Conference in November 1924. The delegation again proposed the total prohibition of heroin to the Committee of Experts, only to have the proposal firmly rejected. It was agreed, however, that the exemption previously granted to doctors from recording preparations of heroin containing less than 0.1% should be withdrawn. When this was translated into UK law, by the Dangerous Drugs Act of 1926, there were some mild protests from the medical profession, directed more at the additional clerical burden for dispensing doctors than at the removal of the exemption.

**The 1930s**

The prohibition of pharmaceutical heroin returned to the international agenda in 1930–1931, at the Conference in Geneva which produced the 1931 Convention for Limiting the Manufacture and Regulating the Distribution of Narcotic Drugs (known as the Limitation Convention). On this occasion the Committee of Experts, of which Professor W. E. Dixon was a member, expressed the belief that heroin could be dispensed with entirely and that doctors in countries where it was currently being used would find that the morphine derivatives to which the Committee had drawn attention were adequate substitutes. However, the Conference decided that member countries should once more only be invited to consider the feasibility of abolishing or restricting its use. The League Secretariat, recognising that this would necessitate 'rather difficult enquiries and negotiations with the medical profession', did not formally contact member countries for their views until May 1934. In the meantime, Article 10 of the Limitation Convention required governments of countries wishing to import heroin to provide the exporting country with a certificate authorising the transaction.

In June 1932, the Home Office suggested that the possibility of complying with the Conference recommendation should be considered. The Ministry of Health, clearly taking the view that primary responsibility rested with the Home Office, declined to become involved and offered to provide the names of the appropriate bodies to be consulted, but thought it unlikely there would be a different opinion from that obtained in 1924. 'Pressure of more important work' in the Home Office saw no further action until July 1933. Then, anticipating an imminent request from the League for a reply, the Ministry of Health was again approached with the suggestion that the views of one or two leading members of the medical profession might be sought. Once more the Ministry declined to become involved and suggested the Home Office could consult the Royal Colleges of Physicians of London and Edinburgh, the General Medical Council and the British Medical Association, or convene a special conference to consider the matter.

There was no great enthusiasm in the Home Office for either option. Not only would it be wrong for the Home Office to summon doctors to a conference but the profession might well interpret what were innocent enquiries as government interference. Sir Malcolm Delevingne decided the matter should be 'allowed to stand over' as it would undoubtedly come up again at the next meeting of the Opium Advisory Committee and only one country, Belgium, had so far responded. He suggested the meeting might afford an opportunity of referring the matter to the Health Committee of the League, the outcome of which could strengthen the government's position *vis-à-vis* the medical profession.

In May 1934 the League's formal request for a statement of the government's position was received but was then 'lost' in the Home Office for two months. On 28 September 1934, T. H. Hutson of the Home Office's International Division, recorded the outcome of an informal discussion with Dr Morgan of the Ministry of Health as:

> Heroin is nearly unnecessary, being replaceable in at least 75% of cases by codeine. Medical opinion of an enlightened third would agree with that; but there is, he thinks, an articulate body of unenlightened opinion which would fight it. Any move by the Home Office or the Ministry to consult the bodies representing the medical profession could arouse that articulate body. Morgan genuinely felt the profession would take it better from the Home Office.

Although both the Home Office and the Ministry of Health hoped any decision could be deferred as long as possible, a reply to the League's letter was sent on 11 October 1934. It was very much based on Dr Morgan's advice: there was a tendency among the medical profession in the UK to restrict the use of heroin, and to substitute codeine wherever that course was considered practicable, but 'advanced medical opinion' was not yet in favour of its total abolition. Therefore, HM Government was not, at the time, in a position to take any steps to abolish or further restrict the use of heroin.[9]

The League's enquiries had found that of the 40 countries which took definite positions, only 16, including the US, and the USSR, favoured total abolition. Of the rest, 12 favoured restricting use, and 12, including the UK, opposed prohibition. The opposing countries offered a variety of reasons for rejecting the proposal, including: the belief that it was of value in the treatment of certain conditions (Canada, Italy, Switzerland); the absence of any record of harmful effects and its low cost compared to morphine (Finland); and the undesirability of restricting the right of doctors to prescribe (Sweden). If this was a setback to the US vision of a world in which there was no legitimately produced heroin, they could derive some satisfaction from the effects of the Limitation Convention, which had come into effect in July 1933. World production of heroin had decreased from 3,652 kilograms in 1929, to 870 in 1936, with a corresponding drop in consumption from 2,127 in 1929 to 853 in 1936. Exports in the same period had also fallen by nearly 75%, from 851 kilograms in 1929 to 208 in 1936, no doubt largely due to the requirements of the Limitation Convention with regard to the import and export of heroin.[10]

**The 1940s**

The first Report of the reconstructed Permanent Central Opium Board in 1949 suggested that there was an *a priori* case for the prohibition of heroin. Few would argue with the statement that 'heroin, if injudiciously prescribed will easily produce addiction'. The Board noted that in 1947 29 countries had managed to do without it and expressed the belief that doctors in certain countries were either insufficiently acquainted with the results of modern research, which had found efficient and comparatively harmless substitutes for heroin, or else were far too lax with regard to the dangerous consequences that may follow the prescribing of heroin. This thinly-veiled attack on the UK medical profession would have carried more weight had the Board not then suggested that heroin was 'popular with medical men in some countries because it is simple to administer and quickly alleviates pain and cough', which would seem to be ample justification for the continuing availability of heroin to any rational person, and potential patient, if not to the Board, on which there was not one practising clinician.

Whether this was the first shot in what the Home Office soon recognised as a concerted drive by the Board and the Drug Supervisory Body and the World Health Organization (WHO) to achieve the prohibition of heroin in medical practice is not entirely clear. A 'scientifically and psychologically planned campaign' was advocated by Professor Fischer, a member of the Board, in a statement to the WHO Expert Committee on Drugs Liable to Produce Addiction in January 1949.[11] He argued that the banning of heroin was 'an urgent necessity in the struggle to control the use of drugs which are a menace to public health'. This introduction of a more subtle European approach is interesting, given that the Chairman of the UN Permanent Central Opium Board in 1949 was Herbert L.

May, who had been the US representative on the Board since it was established in 1928.

The Board's Report drew support from the *British Medical Journal* in a leading article on 15 January 1949.[12] This article, which is particularly relevant to the controversy of 1955, argued that the introduction of pethidine and similar compounds had widened the choice of effective analgesics and morphine or some related drug could always be used as effectively as heroin. It went on to say that pharmacological opinion had long held that heroin's social dangers overshadowed its therapeutic importance and there was justice in the Permanent Central Opium Board's claim of 'an *a priori* case for its total abolition'. After noting the 'well-known' dangers of heroin, the very high per capita consumption of heroin in Finland, and the fact that a rise in legitimate use preceded an increase in addiction and illicit supply, the article concluded that 'It is clearly the duty of the medical profession to examine again the therapeutic value of this substance and to weigh it against its social dangers'.

This hint of a possible changing attitude by the British Medical Association, the publishers of the Journal, passed virtually unnoticed. There was one letter, on 15 February 1949 from Dr James Ross[13] who declared that heroin was unrivalled as a potent analgesic and in his experience opium derivatives were often withheld unjustifiably from patients because many doctors had only a vague and flimsy knowledge of addiction. Further support for heroin appeared in a letter in *The Lancet* on 26 March 1949 from Dr J. Hartsilver[14] who described it as one of the sheet anchors in therapy when all else had failed to produce the desired effect. He went on to say that, provided proper care was taken in keeping a careful check on supplies, addiction should not occur but when it did, and heroin was not available, the addict would never fail to find a substitute.

On 7 February 1949, anticipating there might be trouble at the next meeting of the Economic and Social Council of the United Nations (to which responsibility for drug matters had passed from the League of Nations) Hutson asked if the Ministry of Health would once more seek the views of the profession.[15] This time there emerged a clear divergence of opinion between the profession in Scotland and in England and Wales. The Department of Health for Scotland reported that after extensive personal enquiry by the Chief Medical Officer among leading physicians, surgeons and pharmacologists, the 'all but unanimous' view was that in the case of adults the use of heroin could be abandoned without detriment. There was only one surgeon of standing who used heroin regularly and even he had said he would have no serious objection if its use were to be prohibited. On the other hand, there was a considerable body of opinion which regarded heroin as the opiate of choice in the post-operative treatment of children. There was no support for its continued use in cough mixtures.

A sub-committee of the Ministry of Health's Standing Medical Advisory Committee for England and Wales took a different line. Their reply pointed out that heroin addiction was not a major problem in the UK, and consumption of the drug for therapeutic purposes was not rising. There was a widespread belief among surgeons that the newer, less habit-forming synthetic opiates offered no efficient substitute as a post-operative sedative, since vomiting and constipation were less frequently encountered side-effects of heroin compared with other analgesics. The other major use of heroin was sedation in unproductive and exhausting cough. The sub-committee did not feel justified in advising the Minister to prohibit the manufacture and sale of heroin.

The statement that heroin consumption in the UK was not rising was not strictly true. From 1946 to 1948 the quantities used had risen from 94 to 103 kilograms.[16] The Permanent Central Opium Board had already drawn attention to an increase in per capita consumption of heroin, from 1.1 kilograms per million of population in 1936 to 1.9 in 1947, prompting *The Chemist and Druggist* on 3 September 1949[17] to confess to an inescapable feeling that 'the essential therapeutic application of narcotics is being submerged in a flood of figures'. The Board had singled out Finland for special criticism as there had been an even greater increase in that country in the consumption of heroin over the same period. The Finnish authorities explained this was because of significant rises in diseases such as tuberculosis during the war.

**The 1950s**

In September 1950 the WHO launched an enquiry into the possibility of abolishing the medical use of heroin in those countries which had not yet done so. Samuel Hoare, the Assistant Under-Secretary of State who was Head of the International Division of the Home Office from 1948 to 1961, was not too happy with the outcome of the recent consultations with the medical profession. The advice offered was far from convincing, being largely impressions rather than the results of any controlled experiments. Moreover, there was divergence in the profession over the value of heroin in the post-operative care of children, although it was agreed that it had no advantages over codeine and morphine for treating cough. Hoare felt that the UK ought to make sacrifices for the common good and, but for the fact that heroin was cheaper than the available substitutes, he would have been inclined to suggest the best tactic would be the elimination of its use as a cough linctus.

It was at this point, for the first time, that legal rather than medical advice was sought. In his reply to Hoare on 10 October 1950, G. T. B. Barr, a senior legal adviser in the Home Office, had little doubt that legislation would be needed if the manufacture of heroin was to be prohibited. This was a crucial opinion which, if it had been heeded, would almost certainly have saved the government from much subsequent embarrassment, and the events of 1955 would have taken a different course. Barr wrote:[18]

There seems to be no power outside Section 7 of the (Dangerous Drugs) Act of 1920. I feel fairly confident that Regulations under that Section cannot prohibit absolutely the manufacture or use of a drug. Whether the lesser objective (regarding cough mixtures) could be achieved is another matter. It is just possible it could – much further consultation would be required – but to do it in the Regulations would be altogether novel and alien of the present lay out. It would have to be done in the Regulations and not as a condition of a licence because doctors and chemists are expressly authorised in the Regulations (5 and 6 respectively). Further, any restriction on a chemist would, I am inclined to think, be contrary to Section 7 (2) and therefore ultra vires.

Nevertheless it was decided that the further reference to the Ministry of Health's Standing Medical Advisory Committee should include a recommendation for the total prohibition of heroin. It was conceded that if the Committee agreed, and if this was made public, there would be pressure on the government to legislate. An early draft of the referral proposed that the Committee should be invited to recommend to ministers that the use of heroin as a cough mixture should be discontinued, but this was withdrawn when the Ministry of Health pointed out that while ministers could draw the attention of doctors to the findings of the Committee, they could not advise them to discontinue using a particular drug.

In the meantime, in a letter dated 1 November 1950, the WHO was told that the manufacture and use of heroin in Great Britain would not be banned. While there was general agreement that heroin offered no significant advantages over codeine and morphine as a cough suppressant, there was a considerable volume of medical opinion which took the view that there was no effective substitute for the drug as a post-operative anodyne. Moreover, total prohibition of its use, or even only as a cough linctus, required legislation and, having regard to medical opinion, together with the absence of addiction to heroin on any substantial or increasing scale in the country, such action would not be justified.

The response of the Standing Medical Advisory Committee to the further reference of the matter was to consult the British Pharmacopoeia Commission. This appears not to have been disclosed formally to the Home Office until some five years later, at the height of the controversy to ban heroin, when the Secretary of the Commission wrote on 14 December 1955 to the Ministry of Health setting out its role in the affair.[19] He explained that the Commission had decided in November 1949 to defer any decision on the possible deletion of the monograph on heroin from the next edition of the *British Pharmacopoeia*, due in 1953, because medical opinion was 'extremely divergent'. However, when the question was reconsidered, at the request of the Standing Medical Advisory Committee, there was a clear majority for deleting the monograph on the ground that omission of the entry would leave the situation open and avoid any embarrassment to the government should they decide to ban the drug.

The letter went on to say that it was not the function of the Pharmacopoeia Commission to prohibit the use of a drug but to decide whether, on the available evidence, it was so important a substance as to warrant inclusion in the *Pharmacopoeia*. In the case of heroin, the evidence was not sufficiently strong to justify retention, and its advantages as a cough suppressant did not outweigh the grave consequences of widespread addiction in certain countries. The British Medical Association had been consulted and had agreed to the deletion 'on account of social disadvantages though it has therapeutic value'.

The Pharmacopoeia Commission's reply, that they would be prepared to delete the monograph in the forthcoming issue of the *Pharmacopoeia*, was qualified by the words 'if international agreement were reached prohibiting the manufacture and sale of heroin'. Although no such agreement was imminent, the heroin monograph was included in the list of proposed deletions forwarded in May 1952 to the Pharmacopoeia Committee of the General Medical Council. (It was to be alleged later that pressure had been brought to bear on the Commission, since it would be difficult, or impossible, for the government to ban any drug which was the subject of a monograph in the *British Pharmacopoeia*.) What the Commission's consideration of this question did reveal was the personal views of two eminent physicians who were to play key roles in later events. Sir Henry Cohen, President of the General Medical Council, personally favoured the provisional retention of the monograph, while Sir Russell Brain, President of the Royal College of Physicians, expressed his belief that in some cases no other drug could take the place of heroin as a post-operative analgesic for patients who could not tolerate morphine. There seemed to be no justification for abolishing the use of heroin in the UK if, as seemed to be the case, it was believed to have no adequate substitute.

Taking their lead from the Pharmacopoeia Commission, the Standing Medical Advisory Committee informed the Ministry of Health on 2 January 1951 that 'it would be justifiable to prohibit the use of heroin in this country if international agreement were reached to prohibit its manufacture and sale'. But it was decided that as far as the international agencies were concerned, the UK position would remain as set out in the letter of 1 November 1950, and our willingness now to consider prohibition would not be disclosed.[20]

At this stage there was little public interest in heroin, with only one Parliamentary Question on the subject between 1948 and February 1955. On 1 February 1951 Mr Dodds Parker asked the Home Secretary for the quantity of heroin used in the UK in 1950 compared with 1938 and to what causes he ascribed the difference. In an Oral Answer he was told 46kgs has been used in 1938 and 136kgs in 1949, while the amount for 1950 was not yet available, and that diamorphine (heroin) was used for cough linctuses, which might account for some of the increase. A year later Mr Dodds Parker wrote to the Home Secretary, on 5 February 1952, asking if there were any signs that heroin was leaking into the illicit drug trade. In his reply, on 9 February, the Home Secretary said he had no grounds for suspicion that there was anything seriously wrong; there had been no seizures of heroin by police or Customs in 1950, and the only two cases of unlawfully supplying or procuring heroin had involved individual addicts, with no suggestion of any large-scale organisation for the diversion of lawful supplies.[21]

The international agencies continued to chip away at what they no doubt saw as typical British obstinacy. Early in 1952, in its Report for 1951, the Permanent Central Opium Board drew attention to the increased consumption of heroin in the UK, which had risen from 6th to 4th place in the international league table. In May 1952 the WHO again asked whether the UK could now dispense with heroin altogether. In his advice on the government's response J. H. Walker, the Assistant Secretary in charge of the Home Office Drugs Branch and the UK representative on the United Nations (UN) Commission on Narcotic Drugs, suggested that it might be time to reconsider our position as there had been a number of developments on the issue. These included the willingness of the Standing Medical Advisory Committee to accept prohibition if there was an international agreement, and a hint from Dr Nicholls, the Deputy Government Chemist, that there might now be a shift in medical opinion. Prohibition was not a total solution to the heroin problem but it was difficult to resist the argument that it would help make the suppression of the illicit traffic easier. By holding aloof, we were undoubtedly creating the impression that we were indifferent to other countries' problems and were only prepared to co-operate in international agreements of this kind when it was in our direct interest to do so.

At the recent 7th Session of the Commission Walker had come under some 'friendly private pressure' from other delegates who expressed their disappointment at the UK's stance. The reasons for persisting in our refusal to ban heroin were now so tenuous that it would be extremely difficult to refuse to adhere to an international agreement for its total prohibition. Before long, either the WHO or the Commission were bound to sponsor such an agreement, which most other countries would accept, and it would be better to reconsider our position now rather than appear to give way at the last minute with bad grace.[22]

Hoare also thought it would be undesirable to give a blank negative to the WHO, and tactically inadvisable to say we were prepared to take action only if there was an international agreement. If we were obliged to legislate there could be opposition from the medical profession, who might not all share the views of the Standing Medical Advisory Committee (an accurate prediction of what was to happen three years later). It was therefore decided to tell the WHO that, as medical opinion now regarded the drug as having limited advantages, the deletion of the heroin monograph from the *British Pharmacopoeia* was being considered but complete prohibition of the medical use of heroin would require legislation, which the government was not prepared to sponsor at the present time. The matter would, of course, be kept under review.

The Pharmacopoeia Commission's decision to delete the monograph on heroin from the edition to be published in 1953 was not, however, supported by the British Pharmacopoeia Codex Committee. Following their normal practice of reviewing all items to be dropped from the *Pharmacopoeia*, and after encountering opposition from the Council of the Pharmaceutical Society of Great Britain, the Codex Committee accepted that heroin was still a valuable medicinal agent. It should not be denied to patients requiring it, merely because of its misuse by addicts, who were few in number in the UK. The Committee agreed to include a monograph in the 1954 Codex. The Ministry of Health was not happy with this decision, which would give unnecessary publicity to the two preparations (hypodermic tablets and linctus) that accounted for the bulk of the heroin consumption in the country, and which the Ministry had been advised, could be replaced by equally effective and less potentially habit-forming drugs. Walker raised no objection but was anxious the Codex Committee should be aware of the international sensitivity about heroin, which could well result in an agreement to prohibit its use in all forms before the next issue of the Codex was published.

## The 1954 resolution of the United Nations Economic and Social Council

In May 1953 a recommendation, accepted unanimously by the WHO Assembly, that the licit production and importation of diamorphine (heroin) should be abolished throughout the world, prompted an important comment in the *British Medical Journal* on 25 July.[23] This was to have a bearing on the government's decision to proceed with a ban, as it was seen as indicating there had indeed been a shift in medical opinion. After examining the indications for the use of heroin in preference to other drugs, the Journal concluded:

> ... they did not perhaps constitute very convincing arguments for its indispensability in comparison with the cogent reasons for its abolition ... There would thus be the most respectable precedent for Government authorities should they decide on the revolutionary step of making the use of the drug illegal in Britain.

In September 1954 the UN Economic and Social Council passed a resolution urging governments to prohibit the manufacture, import and export of heroin. Having no specific instructions, Walker, on behalf of the UK, had abstained but hinted that the resolution would be favourably received. The Dutch and French delegates made it clear that in their countries heroin was still regarded as indispensable in the treatment of certain illnesses and that, in any event, the prohibition of medical use would not result in a decline in the number of addicts.[24]

On his return from New York, Walker set in motion the consultations necessary to enable the UK to comply with the resolution. On 14 December 1954 the Ministry of Health Central Health Services Council approved the action of the Standing Medical Advisory Committee, which had told the Minister of Health that the resolution should be accepted. As the manufacturers' associations had also raised no objection, because their export markets for heroin had declined substantially, Walker was able to put forward, on 7 February 1955, the proposal 'that when the current licences (for the manufacture of heroin) expire they should not be renewed except in respect of small quantities for two purposes'.[25] The two purposes for which manufacture would still be permitted were 'for such small amounts as may be necessary for scientific purposes only', which was mentioned in the resolution, and as an intermediary in the manufacture of nalorphine, an opiate antagonist.

Walker's proposal excited little interest, and no opposition, from the higher reaches of the Home Office. In his submission seeking the Home Secretary's approval, while conceding that it was by no means clear that prohibition would materially affect the illicit traffic in heroin, despite his earlier expressed view, Walker assured him that:

> ... adequate and less dangerous substitutes were available, that legislation would not be required to implement the decision, and that as the Health Ministers agreed, it hardly seemed necessary to trouble the Cabinet.

Whether Walker was unaware of Barr's 1950 opinion that legislation would be required, or simply chose to ignore it, it is impossible to say.

## The ban on the manufacture of heroin

The Secretary of State announced the decision to ban the manufacture of heroin to the House of Commons on 18 February 1955 in a Written Answer to Sir Hugh Linstead's arranged Question. The current licences to manufacture heroin would not be renewed on their expiry at the end of the year. In future licences would be issued only for the manufacture of such small quantities as may be required for purely scientific purposes and for the production of nalorphine and there would be no further exports of heroin.[26] There was already a ban on the importation of heroin as part of a well-established policy that drugs which were manufactured in the UK were not also imported. (Copies of the Question and Answer were sent to the Permanent Central Opium Board and the WHO.)

Although understanding, and accepting that our international obligations had made the decision inevitable, Sir Hugh, who was one of the joint secretaries of the Pharmaceutical Society, expressed his personal regret at the necessity for it. He had been surprised, when the matter was raised some years earlier, that the medical profession had not taken a stand on the simple principle that it must claim the freedom to prescribe heroin in appropriate circumstances, however few these might be. But they had been divided and political pressures had now caught up with them.

Apart from a comment in the *Pharmaceutical Journal* of 26 February 1955, noteworthy for the statement that 'there are no known addicts in the UK', the announcement attracted little attention in the lay or medical press. The first signs that the medical profession were waking up to the implications of the government's decision appeared early in April when Sir George Godber (a senior medical officer at the Ministry of Health) was 'buttonholed' by a number of doctors at a dinner given by the Royal College of Physicians. They expressed their concern that the Minister of Health had been advised to accept the UN resolution despite the protest of their president, Sir Russell Brain. This was immediately followed by a letter in the *British Medical Journal* of 9 April 1955 from Dr A. H. Douthwaite[27] (a senior physician at Guy's Hospital in London) who had made the only protest to the Journal's leading article of 25 July 1953[28] when he had argued that 'widespread addiction was the outcome of poverty, ill-health, and misery, and it is to the remedy of these conditions rather than interference with therapeutics that governments should direct their energy and money'.[29]

The Council of the British Medical Association discussed the proposed ban at their meeting on 13 April 1955 at which Dr Solomon Wand, one of the BMA's members on the Standing Medical Advisory Committee, explained that when first informed of the government's intention he had felt it was uncalled for. However, having heard the arguments, and knowing from personal experience that there were adequate substitutes for heroin, he had been persuaded that if the UK 'stayed out' it would intensify a grave international problem. Following this meeting Dr A. Macrae, the BMA's Secretary, wrote to the government's Chief Medical Officer, Sir John Charles, to enquire how the matter of the proposed ban now stood. In this letter he disclosed, for the first time as far as the Ministry of Health and the Home Office were concerned, that in November 1954, after receiving an enquiry from the World Medical Association, the Council of the BMA had resolved:[30]

> That the World Medical Association be informed that it is the duty of the Government to legislate against the misuse of heroin, but the medical profession should not in any way be deprived of the use of this or any other drug which may assist in the treatment of patients.

The reaction in the two departments to this revelation was predictable, although this might have been tempered if it had been known that, through an oversight, the resolution had never reached the World Medical Association.[31] Sir

George Godber contacted Sir Henry Cohen, Chairman of the Standing Medical Advisory Committee, who was in no doubt that the ban was right and reminded Sir George that the BMA had made no protest when it was decided to delete the heroin monograph from the 1953 *British Pharmacopoeia*. At the Home Office, Walker and his immediate superior, Sir Austin Strutt, were equally taken aback at Macrae's disclosure and in a letter to Dame Enid Russell Smith at the Ministry of Health on 25 May, Strutt wrote:[32] '... in the circumstances you will not be surprised if I say that in future we may be inclined to attach rather less importance than hitherto to the view of the BMA in such matters.'

In this letter, which had been prompted by exchanges in the House of Lords on 27 April 1955,[33] Strutt sought confirmation that there were adequate substitutes for heroin and the Ministry of Health decided to seek the opinions of their Consultant Advisers, Dr R. R. Bomford, Professor R. V. Christie and Dr J. Maxwell, as well those of Sir Henry Cohen.[34]

Dr Bomford shared with many colleagues the impression that heroin was a unique drug for treating painful incurable conditions and he disliked the idea of it being banned, apparently without consultation with the profession. Heroin was not indispensable for cough in most people but for analgesia there were no rational grounds for dropping it, especially as he knew there had been no trial comparing it with the available substitutes. Dr Maxwell, who was clearly not impressed by the new synthetic analgesics, could not imagine who had advised the government that adequate substitutes existed. He regretted the decision to abolish the only drug which gave adequate relief in quite a high proportion of cases of terminal malignant disease of the chest, and in some cases of aneurism. He therefore thought the proposed ban was unjustified and he wondered whether it was not too late to reverse it.

Sir Henry Cohen maintained the position he had adopted from the outset: the skilful physician, selecting his drugs with careful reference to the special needs of his patient, could dispense with heroin without any impairment of therapeutic control. Professor Christie also thought that if heroin was no longer available the loss to therapeutics would be insignificant. Although he had little experience of some of the new synthetic analgesics such as methadone or levorphan, he had been told levorphan was not as good as heroin, and pethidine was not often adequate. In his opinion, there was no firm argument for keeping heroin for suppressing cough.

Despite these differing opinions, a number of alternative drugs were listed in subsequent ministerial background briefing papers.[35] For cough, these were linctuses containing opium, morphine, methadone, codeine or hydrocodone, and for pain, morphine, methadone, pethidine and levorphan. (The fact that in 1954 there were probably more known pethidine addicts than heroin addicts was not mentioned in any of these briefs.) Ministers were, however, advised to avoid, if possible, actually mentioning any of these drugs by name, as the choice of drug in a particular case was essentially a medical matter. But in the House of Lords on 8 December, Lord Mancroft, joint Parliamentary Under-Secretary of State at the Home Office, had no alternative but to name these drugs when he was asked by Viscount Elibank what the government considered was an adequate and equally effective substitute for heroin.[36]

## Opposition from the British Medical Association

Prompted by Dr Douthwaite's letter of 9 April 1955, other doctors wrote to the *British Medical Journal* to protest against the proposed ban, and local divisions of the BMA began to adopt resolutions seeking its reversal. On 19 May the Annual Conference of Local Medical Committees debated a resolution protesting at the decision. At this meeting, Dr Wand again spoke in support of the Standing Medical Advisory Committee's advice to ministers, arguing that as medical men in a country to which others looked for a lead, they could not allow heroin addiction, as a world problem, to go unchallenged. Shortly after the BMA meeting, on 21 May 1955, a letter from Dr A. G. Donald was published in the *British Medical Journal* in which he argued that the principle of a few people being asked to make a sacrifice for the good of a supposedly larger number of fellow creatures was unethical and unacceptable to British medicine; it was the same principle under which 'the Germans carried out their much discussed experiments on human subjects'.[37]

Inevitably the issue was raised at the BMA's Annual Representative Meeting attended by about 450 members, the majority of whom were general practitioners, and on 3 June the following resolutions were passed:[38]

That this meeting protests against the threatened withdrawal of the most excellent sedative heroin, which is of inestimable value in so many conditions, and recommends that it should still be manufactured in this country for use by medical practitioners but not exported.

That the meeting instructs the Council to seek direct access to the Government to obtain the reversal of the decision on the banning of heroin.

That this representative Meeting of the British Medical Association wishes it to be known that the Association has not been consulted or asked for an expression of its views in any way on the question of the abolition of the manufacture and use of heroin. The Association, representing as it does the doctors of this country, considers this a serious omission on the part of the Government, and in the absence of such consultation the Government cannot claim to have ascertained the views of the medical profession before arriving at its decision.

The passing of these resolutions raised the temperature of the debate considerably and parliamentary interest began to be aroused. On 6 June, no doubt as a result of the Questions which had been put down for Answer on 16 June,[39] the Minister of Health, Iain Macleod, asked for a note setting out the background. In this he was told that the decision whether or not to prohibit the manufacture of heroin was a matter for the Home Office but the Ministry's Standing Medical Advisory Committee had been consulted and had advised that it was an acceptable course of action. The Committee's Chairman, Sir Henry Cohen, again recently consulted, was emphatic the ban could remain and that it would do 'no medical harm whatsoever'. Walker proposed an arranged Written Parliamentary Question to answer the 'numerous untruthful insinuations in the lay and medical press that the decision had been taken hastily and without consultation'. Neither the Scottish Office nor the Ministry of Health favoured this response as it would only prolong the controversy and it was best to let the dust settle.[40]

The first editorial comment from *The Lancet* appeared on 11 June 1955[41] in the form of a footnote to a letter from Dr W. F. W. Southwood of the West London Hospital, who protested at the way the ban was being imposed and suggested the heroin problem in the UK was insufficient to warrant such action. The footnote explained that the UK government's action was intended to support the international effort, the success of which would be prejudiced if we disassociated ourselves from it. This drew an immediate response from Dr D. R. Laurence of University College Hospital Medical School, who, in a letter to *The Lancet* on 18 June, demolished the argument that the ban would assist the international effort to suppress heroin addiction.[42] He pointed out that the clandestine manufacture of heroin was 'child's play', and as long as opium and morphine were available illicitly it would be impossible to control heroin production and addiction; the only way to do so would be to remove the weaknesses in the control systems of the opium-producing countries which were at the root of the problem.

On 25 June *The Lancet*[43] supported Dr Laurence's argument with two quotations from the *United Nations Bulletin on Narcotics*. The first confirmed that leakage of legitimately produced heroin was not at the centre of the international concern; the second was a comment by Professor Georges Brouet of Paris in 1953, that 'if morphine continues in current use, heroin is so easy to prepare that there is little point in banning it internationally'. But having seemingly moved a shade towards opposition to the proposed ban, *The Lancet* then offered a way out of the dilemma by suggesting it was perhaps not too late to test the rival claims about the indispensability of heroin by a controlled trial, even though this would be lengthy and very difficult. If the results showed heroin to have unique virtues 'we should not be blameworthy if we reverted to the manufacture of heroin for use within our borders'. If, on the other hand, no clear advantage emerged, we should maintain the ban without further question. In the meanwhile, the one thing we should not do was 'to insist on retaining the *status quo* on the basis of the present unsatisfactory evidence'.

On 11 July 1955, Dr Gregg, Chairman of the Council of the BMA, led a deputation to see the Home Secretary (Major Gwilym Lloyd-George) and the Minister of Health (Iain Macleod). The deputation included Mr A. Lawrence Abel (later to be a member of the two Brain Committees), Dr A. Douthwaite and Dr R. Hale-White (whose father, Sir William, had advised the Royal College of Physicians, when first consulted by the government in 1924). The essence of the BMA case, apart from the issue of clinical freedom and the need for heroin in medical practice, was that the profession had not been fairly treated. The BMA was the only organisation capable of providing a fully representative view on behalf of the profession, particularly of general practitioners. Although BMA members served on the advisory bodies on which the government had relied for advice they did not do so as representatives of the Association. (This was a point the BMA was to stress repeatedly during the controversy.)

The Ministers were not persuaded by the case put forward by the deputation and on 25 July Iain Macleod (described later by Dr Macrae, the BMA's Secretary, as 'a very slippery customer') told Lloyd-George that he did not feel in the least convinced by the arguments against the ban. He was satisfied that the consultations had been adequate and was sure that the government's decision should be firmly maintained. It was not until 18 October that the BMA was told the government intended to adhere to the advice received from their expert advisers.[44] This unleashed a further flood of protest and for the next few weeks the columns of *The Times* newspaper, and the medical press, were seldom without some comment on the issue, the vast majority being opposed to the proposed ban.[45]

The debate revolved around a few basic questions. Heroin was a valuable drug for which there were no effective substitutes but if the government was advised that there were adequate substitutes, what were they? How could the prohibition of the manufacture of pharmaceutical heroin in the UK help the addiction problem in America, or elsewhere, when heroin was so easy to produce illicitly and when there was no evidence that the problem was caused by legitimately manufactured heroin? But the most important arguments against a ban were that it would be an unacceptable interference in the freedom of medical practitioners to treat patients as they felt appropriate with whatever drugs they considered necessary, and that the advice received by the government was flawed because it was largely from eminent medical professionals attached to teaching hospitals who were far removed from the 'art' and difficulties of general practice.

## Clinical freedom

The issue of clinical freedom attracted widespread support beyond the medical profession. *The Times* newspaper was very much on the doctors' side, and in two important leading articles on 19 November and 1 December 1955 identified the key issues:

> If a body of medical opinion, neither small nor cranky, is convinced that heroin is necessary for treatment, and if no evil may be shown to spring from its prescription in Britain, what right has a Ministry or a Minister or a Government to stand between a doctor and his patient on the subject?
>
> There is moreover a further question of principle involved. Has the State ever before interfered between doctor and patient by prohibiting an established drug which his professional judgement may deem it essential he should use? In some ways this is the most vital issue of all.

It was the question of the advice tendered to the government which exposed the serious divisions within the profession. If the BMA felt that the Standing Medical Advisory Committee had not truly represented the views of practising clinicians, some members of the Royal College of Physicians were questioning the part played by their President, Sir Russell Brain. But in a letter to the Ministry of Health, dated 13 June 1955, Sir Russell had explained why the Royal College of Physicians refused to take action on the same lines as the BMA. The decision of the Ministry's Central Health Services Council (which had endorsed the Standing Medical Advisory Committee's advice) should be adhered to, and he had little sympathy for the idea that a body which has already taken responsibility for a decision through its 'representatives' on the Council should then be allowed to override the Council's decision. What Sir Russell did not address was the question of how far the views he had expressed in the Standing Medical Advisory Committee could be regarded as truly representative of the members of the Royal College.[46]

In a letter to *The Lancet* on 25 June, Dr J. J. Conybeare complained that members of the Royal College of Physicians had not been consulted.[47] Had they been, the majority of the Fellows would have given different advice to the Central Health Services Council, which could not be regarded as representative of those in active medical practice. Further support for this complaint appeared in *The Times* newspaper, on 24 November 1955, when Sir Francis Walshe, a past president of the Royal Society of Medicine, asked if the *ex cathedra* statements of a small committee could be regarded as 'embodying the corporate wisdom and experience' of the medical profession. He too complained that members of the Royal College of Physicians had not been invited to place at their President's disposal their considered views so he had not been in the fortunate position of being able to represent these views to the Minister, 'or even to know what they might be'.

By this time, the matter had reached the Cabinet where, on 30 November, the Minister of Health said he had invited some of the distinguished members of the

Standing Medical Advisory Committee to confirm their view that heroin could be dispensed with. This they had done in a letter published in *The Times* newspaper that morning. In this letter, Sir Russell Brain (Royal College of Physicians), Sir David Campbell (General Medical Council), Dr Roger Gilliatt (Royal College of Obstetricians and Gynaecologists) and Sir Harry Platt (Royal College of Surgeons) had declared that the decision to ban heroin involved a choice of values which could not be made by doctors alone but only by government.

The Minister went on to say that the agitation which the decision had aroused was due much to the efforts of the Fellowship for Freedom in Medicine, a professional group hostile to any direction or control which might be inconsistent with the professional freedom of medical men. Press interest had centred in *The Times* newspaper in particular but the issue had not been taken up in Scotland. One general practitioner member of the Standing Medical Advisory Committee had retracted and it was possible that some other general practitioner members might follow. There was a conflict of medical opinion but support was coming from *The Lancet*. The government would be criticised whether the ban was confirmed or reversed and it would be difficult to justify a reversal to the WHO, as a number of Commonwealth countries had already followed our lead. He was supported by the Home Secretary, who said the question was one of weighing the alleged need for heroin against the opinion of leading medical professionals who, in advising that adequate substitutes for heroin existed, would scarcely have risked their professional reputations on such a matter. The Home Secretary also commented that we had traditionally played a leading part in international action against drug trafficking. Although some Ministers expressed grave misgivings, and the issue was clearly 'delicately poised', it was concluded that, were it not for the question of interference in clinical freedom, there was no doubt there would be general support for the ban among responsible members of the medical profession.[48]

*The Lancet* support referred to by the Minister of Health appeared in the form of a leading article on 3 December 1955.[49] As a draft of this had been sent to the Ministry a few days earlier it must be seen as the government's non-parliamentary defence. Two days later a pamphlet appeared, 'The BMA Case against the Ban',[50] rehearsing the by now familiar arguments, and was circulated to members of both houses of Parliament. As many of the points had already been dealt with in official statements, the Ministry of Health decided it would be 'undignified' for a Minister to reply to the charges.[51]

On the same day, 5 December, at Question time in the House of Commons, the Minister of Health agreed to consider the suggestion of Herbert Morrison, for the Opposition, that a White Paper should be prepared, although this was later abandoned.[52] The Minister denied there had been any pressure from the United States and undertook to consider the suggestion of a clinical trial. That evening he and the Home Secretary met some 60 backbenchers at a meeting of the Conservative

Joint Home Affairs and Health Parliamentary Committee. As later reported by Nigel Fisher, the Committee's Secretary, in a note to the Home Secretary, the 'sense of the meeting was against the ban but probably all who feel strongly were there and therefore the numerical strength of the opposition seemed larger than it really is. The Socialists are not opposing the ban as a party and there is therefore no Parliamentary risk in adhering to it'.[53]

## Withdrawal of the ban

Although it was not immediately apparent, the end of the affair was in sight. On 9 December Lord Jowett informed the Home Office that in the forthcoming debate in the House of Lords on 13 December, on his motion that 'in view of the apparent conflict of expert medical opinion over the banning of heroin in this country, the period of the present licences to manufacture should be extended pending the institution of further enquiries', he proposed to question the *vires* of the government's decision. Whether Lord Jowett had himself spotted this possible flaw in the government's case, or had his attention drawn to it, is not known. But the same doubt had been raised in the Counsel's Opinion, obtained by the BMA shortly before the debate.[54]

The result of this bombshell was a hastily convened meeting of Ministers on 12 December to decide on the line to be taken by the government spokesman in the debate next day. In addition to the Home Secretary, the Home Office was represented by Sir Frank Newsam (Permanent Under-Secretary of State), Sir Leslie Brass (Chief Legal Adviser) and Sir Austin Strutt. The Law Officers immediately agreed with Lord Jowett's view that the proposed action was *ultra vires*, although their formal Opinion was not delivered until 19 December. The basis of their Opinion was that Section 9 of the 1920 Act, under which the ban was to be effected, gave a 'power to control manufacture for the purpose of preventing improper use', which was not the same as a 'power to prohibit'. (In the debate on 13 December Lord Jowett dealt with this point more colourfully by enquiring whether someone in charge of a horse, dog or child, and told to control it, could be said to be doing so if he shot it through the heart.)

The Law Officers also noted that the reference in the Act to 'improper use' implied that there may be a 'proper use'. Furthermore, Section 9 (2) required Regulations to be made authorising pharmacists to manufacture heroin or any drug, and the existence of this mandatory provision was inconsistent with the grant of a power to prohibit manufacture generally. However, the Law Officers had no doubt that under Section 8 the Secretary of State had the power to refuse to grant licences to import or export heroin. On receiving the formal Opinion, Newsam asked Brass what the position would be if the Secretary of State was honestly of the view that there was no proper use for heroin. Brass replied that this would be a matter for the courts, on the basis of expert evidence, since Section 9 did not qualify the words 'improper use' with 'in the opinion of the Secretary of State'.

Macleod was not happy with this turn of events and said the matter could not simply be settled by retreat. The Cabinet had decided to go ahead and there was a majority in the House for their action. Not only did we have international obligations but it was most important that the eminent medical professionals, who advised the government, should not be left to feel that the government had rejected their advice in face of a popular campaign. The government ought therefore to consider legislation. However, it was agreed that in the House of Lords debate the government spokesman would say the legal point was a serious and difficult one, which would have to be examined, and in the meantime the government would not adhere to the previous decision not to renew the current manufacturing licences after 31 December 1955.[55]

On 14 December the Lord President of the Council, Lord Salisbury, reported to the Cabinet on the previous day's debate.[56] In view of the legal argument the government felt obliged to announce that the manufacturing licences would be renewed for a further year, during which time Parliament would have time to consider the matter further. He thought any attempt to seek legislative authority to prohibit manufacture would be defeated in the House of Lords where the opposition was overwhelming. One of the most significant contributions to the Debate had come from Lord Waverley, a former Home Secretary and Permanent Secretary of State at the Home Office, who could not see what possible good such a ban would do in other countries and was against preventing a doctor from prescribing what he genuinely believed was necessary for the treatment of his patient.

The question was now essentially a political one as Sir Austin Strutt noted in a submission to the Home Secretary on 17 December.[57] The government had to decide if the necessary legislation was to be introduced. (The Ministry of Health was clearly relieved that the debate now turned on legal issues, which took it into the Home Office's court.) Strutt felt it would be wrong to throw over the advice given to the Minister of Health that heroin was not indispensable. Moreover, by not enforcing the ban, the UK would be falling from the high tradition of being in the van in the world fight against illicit drug traffic. We could make a contribution by prohibiting export, but the total quantity exported from the UK was less than the amount involved in three recent seizures in North America.

On the other hand, the atmosphere in the House of Lords had been hostile and the government would have been defeated if the issue had proceeded to a vote, while in the House of Commons opinion had veered in support of the government. A bill providing the necessary powers would not be difficult to draft but it would be controversial and would turn largely on the question of what right a government had to dictate to doctors what they should prescribe. Strutt's assessment of the state of opinion in the House of Commons was not shared by the Commonwealth Relations Secretary who, in a personal note to the Home Secretary, said the government faced 'resounding defeat' in both Houses. The Lord President of the Council agreed and suggested the case for a total ban could be reconsidered if the controls over manufacture and exports proved ineffective.

The matter returned to the Cabinet on 3 January 1956, by which time Iain Macleod had been succeeded as Minister of Health by R. M. Turton. The Home Secretary found little support for his suggestion that in the proposed White Paper, or in a debate on the White Paper, he should say that the government had no intention of withdrawing from their current position and that, if it should be found that further legislative authority was required they would consider seeking it from Parliament. When sent a draft of what the Home Secretary intended to say in Cabinet, the Attorney-General objected strongly to the implication that the legal position was unclear, when as the Home Secretary would know, the Law Officers had no doubt that existing powers to do what was proposed were inadequate. (Strutt had dismissed this as 'a silly point'.) But after discussion, the Cabinet decided it would not be justifiable to promote the required legislation as the legislative programme for the current session was already congested. It was doubtful if a bill, even if it successfully passed through the House of Lords, could become law by 1 January 1957, when the manufacturing licences were again due for renewal. The Home Secretary would therefore make a statement announcing the government's decision but this would not refer to the difference of opinion in the medical profession about the medical use of heroin. In view of this there would be no need for a White Paper.

A draft of the proposed statement was approved by the Cabinet on 17 January 1956[58] and on 26 January 1956 both Houses of Parliament were told that the government had decided to prohibit from 1 January 1956, all exports of heroin to countries outside the British Isles, and all imports.[59] Manufacture within the UK would be restricted to the quantities actually required for home medical consumption and scientific use. But there was one matter outstanding.

When winding up the debate for the government on 13 December 1955,[60] Lord Woolton had undertaken to consider whether it would be practicable and advantageous to have a special series of scientific trials to assess the therapeutic value of heroin. The Medical Research Council was approached, but on 6 February 1956 replied that it was very unlikely such trials could be devised. In any case, as heroin was rarely prescribed there would be difficulty in finding enough patients and any trial would therefore take a very long time and it was doubtful if it would yield decisive results.[61]

## 'Woolly thinking'

Looking back on this affair now it is difficult not to agree with Dr Hale-White's comment in the *British Medical Journal* on 30 April 1955[62] that the public debate was being dominated by much 'woolly thinking', or, when it was all over, with the Journal's view that it was 'all rather a sorry muddle'.[63] Certainly the government had no case, apart from a desire for international solidarity, yet they persisted with the claim, for which no tangible supportive evidence was ever produced, that the removal of heroin from medical use in the UK would assist the task of enforcement officers in other parts of the world. *The Lancet* had endeavoured to help out by asserting that the task of those checking the illicit traffic would be made easier because 'wherever the ban operates any heroin found is certainly illicit'.[64]

*The Times* newspaper drew attention to the weakness in the government's argument, in a comment on 14 December 1955 on the House of Lords debate, pointing out that Lord Mancroft, for the government, had given no reasons to support the supposition that control of illicit supplies was made more difficult by the existence of legitimately manufactured heroin. Moreover, the US Treasury Department, responsible for the Federal Bureau of Narcotics, had dismissed the implication that heroin manufactured in the UK was being smuggled into America, as most of the heroin entering that country came from illicit laboratories in Europe, the Middle East and the Orient, with a small amount coming from Mexico.

If the government's case was weak, the BMA failed abysmally to exploit that weakness. Instead of taking a firm stand on the simple and clear-cut issue of principle, that doctors should be free to treat patients with whatever drugs they felt were appropriate, the BMA spent a disproportionate amount of time and energy complaining about the lack of prior consultation, the manner in which the government had obtained their expert advice, and the nature of that advice. Did no one at the BMA anticipate the likely implications of the WHO's 1953 resolution or see any significance in the approach from the World Medical Association?

But there are also unanswered questions about the government's handling of the issue. One of the most important is how did the Ministry of Health, upon whom the Home Office were entitled to rely for guidance, so completely misread the likely reaction of the profession. Were medical administrators so cocooned in their ivory towers that they had lost all contact with grassroots medical opinion? Or was it simply misplaced confidence that because the proposal had been endorsed by some of the most eminent members of the profession it would be accepted by the rank and file without challenge? There had been ample evidence over the years of the sensitivity of the profession to any perceived threat to clinical freedom. In 1924, when the question of substitutes for cocaine was being discussed, the *British Medical Journal* gave a strong warning that 'the proposal to prohibit medical practitioners from using a particular drug is open to serious objection'.[65] As recently as 1950, the Central Health Services Council, in its annual report, had advised the Minister of Health that there should be no absolute restriction on the prescribing by general practitioners of any drug which, in their opinion, was necessary for the treatment of their patients.[66]

The most incomprehensible aspect of the whole affair, however, is how the Home Office managed to cause the government such embarrassment. Walker's failure to heed Barr's 1950 advice was at the centre of the fiasco. But the unanswered question is why he chose to do so, because there is ample evidence that he was familiar with the papers on which it was recorded. It had been only three years since the WHO had been told legislation would be needed if the manufacture of heroin was to be banned in the UK. Why did his superiors not query the absence of any reference to the legality of the proposed action in his minute of 7 February 1955, proposing acceptance of the UN resolution? Barr's advice had been unambiguous and was later confirmed by other lawyers, including Counsel consulted by the BMA, the Law Officers and Lord Jowett.

As far as the government was concerned the statement of 26 January 1956 marked the end of the matter. There was little further direct international pressure for the UK to come into line. In fact there was some satisfaction that 'the relatively small residuum of licit use of diacetylmorphine was tending to be further reduced'.[67]

The international pressure for a worldwide ban eased with the coming into force in 1965 of the Single Convention on Narcotic Drugs 1961. The Convention established the right of individual governments to determine for themselves the control regimes to be applied to a small number of drugs generally but not universally accepted as having no legitimate therapeutic use. It was left to each Party to the Convention to decide if 'the prevailing conditions in its country' required the prohibition of the production, manufacture, export and import of, trade in, possession or use of any such drug, as 'the most appropriate means of protecting the public health and welfare' except for amounts which may be necessary for medical and scientific research only, including clinical trials therewith to be conducted under or subject to the direct supervision and control of the Party'.

The inclusion of this provision represented a considerable victory for those delegates to the Plenipotentiary Conference who had opposed the original proposal for a mandatory prohibition in the Convention. It means that as long as HM Government is satisfied that the normal control measures, as applied to other narcotics such as morphine, are sufficient to protect the public from the dangers of legitimately produced heroin, it can continue to be manufactured and used in the UK. However, there now seems to be a threat to the long-standing policy of prohibiting the import of drugs which are already manufactured in the UK. This comes, not from any change in international thinking but from what the *Sunday Telegraph* newspaper on 12 January 1992 called 'the all-embracing tentacles of the

Treaty of Rome', under which the UK may be compelled to permit the import of heroin from the Netherlands.

## Use of heroin in the care of the terminally ill

Since about the mid-1970s the growth of the hospice movement, and a more widespread use of heroin for pain relief of the terminally ill, have resulted in a dramatic increase in the quantity of heroin consumed in the UK. When the Permanent Central Opium Board first expressed concern in 1948 consumption was around 100 kilograms a year, a quantity which gradually decreased, and until the period just before the Brain Committee was reconvened in 1964 to look into the prescribing of heroin to addicts, the annual consumption was only 50 kilograms. Today the UK's annual consumption of heroin is about five times what it was in 1964, averaging around 250 kilograms a year, used almost exclusively for pain relief.

To some, this may be seen as merely confirming what they have always regarded as the British cavalier attitude to heroin. But as the British National Formulary[68] makes clear, in treatment of severe pain in terminal care 'Diamorphine (heroin) is preferred (to morphine) for injection because being more soluble it can be given in smaller volume'. (In 1995 heroin was also available in linctus form to control distressful cough in terminal lung cancer.[69]) This advice is hardly a 'green light' for the indiscriminate prescribing of heroin for any painful condition and is certainly not interpreted in that way by UK doctors. But I suspect it is the philosophy set out in the Formulary that sets our doctors apart from those in other countries who have readily surrendered their fundamental professional freedom to bureaucracy and politicians. The basic aim in the treatment of terminally ill patients, 'is to keep them as comfortable, alert and free of pain as possible',[70] an aim which has always been fully recognised and supported by all concerned in drug control in the UK.

# 4

# Rolleston reviewed: the first report of the Interdepartmental Committee on Drug Addiction

An Interdepartmental Committee on Drug Addiction, under the chairmanship of Sir Russell Brain, past president of the Royal College of Physicians, was appointed by the Minister of Health on 3 June 1958 with the terms of reference:[1]

> ... to review, in the light of more recent developments, the advice given by the Departmental Committee on Morphine and Heroin Addiction in 1926; to consider whether any revised advice should also cover other drugs liable to produce addiction or to be habit-forming; to consider whether there is a medical need to provide special, including institutional, treatment outside the resources already available, for persons addicted to drugs; and to make recommendations, including proposals for any administrative measures that seem expedient, to the Minister of Health and the Secretary of State for Scotland.

There has been much speculation about the reasons for the appointment of the first Brain Committee. Bean[2] thought the background 'something of a mystery' and was puzzled by the words 'recent developments' in the Committee's terms of reference. On the other hand, Stimson[3] had little doubt they related to evidence of changes in the extent of drug misuse, with cannabis now becoming popular beyond the ethnic communities within which it had previously been largely confined, and with signs of a growing interest in heroin in and around some of the jazz clubs in the West End of London.[4] If only this had been the case. Had the Committee sensed that a fundamental change was occurring in attitudes to drug use, we would perhaps have been spared the necessity for a second enquiry in 1964–1965 and five vital years would not have been wasted.

## The origins of the first Brain Committee

It was J. H. Walker who was indirectly responsible for the Committee's appointment. After moving to a new post, he sent his successor in charge of the Drugs Branch, T. C. Green, a long memorandum on 25 October 1955 setting out a number of issues which he thought needed attention.[5] Walker suggested that the time had come for 'some sort of review' of drug control policy and its administration even though currently there was no serious public alarm about drugs. He thought that the control system, which had been established under the Dangerous Drugs Act of 1920 and extended in conformity with subsequent international agreements concerned mainly with international trade and the control of new drugs, had worked well with little criticism and 'with economy' ('value for money' in today's terminology) but the treatment of morphine and heroin addiction had not been reviewed since the Rolleston Committee's report in 1926.

As Walker had been the United Kingdom (UK) representative on the United Nations (UN) Narcotics Commission, much of his memorandum was devoted to likely international developments and, in particular, to the draft of the new Single Convention on Narcotic Drugs then under consideration by the Commission. He felt that 'a wide-ranging independent review', to be completed by the spring of 1957, would considerably strengthen the government's hand in resisting some of the proposed provisions of the Convention which were not in harmony with UK policies and thinking. One of these would require parties to the Convention to prohibit the use of drugs designated by the Commission on the advice of the World Health Organization (WHO). The likely candidates for prohibition were cannabis, desomorphine, ketobemidone and heroin, with the proposed banning of heroin currently the subject of fierce controversy. (In the light of the part Walker played in this, his comment that 'it seems intolerable that any government should be forced to prohibit any drug which its own medical advisers may think desirable' is intriguing.)

Other issues which Walker felt needed to be looked at by an independent committee were the control of new synthetic drugs, policy on addiction, addict doctors, compulsory treatment and the improper prescribing and supply of dangerous drugs. He drew Green's attention specifically to my recent report on the developing heroin problem (see Chapter 2 on 'Mark's' activities and Drs Rourke and Maguire) from which it was obvious that the guidance offered by Rolleston on the prescribing of drugs to addicts was 'far from being universally observed'. Walker saw the potential threat posed by these new addicts and commented:

> Mr Spear's report makes it clear that there is a small but potentially dangerous group of drug addicts (mainly heroin addicts) in London at the present time and that many of them have become addicted quite recently at a fairly early age … In these circumstances where a group of youngish addicts is thrown together frequently, the risk of proselytism, which is always one of the more dangerous features of drug addiction, is greatly increased. This particular group of addicts could very easily lead to a widespread problem …

The proposal for a wide-ranging review of drug control policy did not find favour with Green's superiors, Samuel Hoare and Sir Austin Strutt. It was sent to Hoare on 8 January 1956 and did not come back to Green until the end of August, Hoare's excuse being that he felt the moment was 'not propitious' for the appointment of an independent committee to examine the whole field of dangerous drugs. He was not convinced that such an enquiry would give greater weight to any objections the government might have to unacceptable proposals in the draft Single Convention. Other countries would probably not believe that such a committee was truly independent, nor was it any good going to a committee unless the Home Office already had some idea where to find solutions to the various problems, although he conceded there could be a case for a committee to look into the specific questions Walker had raised.

In Hoare's view these questions were 'not urgent' and could be considered 'without regard to the progress of the draft Single Convention'. Sir Austin Strutt concurred, and it was not until 19 November 1956, more than a year after Walker sent his memorandum to him, that Green wrote to the Ministry of Health setting out the issues on which the Home Office felt in need of advice. In his letter he drew heavily on Walker's memorandum but for some inexplicable reason he did not mention the emerging heroin problem. The issues he did identify were the increasing range of new synthetic analgesics being developed and placed under international control, policy on addiction treatment, addict doctors and 'script' doctors.[6]

### Control of new synthetic drugs
Green noted that the control of the ever-increasing range of new synthetic drugs, 'many with unmanageable names', placed an unwelcome burden on retail pharmacists, who had to have separate sections in their Dangerous Drugs Registers for each drug, as well as on the police who inspected those records. There was likely to be little demand for many of the drugs and Home Office thinking favoured a special type of control until it became clear whether a legitimate demand for a particular drug was likely to develop, which would permit the manufacture and import of small quantities for clinical trials before the drugs could be released to retail pharmacists or general practitioners.

### Treatment of addiction
The issue with regard to the treatment of addiction was whether the advice offered by Rolleston about 'maintenance' prescribing still held, as evidence available to the Home Office suggested some doctors were not following the advice. (Green suggested that if an addict could work while receiving a drug, he might be able to work even better if he could be helped to do so without it.) Moreover, Public Health Service doctors in the United States (US) had demonstrated that they could withdraw drugs even 'in patients enfeebled with old age', and, although this had been achieved so far only in closed institutions by doctors with highly spe-

cialised experience, it might soon be within the resources of general medical practitioners. The view strongly held in North American circles was that it was unethical to condemn a patient, especially a young one, to permanent addiction.

Green noted that discussions in the UN Narcotics Commission showed it was clear that many countries believed treatment of addiction could only be carried out satisfactorily under compulsion in closed institutions. It had been proposed that this should be made obligatory under the new Single Convention but the UK had succeeded in having the draft watered down by the inclusion of the words 'where the seriousness of the problem of drug addiction and their economic resources warrant such measures'. But other countries would be suspicious of our motives in maintaining this attitude and we ought to ensure it was in line with our own current medical thinking so that in future discussions in the Commission we could maintain our position with a clear conscience.

Green posed three questions in respect of treatment:

1  Did present practices still meet with the approval of the majority of doctors, or had there been any substantial change of opinion since 1926?
2  Had treatment methods advanced sufficiently far in this country to make it practicable to take a stricter line in insisting on serious attempts to effect a cure in nearly all cases before resorting to permanent maintenance doses?
3  Was it desirable to tighten up the present instructions given to doctors about the treatment of addicts?

The third question clearly referred to DD 101 (the 'Memorandum as to the Duties of Doctors and Dentists'), and showed that it was not only visitors from North America who failed to appreciate that DD 101 had no legal status. Even though this was an internal letter, it is a little surprising, given the delicate relationship between government and the medical profession at the time, that it did not bring a swift rejoinder from the Ministry of Health to the effect that government departments did not give 'instructions' to doctors.

### Doctor addicts

Green then turned to the handling of doctor addicts, currently representing about 25% (85) of the known addict population. Walker's comment in his October 1955 memorandum that doctor addict cases, though not numerous, were 'tiresome' because the Home Office had not yet found a satisfactory way of dealing with them, was both misleading and unfair to the Inspectorate and their use of the Undertaking procedure.[7] What really concerned Green was the difficulty of deciding when it was safe to restore the authority to possess and supply dangerous drugs to doctors from whom it had been withdrawn because of their addiction.

Current policy was for no application for restoration to be entertained until the doctor had been free of drugs for at least two years. The application had to be accompanied by certificates from two doctors saying so and that the applicant was unlikely to relapse. Experience showed that these supportive letters were usually from doctors with no expertise in the treatment of addiction and said little more than that Dr X was a competent practitioner and a good sort who was likely to be-have himself in the future. Unfortunately, experience also showed that it was often necessary for a further withdrawal of the doctor's authority when he found unre-stricted access to drugs too great a temptation. Green asked if it would be possible to set up simple machinery for the examination of a previously addicted doctor by someone with experience of addiction, who could give a reasonably good opinion of the doctor's prospects.

### Indiscriminate prescribing

Following the failure of the case against Dr Rourke (see Chapter 2) it was under-standable that Walker should have included the problem of 'improper prescription and supply' in his memorandum. But what is less easy to understand is why he should then argue that a tribunal was not the best solution to this problem. The Franks Committee on Tribunals had been appointed and he had virtually com-pleted discussions with the General Medical Council and the British Medical Asso-ciation about the updating of the tribunal procedures. Furthermore, the intention to restore the machinery had already been announced in Parliament by the Home Secretary, Sir David Maxwell Fyfe, in answer to an arranged Written Question.[8]

If anything, the abortive attempt to deal with Rourke through the courts should have confirmed the need to test the tribunal procedure proposed by the Rolleston Committee in 1926. Yet Walker was still firmly attached to the idea of tackling the problem through the criminal law. He conceded it would be difficult both to counter a doctor's claim that the prescribing of a drug was medically nec-essary and to satisfy a court that such a claim was in fact false. It would be equally difficult to amend the law to trap 'a wilful script doctor', without imperilling doc-tors' clinical freedom to prescribe such drugs as they consider, in their professional judgement, to be necessary for their patients, or without putting in jeopardy doc-tors who might err through inexperience or genuine error. The suggestion that a doctor who made a genuine error of judgement would face severe disciplinary ac-tion showed how out of touch Walker was with Drugs Inspectorate practice. Never, during my 30-odd years of dealing with dubious prescribers, was a doctor who had been 'conned' into prescribing, or who had made a genuine error, in dan-ger of receiving more than a few well-chosen words of advice.

Walker's catalogue of the practical difficulties of using tribunals was equally unconvincing. Although he conceded that tribunals appeared to have worked ef-fectively in Northern Ireland, he reminded Green that there was no power to com-pel the attendance of witnesses, and that adequate evidence, which would have to be of the same standard as would be acceptable in a court of law, would be difficult to obtain. But there had apparently been no problem in preparing a case against Dr Quinlan for submission to the General Medical Council; the Council's decision not to proceed with it was based on political, rather than evidential grounds. Walker also suggested that the power to set up tribunals was 'not clear beyond doubt'. This doubt was not mentioned in the note on tribunals which the Home Office put before the Interdepartmental Committee on Drug Addiction on 9 February 1960.[9]

Walker had suggested that one remedy to the problem of 'indiscriminate or wrongful prescribing', currently being canvassed in international circles, was the special prescription form. Doctors would be required to use special forms for all narcotic prescriptions, the counterfoils of which would then be forwarded to a central point for scrutiny and where necessary, further enquiry. Such a scheme could be operated 'without any threat to professional secrecy by omitting the name of the patient from the counterfoil submitted to the State'. Leaving aside the question of the resources needed, which Walker himself acknowledged would be 'tremendous', the omission of the patient's name would render the whole scheme useless, as it would be quite impossible to identify the person being prescribed a reasonable or excessive quantity of drugs. That he could seriously put this forward as a possible answer to the 'script doctor' further illustrates the wide gap which often exists between theory and practical reality. What neither Walker nor those who were to put the Home Office case before the Interdepartmental Committee seemed to understand was that our problem was not the detection of dubious prescribing, but our total inability to do anything about it. There was a limit to what the Inspectorate could achieve by persuasion, reason and bluff.

As the surviving papers show, Walker's view that it was all too difficult prevailed, and merely identifying the problem seems to have been about as far as those Home Office officials who were involved with the 1958–1960 Interdepartmental Committee on Drug Addiction were prepared to go. Our inability to tackle the overprescribing which was a major loophole in our control, through which significant quantities of heroin were already leaking, was never pressed.

## Meeting with the Ministry of Health

On 5 December 1956, after some initial discussion within the Ministry of Health, it was suggested that a meeting might be arranged with the Home Office to discuss the problems in more detail. The preliminary thoughts of the Ministry officials and medical administrators indicated there was no enthusiasm for compulsory treatment, which would certainly arouse political opposition. Doctor addicts posed difficult medical and ethical problems. The response of the Chief Medical Officer, Sir John Charles, to 'script doctors' showed that he had as little understanding as currently existed in Home Office administrative circles of the threat posed by just one prescriber like Rourke. He thought 'script doctors' presented a 'very tricky problem' but if it was so small was it worth bothering about? He had no idea what effective measures could be taken to deal with them and any attempt to do so would 'come up against the old problem of professional discretion and freedom'.[10]

The meeting took place on 22 January 1957, the Home Office being represented by Green, Len Dyke (who had been appointed Chief Inspector in 1956) and Jack Stephens, the junior official dealing with policy matters. Compulsory treatment was quickly ruled out as a non-starter. The suggestion that doctors applying for the restoration of their authority to prescribe dangerous drugs should be examined by a specialist suffered a similar fate on the grounds there were few doctors who could be regarded as specialists and none of these might wish to be known as 'a Home Office specialist'. The problem posed by 'script doctors' was also perfunctorily dismissed; little could be done about them because of the difficulty of obtaining evidence. Green's note of the meeting shows he had failed to, or had chosen not to, appreciate that detecting such prescribers was not the problem. Counterfoil prescription forms and better information through the NHS about doctors regularly prescribing dangerous drugs, both of which prompted lukewarm responses from the Ministry of Health officials, would do nothing to stop prescribers like Rourke and Maguire.

Only one of Green's original items now remained on the agenda – whether the advice given to doctors needed to be tightened up. (None of the Ministry of Health doctors present had apparently ever seen a copy of DD 101.) It was during the discussion on how this might be done that the idea of setting up 'a Rolleston type committee' emerged. There were some doubts whether a special committee to deal with such a comparatively small problem might not be regarded as 'making too much of it' but the proposal was welcomed by the Home Office. If set up, the committee could consider whether the 1926 guidance should be revised and whether the terms of reference could be extended to cover other narcotic drugs, including the new synthetics. It could also consider the feasibility of providing special treatment for drug addiction.

An official of the Ministry of Health wrote to Green on 4 April 1957 to say that the Ministry's advisors had confirmed that the advice given by the Rolleston Committee in 1926 was now out of date and there was a case for a new committee with wider terms of reference. The Department of Health for Scotland noted that the Presidents of the Royal Colleges of Physicians and Surgeons of Glasgow and Edinburgh, although giving unofficial approval, were doubtful of the need for such an enquiry.

While the Home Office set about preparing evidence to place before the committee, the Ministry of Health proceeded with the drafting of terms of reference and the selection of the chairman and membership.[11] The first choice of chairman was Sir Aubrey Lewis, an eminent professor of psychiatry, but for unrecorded reasons it was felt it would be better to have a general physician, and Sir Russell Brain, past President of the Royal College of Physicians, was appointed. Of the other seven members of the committee, six were doctors and one was the president of the Pharmaceutical Society.

At the end of June 1957 Green sought the Home Secretary's approval for the proposal to convene the committee.[12] In his minute he noted that:

> The enthusiasm of the Ministry of Health for this proposal has noticeably increased of late as they see in it a possible answer to any awkward questions which may be asked about the use of dangerous drugs by Dr John Bodkin Adams, after the Courts have dealt with him.

This was a reference to the impending prosecution of Dr Adams, a general practitioner in Eastbourne, charged with the murder of an elderly patient by administering heroin.

By this time Sir Austin Strutt had been succeeded by E. H. Gwynn as the Under-Secretary of State responsible for domestic drug policy. Gwynn thought the committee should provide up-to-date authoritative medical advice of value, both domestically and for the purposes of discussion at the UN Narcotics Commission. But he was doubtful that the committee's findings would be of much practical help to the Home Office in the administration of the Dangerous Drugs Act and Regulations as:

> We shall still have to seek our own solutions of current problems. It was just as well the committee was not to tackle the problem of script doctors, if it were to do so it would need to be differently constituted and the Home Office would probably have to take some responsibility for it.

## The joint Home Office and Ministry of Health memorandum to the Committee

On 11 March 1958 Green sent the Ministry of Health, for comments, a draft of the evidence the Home Office proposed to submit to the Committee, and directed attention to four specific points on which he felt the need for guidance. These were the distribution of DD 101 (the current means for bringing advice to the notice of doctors), special prescription forms and the treatment of addicts. Ministry officials were not entirely happy with this draft. They did not think it should be the Home Office which posed questions about treatment matters, and therefore suggested the evidence put before the Committee should be a joint effort of the two departments. Green readily accepted this suggestion and by July a final text had been agreed.[13]

The foundations of the first Brain Committee's anodyne report of November 1961 were undoubtedly laid by the joint memorandum. Unlike the document Delevingne had submitted to the Rolleston Committee seeking specific answers to difficult practical control problems, the 1958 memorandum was little more than an instruction manual for a routine servicing of the 'British system'. There was no real problem, a few doctors were not following the Rolleston advice, upon which recent treatment methods in the US now cast some doubt (there was no reference to the extent of addiction in the US), and since 1926 many new drugs capable of producing addiction had been developed and placed under international control. Of the recent changes in the extent of heroin addiction there was no mention.

The Committee was told that the action taken as a result of the advice given by the Rolleston Committee had ensured that the problem of addiction had remained very small. There appeared to have been a considerable reduction in addiction to opiates between 1936 and 1947, but since then the numbers had steadily increased – which was 'disappointing'. What was not explained, for which Len Dyke must take some responsibility, was that this apparent decrease in the number of addicts was merely the result of a major change in the method of compiling the statistics.[14] It was noted that since 1947 addiction to the newer synthetic drugs had increased, and the rate of increase in the total number of known addicts had accelerated in the period since 1954. However, the significant rises between 1954 and 1959 in the albeit small numbers of heroin (from 55 to 68) and cocaine (from seven to 30) addicts were not emphasised.[15]

Any fears that the situation was worsening were quickly dispelled. The 'disappointing' increase in the number of addicts could be 'more apparent than real', and could be due to a combination of circumstances, including the development of the National Health Service, which had led to the wider use of drugs of all kinds, the improved reporting by the police of regular supplies of dangerous drugs, and doctors' lack of knowledge of the dangers of the newer drugs. But whatever the reasons for the increase, it was clear that the advice given by the Rolleston Committee for the treatment of addiction was not always followed in 1958. How could any new advice be brought more effectively to the notice of doctors and how could the principles underlying that advice be brought out more clearly so as to avoid misinterpretation?[16] This was the central theme of the memorandum. What was to be done about the minority of doctors who continued to misunderstand or ignore advice received far less emphasis.

Doctor addicts were said to be 'difficult to detect', a statement which Inspectorate experience showed was certainly not the case, and 'even more difficult to deal with when detected'. But the specific difficulty which had been troubling Walker, of how to respond to a doctor addict's application to have his or her authority to prescribe dangerous drugs restored, was not mentioned. It was suggested the Committee might feel it desirable to consider 'whether there is any way of preventing doctors from freely using dangerous drugs on themselves or members of their families'. This was another 'very delicate question' for which one possible answer might be to require all doctors to keep a record of all dangerous drugs administered or dispensed, including any for themselves or their families.[17] It was not explained, if self-administration was an unacceptable practice, how an additional record-keeping requirement would stop it, as it was hardly likely that doctors would record that they were giving morphine to themselves or members of their families because they were addicted.

Although it had been agreed that the 'script doctor' problem was too difficult, Green's original draft did contain a reference to the possible re-establishment of the Rolleston tribunals. This was deleted on legal advice, although a note from the Home Office in January 1960 specifically asked for the Committee's views 'on the desirability of proceeding with the reconstitution of the medical tribunals'.

In the meantime, the 'Committee's attention was drawn to the 'small number of doctors who deliberately ignore the Rolleston advice, even when it is brought to their notice' and were asked if 'any fresh action' was practicable to put a stop to such activities.[18] (The fact that there was currently no action which could be mounted against these doctors was not emphasised.) The doctors concerned were originally referred to in the memorandum as 'the *so-called script* doctors who regularly supply addicts with drugs, without, it appears, any attempt to effect a cure or achieve a reduction in the quantity taken *and sometimes, it is suspected, for financial gain*'. The Chief Medical Officer, Sir John Charles, was rather upset by the words shown in my italics and members of the Committee were asked to delete them from their copies. Sir John felt that in a document which might eventually be published, it was inadvisable either to mention the suspicions, which he understood could not be proved, that some doctors might be prescribing for financial gain, or to coin a new term of opprobrium, 'script doctor', which was not in use outside the Home Office. (Today such doctors are either 'irresponsible' or 'non-*bona fide*' prescribers, the terms used respectively in the Misuse of Drugs Act 1971 and by the General Medical Council.)

International matters were barely mentioned in the memorandum. The only reference (at paragraph 28) to the new synthetic drugs brought under international control by the 1948 UN Protocol said these were covered by the Dangerous Drugs Acts, 'which already provided for bringing under control any drug likely to be productive, if improperly used, of ill effects substantially of the same character or nature as those produce by morphine or cocaine.' Smart[19] is therefore incorrect in her suggestion that the motivation for setting up the Committee was mainly 'from a concern to respect international treaties on drug addiction' because Britain was due to ratify the 1961 Single Convention. She made this assumption on the basis of a single sentence from a letter to the British Medical Association inviting it to nominate a member, which said 'it would be very helpful for those who represent the government on international bodies to be fully acquainted with current medical views in this country'.

## Evidence collected by the Brain Committee[20]

As the Brain Committee has been heavily criticised for failing to detect the changes then occurring in the drug misuse scene, with Lord Brain[21] offering the defence that he and his colleagues could only act on the evidence put before them, what steps did they take to confirm, or augment, the cosy picture presented in their official briefing? Appendix I of the Committee's report contains an impressive list of witnesses, but the Committee decided, 'as a general rule', not to seek oral evidence. On 4 November 1958 a number of organisations were invited to respond to a questionnaire, listing 12 points which the Committee felt were of importance. A year later this invitation was extended to a number of doctors with special experience of treating addicts, whose names were supplied by the Drugs Inspectorate. By means of a press notice they also invited 'anybody interested to submit representations.' As there is no evidence that members of the Committee carried out any field visits, it has to be assumed these initiatives constituted the 'widespread enquiry' which enabled the Committee to state with such certainty that there were no doctors whose prescribing currently gave rise to concern, and that there was no cause to fear that any real increase in addiction was at present occurring.[22]

Only two of the points on which the Committee sought information and comment in the questionnaire, related to the current extent of the problem:

1   Information available to the Home office suggests that the number of addicts to opiates and synthetic opium substitutes has increased to some extent over recent years. Do you consider that addiction to dangerous drugs is becoming a more serious problem in the United Kingdom?
2   Of the known addicts, doctors, nurses and pharmacists, the so-called 'professional' addicts, form a large proportion. Have you any data to suggest that the number of these addicts is increasing or diminishing? And if so, can you suggest any reason?

The remaining questions concerned: compulsory notification or registration; the use of special prescription forms; the concept of the 'stabilised' addict; institutional versus ambulatory treatment; compulsory treatment; the success of current treatment methods; the dissemination of information to doctors and medical students; whether new analgesics should be restricted until they had been adequately investigated; the use of sedatives, hypnotics, stimulants and tranquillisers; and whether all drugs acting on the central nervous system should be released for general prescribing only after adequate clinical trials had been conducted. The most noticeable omission from this questionnaire was any reference to unjustifiable prescribing.

What was the response to the Committee's general request for information and how did it affect their final conclusions? Were there, in fact, any clues which, if followed up, might have revealed that the situation was not quite as described in their briefing from the Home Office and Ministry of Health? The replies from those organisations which felt able to offer a positive reply contained little to challenge the view that addiction was still not a serious problem in the UK. But there were some interesting individual comments, both in relation to the current situation and having a bearing on future developments.

Probably reflecting a fairly widespread view of drug addiction, the Medical Defence Union believed it was a stable but serious problem, with 'pockets of drug addiction close to seaports and in some large cities with a considerable coloured population'. Two bodies which might have been expected to make positive contributions were almost equally unhelpful. The Royal Medico-Psychological Association (the forerunner of the Royal College of Psychiatrists) did not think addiction was becoming a more serious or dangerous problem, nor was there evidence to suggest the number of 'professional' addicts was increasing; institutional treatment was essential but the mental hospital was not the right place in which to treat addicts; the NHS 'should provide either independent units, or special units, within the curtilage of existing hospitals'.

The reply on behalf of the Society for the Study of Addiction came from its past Secretary and one of its oldest members, Dr John Yerbury Dent. The Society had no corporate opinion on addiction but he was certain many members would agree with his answers to the Committee's questionnaire. He thought addiction to barbiturates was growing and was a serious menace, but addiction to morphine, cocaine or heroin was not, and this could be due to their replacement by pethidine and others of the newer range of synthetic analgesics. Addiction to opiates was not a very serious national problem because there was only a very small black market and addicts could get their drugs legally and under medical control. Not surprisingly, given his known strong belief in the particular treatment, Dr Dent thought addiction was now 'easily curable with apomorphine in the majority of cases' and this should be available under the NHS.

Of the individual replies the most important were those of Dr Denis Parr of St George's Hospital and Dr J. C. Batt, of St Ebba's Hospital, both of whom had had some of the new heroin addicts as patients and were well placed to comment on the changing situation. Although he expressed no opinion on whether the number of addicts was increasing or whether the overall problem was worsening, Dr Parr addressed some of the practical difficulties which his patients created. He firmly believed addiction should be a notifiable disease and that additionally there should be 'registration' for patients being prescribed drugs outside the hospital setting. He wrote:

> I do not believe that ambulatory treatment can in itself lead to the cure of established addiction to dangerous drugs. I am strongly of the opinion, however, that the present tendency for addicts to drift from one to another of a small number of medical practitioners who are willing to prescribe for addicts until their patience expires is highly unsatisfactory. There are many practical difficulties (and irritations) in prescribing for ambulatory addicts over long periods. Sooner or later, for example, such patients complain that they have lost some of their supplies, or that some sudden crisis has caused them to take more than their allowance. Such problems could be handled more satisfactorily in a clinic than by a private practitioner and continuity of supervision would offer a better chance of stabilising the dosage, so far as possible and paving the way for persuasion to undergo in-patient treatment. I would not propose that attendance at such a clinic should be obligatory for registered addicts but that subtle pressures should be devised to urge them in this direction and encourage outside doctors to refer their cases.

Dr Batt had no doubt that drug addiction was increasing and was probably more widespread than generally supposed. Most of his addict patients were women in the younger age groups who were taking morphia, heroin or cocaine. The 'registered' addict made every effort to obtain a supply in excess of her needs so that at any given moment she would have a spare supply which permitted her to introduce others to the evil. This went on as long as she had enough to stabilise herself, but as most addicts invariably increased their dose, the result was a number of patients who required further supplies. In consequence they became 'registered' at a higher dose than necessary or else went to the pedlar. All addicts said drugs could always be found and also admitted knowing others who were not 'registered'. One of the sources of information was the all-night chemist, which 'acts as a club' for this group of people; they congregated there for their next supply and if one of them knew of an illegal source of drugs, the news spread. It was rare to meet an addict who had not got information in this way. If forced to rely on illicit supplies, women turned to prostitution or other criminal activities. Dr Batt also drew the Committee's attention to the increasing use of cannabis, now 'an accepted pastime in the larger cities', and most of his heroin addict patients had previously used this drug.

The replies from two other doctors with experience in the field are interesting for different reasons. One was from Dr A. A. Baker, then at Banstead Hospital and later Senior Principal Medical Officer at the Ministry of Health with responsibility for setting up addiction services recommended by the second Brain Committee. (As he was later to admit,[23] this was a task on which he felt he had been 'wrongly employed.') Dr Baker did not believe addiction was increasing but felt strongly that there should be some form of compulsory treatment, initially in hospital, with a considerable period of compulsory outpatient supervision. Addicts should not receive maintenance supplies of their drugs, as this often led to deterioration and exploitation of doctors by their patients and sometimes of the patient by other addicts.

Dr Denis Leigh, of the Bethlem Royal and Maudsley Hospitals, showed how eminence and understanding are not necessarily compatible. He did not think addiction was a serious problem but he accepted the concept of the stabilised addict. However, if it were not for 'the legal difficulties, trials and tribulations which may beset the doctor who prescribes drugs for the addict', he thought the stabilised addict would be more common. The present situation was unsatisfactory because 'although no register exists, a good deal of pressure is put on these people by the police and the Home Office'. It seems that at some time previously he had had occasion to differ rather forcibly with 'a doctor from the Home Office', who had wanted information about one of his patients without the patient's knowledge or consent. The present system was neither one thing nor the other and if a doctor tried to help a patient, and be a law-abiding citizen, treating drug addicts could sometimes be very complicated.

During their deliberations, the Committee had access to other data having a bearing on the current extent of the problem – for example, that between 1954 and 1957 first admissions to mental hospitals of drug addicts had doubled, from 27 to 54. The Regional Medical Officer Service, from an analysis of 50 cases randomly selected from 400 prescribing enquiries undertaken during 1958, had identified five addicts, including a 26-year-old who had been taking cocaine 'for many years', and a 37-year-old addicted to heroin since 1954 and currently being prescribed 10 grains (600mgms) a day.

At their 6th meeting on 15 December 1959, the Committee spent some time discussing the results of a survey conducted by the British Medical Association on Merseyside. Although there had been a disappointing response from doctors in the area, the general impression was that the problem had not changed much 'since Rolleston'. The survey had identified 57 'true' addicts and some heavy prescribing of barbiturates and amphetamines.

Copies of the responses to the questionnaire were circulated to Committee members but, for the most part, were merely 'noted' and not discussed in any detail. In fairness to the secretariat, the possibility of asking Dr Batt to give personal evidence was apparently considered but for some unrecorded reason was taken no further. The Committee's assessment of the scale of the problem, that it was still 'very small' and not increasing, was therefore based almost entirely on information coming from official sources.

## Illicit traffic

At their first meeting (on 16 July 1958) the Committee spent some time discussing illicit traffic, which had not been mentioned in the joint memorandum. They noted that there was practically no smuggling of heroin (HM Customs had reported no seizures of heroin between 1945 and 1956, around 500 grams in 1957 and 1958, and around 2 kilograms in 1959 and 1960) and that most drug offences involved Indian hemp (cannabis), which did 'not appear to have very serious effects'. 'Criminal addiction', which was not defined, was not a serious problem.

Illicit traffic was again discussed at the 6th meeting on 15 December 1959, prompted by the statement in the government's annual report to the UN that in 1958 there were 15 addicts 'receiving licit drugs by illicit means'. The Home Office, through S. H. E. Burley, who had replaced Green (who had taken up a temporary academic fellowship), again confirmed there was no organised traffic in manufactured narcotics, the amount stolen was small and drugs were not getting into the hands of the public in appreciable quantities other than by prescriptions. There was no market for illicit supplies and the statement merely referred to a number of addicts who had obtained pharmaceutically manufactured drugs by various illegal means.

Nevertheless, following this discussion W. G. Honnor, one of the Committee's joint secretaries, wrote to Burley seeking an assurance for the Committee that thefts of drugs were small and that in general the Home Office knew of them when they occurred. The exercise enabled Dyke to tell Burley in February 1960, that:

> ... we contend that illicit traffic in manufactured drugs does not exist in this country; such evidence as arises from isolated instances, e.g. theft from a hospital or retail chemist, is very seldom capable of proof that, in fact, the stolen drugs reached the illicit market for use by addicts or others.

This statement was incorrect because in two of the four major thefts there had been clear evidence that the stolen drugs had been sold to West End addicts. Moreover, although in his note Dyke detailed these major thefts, neither he nor Burley in the reply to Honnor, commented on the connection between the theft of heroin, morphine and cocaine from a hospital dispensary in 1951 by 'Mark' and the emergence of the new group of young heroin addicts in London.[24]

## Numbers of known addicts

At the second meeting of the Committee, on 22 October 1958, Green reported a 'remarkable' rise in the number of addicts known to the Home Office, from 347 in 1957, quoted in the joint evidence, to 455 by September 1958 (neither of these figures can be reconciled with any published subsequently), with morphine and pethidine being the main drugs involved. He attributed the increase, at least in part, to the new advice issued to the police at the end of 1957, which had probably led to more cases being reported. What he did not tell the Committee was that a change had been made in the method of compiling the addict statistics in 1958 so that only those known to have been addicted in the year in question would be included in the figures.

The Committee readily accepted the Home Office view that the apparent increase in the number of addicts was mainly due to intensified action for their detection and noted in its Report:[25]

> We are, however, satisfied that the arrangements for recording manufacture and supply, and for inspection, continue to ensure that nearly all addicts are known to the Home Office, to the Ministry of Health and to the Department of Health for Scotland.

Green had expressed doubts about the accuracy of this statement when it appeared in an early draft of the report (with 'virtually' in place of 'nearly'), especially as the joint Home Office/Ministry of Health memorandum had described the arrangements as 'necessarily chancy' allowing cases of addiction to escape notice 'for many years'. But Dyke disagreed and insisted that 'virtually' was correct.

The Committee may have been satisfied that most addicts eventually came to Home Office notice but how that information was translated into the official addiction statistics seems to have been a matter of some confusion to their departmental advisers. The original Home Office/Ministry of Health memorandum had quoted numbers of known addicts for the years 1936, 1947, 1950, 1954 and 1957 but the Committee were urged to treat the 1936 figure with caution, as the basis for its compilation was not known. In June 1960 Burley repeated this note of caution, when he provided the secretariat with a revised table and asked that there should be no special reference to the 1936 figure as 'it would cause embarrassment to us to admit that we did not know in 1960 the basis on which our figures 24 years earlier were compiled'.

The addict statistics for 1958, 1959 and 1960, which appear in Appendix II of the Committee's report relate, in fact, to 1957, 1958 and 1959. At the time, the annual statistical count was being carried out by the Inspectorate in January of the following year, so that the figures available in June 1960 obviously could not refer to the number of addicts coming to notice later in the year. Although this error was pointed out, no correction was made before the report was printed.

If there was uncertainty about how the figures were compiled there was equal uncertainty about what type of case was included and the nature of the information about addicts held in Home Office records. At the Committee's meeting on 15 December 1959 it was suggested, and apparently not challenged by the Home Office officials, that the figures should be broken down into 'true' addicts; persons suffering from malignant or chronic disease; 'stabilised' addicts who were able to lead a normal life on a non-increasing dose; and, 'habituates', that is, persons who for psychological reasons were given small doses but who were not 'true' addicts. This followed an earlier request from Dr Roy Goulding, a joint secretary to the Committee, for information on: the number of addicts who were basically psychopathic personalities and for whom drug addiction was simply an 'outlet'; and the number who were otherwise 'normal' personalities but became addicted because they were introduced to drugs for some ostensible therapeutic indication. It was left to Green, commenting on the final draft report in July 1960, to question the proposed statement that persons receiving dangerous drugs for medical conditions were being included in the addict statistics. They were not.

Instead of it being made clear that the Inspectorate did not have information about addicts' personalities, or the need or power to obtain it, we reviewed some 400 addict files to see what information was available. The review, as could have been predicted, was pointless, showing that in 55 cases there was no helpful information, in 109 the drugs appeared to have been taken initially for 'euphoric' reasons, in 272 ostensibly for therapeutic reasons with some suggestion of personality defects for 85, and for 187 there was no information about any personality problems.

### Doctor addicts

The amount of time the Committee devoted to the doctor addict matched the low-key reference to the problem in the Home Office/Ministry of Health memorandum. It had been proposed to ask in the questionnaire to outside bodies whether it would be wise to have a more peremptory means than was available under existing arrangements for withdrawing the authority of an addict doctor to prescribe dangerous drugs. This was a veiled reference to the tribunal machinery but the question was omitted as it was felt it might arouse suspicions that some such 'moves were afoot'; there was also doubt in the Home Office about the legal basis for the Rolleston tribunals. From the surviving papers it would appear that any detailed discussion about doctor addicts was overshadowed, despite the earlier intentions, by the Committee's consideration of the possible restoration of the tribunal machinery.

It was in the context of the tribunal procedure that the Home Office was asked for information about how doctor addict cases had been handled. A review of 35 cases by the Inspectorate showed that convictions were obtained in 13, in a further 12 proceedings could not be taken due to the age or medical condition of the doctor or because there was insufficient evidence, while in the remaining 10 there was no evidence of offences but clear evidence of addiction. In 10 of the cases where convictions were recorded, the Home Secretary had withdrawn the doctor's authority to possess and supply dangerous drugs, and a further 15 had given formal

Undertakings (see Chapter 2). Only three of the 35 doctors were currently giving any cause for concern. This information was provided in May 1960, when the Committee was considering their draft report and there is no indication from the minutes that it was the subject of much discussion.

In the published report[26] the Committee recognised that doctor addicts, called 'professional addicts', though small in number, presented 'special problems' although these 'problems' were not identified. But the Committee was not content with this brief reference and also pointed out that 'a doctor who decides that medically he requires the regular administration of dangerous drugs may lawfully obtain them for his own use by giving a prescription for that purpose' (a situation which still obtains), although this was likely to attract the attention of the authorities, and whether such self-administration or excessive prescribing amounted 'to infamous conduct in a professional respect' was a matter for the General Medical Council.[27]

Green (now returned to the Home Office but not yet officially re-involved with drug policy) and Burley were unhappy about this 'green light' advice, and in a letter dated 12 July 1960 Burley told Honnor he thought it unwise to state so bluntly that a doctor could lawfully treat himself. It was possible that some doctors were deterred from doing so in the belief that it was illegal. Nor was Burley happy about leaving the question of self-administration, and that of doubtful prescribing, to the General Medical Council since the Council could only act as a result of a formal complaint. His further suggestion, that the difficulties in satisfying the Council that such conduct was infamous should be mentioned, was not taken up.

### Tribunals and 'script' doctors

Although Green's detailed reference to 'script doctors' had, on legal advice, been deleted from the joint memorandum, the Committee did look briefly at the problem at their first meeting. It was accepted that doubtful prescribers were few in number, that their activities raised difficult ethical problems and that it was rare to obtain sufficient evidence for a successful Dangerous Drugs Act prosecution or for reference to the General Medical Council. There is little doubt that from the outset the Committee were being gently nudged towards the negative and defeatist Home Office view that tribunals as envisaged by the Rolleston Committee were unworkable. The Committee returned to the question on 9 February 1960 when the Home Office submitted a paper setting out the history of the tribunal procedure. This did not refer to the earlier legal doubts but did offer reasons why the Rolleston tribunals had never been used, 'partly because of the difficulties of getting satisfactory evidence and partly because other remedies were sometimes available'.

The paper specifically asked for the Committee's views 'on the desirability of proceeding with the reconstitution of the medical tribunals', pointing out that the alternative – reference to the General Medical Council – was seldom practicable because 'it was difficult to satisfy the Council that the conduct of a doctor who prescribed what appears to be excessive quantities of dangerous drugs amounts to conduct infamous in a professional respect.' Included in this paper was a reference to the use of tribunals in Northern Ireland.

The procedure in Northern Ireland appeared to be very informal, almost casual, with 'nothing of the star chamber about it'. A tribunal was set up as required under the provisions of the First Schedule of the 1938 Regulations, which did not lay down the specific procedure to be followed. No publicity was given to the proceedings until the outcome was promulgated in the *London Gazette*. In May 1960, Burley discovered that at a recent tribunal defects in its powers had been exposed, as a result of which the authorities had been forced to suspend the procedure. As consolidating regulations were also urgently required in Northern Ireland, it was decided to go ahead with these and postpone the re-introduction of the tribunal powers until there was an opportunity to reconsider them in the light of the Committee's recommendations.

Discussion of the Home Office paper revived the familiar arguments for doing nothing. The number of doubtful prescribers was small, they presented very undesirable features and there was no practicable method at the present time for bringing them to book. If a doctor claimed to be a specialist in treating addiction, it would be difficult to bring professional evidence to refute that claim. The profession would object to any restriction on their freedom to treat a patient as they saw fit and a statutory provision making it a criminal offence to treat addicts unprofessionally would be almost impossible to administer. Any legislation which made it illegal to treat in some circumstances and permissible in others would also raise grave practical difficulties. Having considered all these negative arguments, with no dissent from the Home Office representatives in attendance, the Committee decided not to recommend the reintroduction of tribunals. They would, however, review the decision before their report was finalised and in the light of any additional evidence from the police.

Dubious prescribers and tribunals were again discussed at the 8th meeting, on 8 March 1960, when the Committee found additional reasons why nothing could be done to resolve the problem. These included the impossibility of countering claims made by doctors that they were prescribing in accordance with medical judgement, and the practical problems which would arise from a statutory requirement that a written second opinion should always be obtained. Who would provide the second opinion? Unless this was very carefully circumscribed we could have been faced with Maguire providing the second opinion for Rourke, and vice versa (see Chapter 2). Would it be binding and for what period would a doctor be able to prescribe before a second opinion was necessary? In any case, such a statutory requirement might be seen as interference with a doctor's discretion. Before reaching a final conclusion the Committee asked that the General Medical Council be invited to give evidence.

The approach to the General Medical Council resulted in a letter from the Registrar, Walter Pyke-Lees, in which he set out the Council's position and the history of the exchanges with the Home Office about Quinlan and Rourke. In turn, this prompted a note from Goulding to his fellow secretary, Honnor, which, in addition to proposing that the Council would have to be invited to meet the Committee, confirmed the suspicion that on this issue, the Committee were being led by their officials:

> Meanwhile the position seems clear. We feel, as do the Home Office, that it would be both impolitic and impracticable to set up these Tribunals. Our Committee is in accord with that view and intends for the moment to say so. The G.M.C. on the other hand, considers this to be the only way out. I think they may be shirking their own responsibilities.

Sir David Campbell, President of the General Medical Council, and Pyke-Lees attended the Committee's next meeting, on 27 April 1960. They explained that the Council could take action only in respect of 'infamous conduct' which attracted the penalty of erasure from the Medical Register. It was doubtful if the sort of prescribing under discussion raised moral issues of the sort usually considered by the Council's Disciplinary Committee and special legislation would probably be needed to enable them to deal with such cases. It would be difficult enough for a specialist tribunal, although such a procedure appeared to have worked well in Northern Ireland, but this was their preference since the procedure would be directed specifically at the doctor's right to prescribe dangerous drugs.[28]

The Committee were unmoved by these arguments and confirmed their original decision not to recommend the restoration of the Rolleston-type tribunals:[29]

> We are impressed by the difficulties of establishing a special tribunal for this purpose. There would be a need for powers to take evidence on oath, witnesses who are themselves addicts are notoriously unreliable and it might prove extremely hard to assess 'sufficient medical grounds' in the face, possibly, of opposing medical opinions.

The Committee also thought there would be too few instances of doctors prescribing excessively to justify 'the introduction of further statutory powers to correct them'. It did 'strongly recommend' that doctors should obtain a second medical opinion in writing before regularly prescribing a dangerous drug, 'for a lengthy period, say, in excess of three months'.[30]

As Dyke did not see fit to share the Committee's thinking with the rest of the Inspectorate, we had to rely for our information on the surreptitious examination of his papers. It was therefore not until the summer of 1960, when drafts of the final version of the report appeared, that we had any inkling that there would be nothing in the Committee's proposals which would help us in our efforts to contain a growing heroin population, supplied almost entirely by doctors' prescriptions. I updated my 1955 report on the extent of heroin addiction, which showed that another 46 new heroin addicts, 45 of non-therapeutic and one of therapeutic origin, had come to our notice since then and that the major source of supply was still prescriptions. There had been changes in the ranks of the prescribers with Lady Isabella Frankau now well established in the field, but not yet prescribing in the bizarre manner which was to lead to the reconvening of the Committee in 1964. My report was not completed until 11 November 1960, after the last formal meeting of the Committee, but as the Home Office had not previously brought the existence of the new heroin group to the attention of the Committee, it would have been pointless, as well as embarrassing, to tell it now that the group was expanding.

**Cannabis**

At the meeting on 9 February 1960 the Committee received a paper requested from the Home Office on cannabis, a subject in which they had earlier shown considerable interest. The paper described the increasing use of cannabis, as reflected in the number of convictions and seizures, and offered yet another clue to the changing situation, which the Committee failed to recognise and pursue. Although it does not appear in the report, the minutes show that the Committee concluded that 'on present evidence addiction to cannabis did not lead to more serious forms of addiction'.

## Responses to the report of the first Brain Committee

That the Home Office was already well content with the Committee's conclusions was confirmed by Burley in June 1960. He had been asked by Hoare how the Committee's enquiry was progressing and had replied, 'It will be harmless and dull'. The final report, published in April 1961, was equally well received in the higher reaches of the Home Office and the Home Secretary was assured 'it was unlikely to lead to much change in Home Office practices but will be examined in detail'.[31]

That examination, by one of Burley's administrative colleagues, displayed a complacency matched only by that of the Committee. He commented that the market in illicit drugs could thrive only if there was sufficient profit, and in the UK no great profit could accrue because addicts were able to obtain their drugs of addiction through the NHS on prescriptions. The vital requirement, that there should be some control over this prescribing, which the Committee had failed to provide, was totally missed, or ignored.

Beyond the Home Office the publication of the report attracted little comment, an indication that the problems of drug addiction had not impinged very much on medical, public or political consciousness. There was a brief exchange of correspondence in *The Lancet* about the definitions of addiction, habituation and dependence, while a leading article agreed that the present arrangements had worked well.[32] The recommendation that a second opinion in writing should be obtained before a doctor embarked on a lengthy period of prescribing was welcomed, although what should be done about a doctor, like Rourke, who would certainly ignore such advice, was not mentioned. The absence of any proposals for 'new statutory tribunals or other powers' was also approved.

It was Irving 'Benny' Benjamin, a pharmacist at John Bell and Croyden (one of the two 24-hour pharmacies in the West End of London) who put the first Brain Committee's efforts in true perspective. This he did at the meeting of the Society for the Study of Addiction on 18 April 1961, at which Sir Russell Brain previewed his Committee's report.[33] In an intervention which shattered the self-congratulatory atmosphere of the occasion, Benjamin suggested that not only was the illicit market larger than the Committee believed but it was mainly in the hands of known addicts who were receiving their drugs on doctors' prescriptions. This demolition of the Committee's main conclusions, that there was no cause to fear that any real increase in addiction was occurring and that there were no doctors prescribing for addicts without providing adequate medical supervision, drew from Sir Russell the rather lame response that the Committee could 'only act on the evidence given to us and the conclusions I have stated had been based on the evidence provided ... We can only act on our evidence'.

As the report of these important and fascinating exchanges shows, Benjamin also dealt more than adequately with the attempt by one of the Committee's joint secretaries to suggest he had been remiss in not making his experience available to the Committee. In further comments on the changing drug scene of the 1960s, Benjamin[34] explained that the main cause of his doubt about the first Brain Committee's conclusion was, whereas the Committee claimed that in 1959 there were 30 cocaine addicts in the whole of Great Britain, his London pharmacy had dispensed cocaine on prescriptions to 33 addicts. He was also surprised to be told there were no doctors prescribing for addicts to a degree that might be open to question.

The first Brain Committee's official blessing that all was well at a time when the heroin problem was becoming critical was undoubtedly disastrous. Just how disastrous was shown by the reconvening of the Committee in July 1964 and its very different second report in 1965. Even if the Committee had been seriously let down by their official advisers, as Sir Russell Brain implied at the meeting of the Society for the Study of Addiction, there were enough clues in the information put before it to have prompted anyone taking more than a perfunctory interest in the proceedings, to ask some penetrating questions. For example, with regard to doctors prepared to issue prescriptions to addicts without providing adequate medical supervision, it is stated, in paragraph 37 of the report, that the Committee's attention had been drawn to the existence of only two 'habitual offenders' during the previous 20 years. But Appendix I to the Home Office/Ministry of Health memorandum summarised the activities of four such practitioners. One of these was Rourke, who together with Quinlan, had also been mentioned in the General Medical Council's evidence. Yet no member of the Committee saw fit to enquire whether Rourke was still practising and prescribing. (It is another mystery how Len Dyke allowed this statement to be included in the report, when from his own experience he could have added the names of Tait and Ripka, and should have known of several others.)

The Inspectorate knew there was a serious loophole in our controls, which had to be closed if the heroin problem was not to get worse. What we did not know, until the background papers became available, and certainly did not anticipate, was that our attempts to have this loophole closed, by the use of tribunals to deal with 'script doctors', were being sabotaged by our administrative colleagues, aided and abetted by our Chief Inspector. There is, of course, no reason to suppose, even if the Committee had been told and fully understood what was happening, that they would have made any different recommendations, but at least they would have been denied the excuse that 'nobody told us'.

The further tragedy was the failure of the Committee to look into the future. Why should they think that because they and their advisors believed there was no questionable prescribing at the time they were sitting, there would be none in the future? The Rolleston Committee, dealing with a totally different situation, had had the foresight to offer a contingency plan. The complacency and short-sightedness of the first Brain Committee meant that it was to be another three years, and several hundred heroin addicts later, before the serious consequences of its failures were appreciated.

# 5

# Cannabis and amphetamine misuse in the 1950s and 1960s

The first Brain Committee had concluded that cannabis lay outside their terms of reference, because it was not a drug of addiction, had 'virtually no place in therapeutics', and they had received no evidence that its use caused medical problems.[1] But in the historical context of drug problems in the United Kingdom (UK), neither cannabis nor the amphetamines, similarly sidelined by the Brain Committee, can be ignored. By the time the Committee's report was published in 1961 there was growing concern about the misuse of both drugs.

## Cannabis

Indian hemp, as cannabis was then known, had been brought under control in 1928 and, according to the UK's 1932 report to the League of Nations, 'The illicit use of and traffic in the drug appears to be confined to Arab and Indian seamen'.[2]

In the immediate post-war decade, cannabis was seen as the drug of the recently arrived immigrants from West Africa and the West Indies, and the majority of those involved both in its supply and use were from those communities, along with 'the occasional pseudo-Bohemian kind of individual'.[3] The 1947 report to the United Nations (UN)[4] noted that:

> There has been a considerable increase in the number of seizures of Indian hemp ... [the drug] would be sold to the petty traffickers who are in touch with both the coloured seamen of the East End and the clubs frequented by Negro theatrical performers and others in the West End of London.

The 1950 report stated:[5]

> ... it is now clear that the traffic in hemp is of much greater importance in the UK than the traffic in opium ... whereas the traffic in opium is still almost entirely confined to the seaports, the traffic in hemp has spread to all parts of the country where there is a large coloured population.

Such blatant linking of illicit drug use to particular racial or ethnic groups would now be regarded as politically incorrect but it must be remembered that these statements, with their emphasis on 'colour', merely reflected in the usage of the period and the picture emerging from the seizure and conviction statistics and supported by anecdotal and other background intelligence. But the picture was to change. The raids by the Metropolitan Police on Club Eleven on 15 April 1950 and the Paramount Dance Hall on 1 July produced clear evidence of the widening appeal of the drug.[6] It was no longer possible to tell the UN that there was no evidence to suggest widespread use of cannabis among the white population in the UK.

The increasing number of prosecutions, particularly when young white English girls were involved, provided the popular press with a rich source of material for lurid articles 'closer to those of the 1920s ... [with] shared assumptions about sex, racial differences and inter-racial contact'.[7] Such contacts were noted in an internal memorandum prepared by a member of the Drugs Inspectorate in 1954:

> Although there has been no tendency for opium traffickers, who with rare exceptions are Chinese, to introduce white persons to their drug, there has been such a tendency among hemp traffickers ... The explanation of this would appear to be that whereas the Chinese community tends to isolate itself to a very great extent, the Africans and West Indians find common ground with young persons of European origin in 'bebop' dance halls and music clubs.

Nowadays these comments no doubt appear naive and simplistic but what has to be remembered is that in the 1950s cannabis was a new drug in our experience, although it had appeared on a very limited scale before the war in some of the night clubs in the West End of London. As reported in *The Times* newspaper on 13 October 1938, it had been described by Charles Daubley, the Metropolitan Police chemist, who analysed the sample found in Freda Roberts' possession, as 'a very dangerous drug', a view which remained largely unchallenged until the mid-1960s.

Nor was opinion in official circles any more enlightened or balanced. This was hardly surprising given the heavy reliance then being placed on the far greater experience of the authorities across the Atlantic. But it was not then appreciated that most of the 'facts' about cannabis emerging from the United States (US) Federal Bureau of Narcotics were either gross distortions of the truth, or the creation, for his own political ends of the Bureau's Commissioner, Harry J. Anslinger. There was no one in this country with sufficient first-hand knowledge or experience to challenge the more outlandish of Anslinger's assertions. Sir Ronald Howe, Assistant Commissioner (Crime) of the Metropolitan Police, in his review of Anslinger's book *The Traffic in Narcotics*, merely contrasted the US situation with that of the UK, where cases similar to the 'most sensational' ones used by Anslinger to illustrate 'the homicidal tendencies and generally debasing effects of marijuana', were almost, if not entirely unknown.[8]

Having no reason to doubt this conventional wisdom and knowing from my visits to police forces in the major cities that they were encountering cannabis with increasing frequency, I completed, in May 1960, a review of its illicit use in the UK over the previous 30 years. During the time I was preparing my review, HM Customs had made the by then largest-ever seizure – 169 kilograms from a ship in Liverpool – providing timely support for my main contention, namely that the traffic in cannabis was becoming well organised, and needed to be addressed before the energies of the traffickers were directed to the supply of other drugs such as heroin. As the enforcement response was unco-ordinated, and very largely dependent on the interest and enthusiasm of a comparatively small number of individual police and Customs officers, I proposed the Home Office should hold a conference at the earliest opportunity to assess the extent of the problem, the practical difficulties being encountered by the enforcement bodies, and any useful measures which could be taken to co-ordinate the enforcement response.

In March 1961 Burley, then head of the Drugs Branch, who had been considering the proposal, asked for the statistics in the review to be updated, and in due course, after further thought, rejected the suggestion that the traffic in cannabis was now well organised. (This is an interesting assessment, given that a predecessor of his, J. H. Walker, in an address to the Canadian Senate Special Committee on the Traffic in Narcotic Drugs in Canada on 17 May 1955, had stated that 'in 1954 … for the first time there were clear traces of an organized international traffic in Indian hemp'.) There the matter rested until T. C. Green returned to take administrative charge of drugs policy.

On 22 November 1962 a meeting was held at the Home Office, attended by senior police officers from the cities where cannabis use was prevalent as well as by officers from HM Customs and Excise working at the ports where seizures of illicit imported cannabis were most frequently made. In addition to confirming the picture of cannabis use shown in my review, and the inadequacy of the enforcement response, the meeting provided a useful opportunity to obtain a police view of the drug scene in the UK. Opium was considered to be no longer a problem in Liverpool or London, where previously most offences and seizures had been recorded and it appeared that the younger members of the Chinese community were not interested in opium-smoking. Nor were there any signs that heroin addiction was a problem outside London, where over-prescribing was the main source of supply to the illicit market. However, to a number of those present the use of amphetamines by young people was a matter of far greater concern than the use of cannabis or heroin. It was this meeting, and not the later publicity given to the 'purple heart craze', which laid the foundations of the Drugs (Prevention of Misuse) Act 1964.

## Amphetamines

The first Brain Committee acknowledged that the misuse of stimulant drugs such as amphetamine and phenmetrazine had led to 'some publicity and concern'. Although cases of addiction and habituation did occur, the Committee believed, as they had in respect of opiate addiction, that such abuse 'was not widespread', again demonstrating the superficiality and ingenuousness of their enquiry. The fact that some 2.5% of the 214 million NHS prescriptions in 1959 were for amphetamine preparations or phenmetrazine might indicate excessive prescribing but to the Committee was 'hardly to an extent that could give rise to concern'.[9]

On 10 July 1961, Kenneth Robinson, then the Labour Party opposition spokesman on health issues, and a future Minister of Health, followed up those comments in the Committee's report by a Parliamentary Question to Enoch Powell, the current Minister of Health, asking what steps he proposed to promote research into the prescribing pattern for habit-forming drugs like amphetamine. The answer, that the matter would be referred to the Standing Committee on Operational Research in the Pharmaceutical Services, is less interesting than Robinson's supplementary comment, on which Powell declined to express an opinion, that there was a view that 'the Brain committee took a rather too complacent attitude' about drug addiction in the UK.[10]

If the first Brain Committee had interpreted, and responded more conscientiously to, their terms of reference in relation to 'other habit-forming' drugs, they might have pondered on the possible effect on the level of amphetamine prescribing of the statement in the Ministry of Health's Annual Report for 1954 that 'drugs of this group [amphetamines] have the advantage of being relatively non-toxic, addiction to them is rare, and there are no serious ill effects'.[11] A more thorough enquiry would also have revealed that by then the demand from the general public for amphetamine preparations had increased sufficiently to prompt the Pharmaceutical Society, whose members were being embarrassed by demands for the drug, to suggest that tighter controls were needed.[12]

In 1954 amphetamine and its preparations were controlled only as Schedule 1 poisons, which meant that they could be sold 'over the counter' without a doctor's prescription but only under the supervision of a registered pharmacist and if the person was known to the pharmacist as someone to whom the drugs might properly be supplied.

The Pharmaceutical Society therefore proposed that control should be strengthened by placing amphetamine and its salts, other than in an inhaler, in Schedule 4 of the Poisons Rules, thus making it available only on prescription. This change in the legal status of amphetamine, made in January 1956, did little to reduce its availability or popularity and was followed by an increased demand for inhalers, which could contain up to 325mgm of amphetamine base.

The police were left in much the same position as their predecessors in 1916 before the introduction of Defence of the Realm Act Regulation 40B. They might find someone in possession of amphetamine tablets, almost certainly not obtained on a prescription, but unless they could offer evidence of a sale, which was usually very difficult to obtain, there was no action they could take. In a very few areas, including London, local legislation, such as the Metropolitan Police Act 1839, did allow for prosecution where there were reasonable grounds for believing, or where it could be shown, that articles or goods found in someone's possession had been stolen or unlawfully obtained. To remedy this unsatisfactory situation, it was proposed, at the November 1962 meeting at the Home Office, that if amphetamine could not be placed under full Dangerous Drugs Act control, there should at least be an offence of unlawful possession, with the onus of proof placed on the person found in possession that they had obtained the drug lawfully.

The misuse of amphetamine which was worrying the police in 1962 was not that to which the first Brain Committee had referred and which had raised issues on which the Committee did not feel 'competent to pronounce'. The 'publicity and concern' about the abuse of stimulants, noted by the Committee, was being expressed in the medical literature and was directed mainly at adults receiving the drugs on doctors' prescriptions who 'presented with severe (though transient) mental disorder'.[13] It was not until 1963 that serious press, Parliamentary and public attention was focused on the increasing numbers of young people taking 'pep pills' which had not been prescribed for them. One of the most popular preparations was Drinamyl, a combination of dexamphetamine and amylobarbitone, widely known as 'purple hearts' (although the tablets were coloured light blue and triangular in shape).

The beginning of amphetamine misuse by young people is a much under-estimated factor in the growth of the British drug problem. There are a number of important accounts of the part this drug played in the all-night club/music scene of the 1960s, which leave little doubt that it was the widespread use of amphetamines which laid the foundations for many of the changes in the nature of drug misuse that were to occur over the next decade.[14]

The first public indication that the Home Office was taking seriously the views expressed by the police in 1962 came on 4 April 1963. The Parliamentary Under-Secretary of State, C. M. Woodhouse, told Laurie Pavitt, in reply to his Parliamentary Question, that while it was not appropriate to bring amphetamine within the scope of the Dangerous Drugs Act, which was concerned with drugs controlled by international agreement, the Home Secretary was nevertheless considering the possible need for its stricter control.[15] This consideration of the problem proceeded at the customary leisurely bureaucratic pace and in December 1963 the Home Affairs Committee of the Cabinet agreed that officials should prepare a scheme of control which could possibly be included in the 1964/1965 legislative programme.

By this time there had been consultations with various professional interests, as the then Home Secretary, Henry Brooke, disclosed on 30 January 1964 in answer to Parliamentary Questions from Kenneth Robinson and Ben Parkin. Robinson had drawn attention to the large number of cases of illegal possession of amphetamines by young people now coming before the courts in London and asked what action the Home Secretary proposed to take. Parkin repeated Pavitt's earlier suggestion that a Dangerous Drugs-type control should be imposed on amphetamines.[16]

In the light of what was shortly to occur, Brooke's reply is particularly interesting as it shows that in January 1964 he had no plans to introduce legislation in the immediate future. He was gravely concerned about the abuse of amphetamines and had drawn the attention of the pharmaceutical industry to the need to take closer precautions to ensure that such drugs did not get into the hands of those who trafficked in, or misused, them. He had also been in touch with the Pharmaceutical Society about the retail trade and the Ministry of Health had suggested to the medical profession steps to make the forgery or alteration of prescriptions for drugs of this kind more difficult and to avoid the prescribing of drugs not needed for therapeutic purposes. Brooke concluded, 'If further action proves necessary, I will not hesitate to take it'.

The political necessity to take further action was triggered the following week by a series of articles by Anne Sharpley in the London *Evening Standard* newspaper, in which she graphically described the West End 'pill scene', with the first article appearing on 3 February 1964. On 7 February the Cabinet Home Affairs Committee agreed with the Home Secretary that stricter controls were urgently needed and authorised the preparation of a bill, to be ready by Easter, to bring these into effect. Brooke informed Parliament on 27 February of his intention to legislate[17] and the bill was introduced on 31 March 1964.

## The Drugs (Prevention of Misuse) Act 1964

The Act started its life as the 'Stimulant Drug' Bill but it would appear that during the drafting stage someone remembered that the term 'Prevention of Misuse' was available. For an Act intended to prevent misuse, it deserves to be remembered more for what it did not contain, than for what it did. Leading critics, as reported in *The Times* newspaper on 20 April 1964, described it as 'a palliative' which, by treating drug users as ordinary criminals, could be harmful, unless the government was prepared to tackle drug misuse at grassroots as a medical and social problem.

The Act gave police the offence of unlawful or unauthorised possession, but not an offence of unlawful supply, which left them in the same unsatisfactory position they had been in under the Poisons Law, of having to obtain evidence of actual sale.

(The offence of 'possession with intent to supply' controlled drugs was created seven years later by the Misuse of Drugs Act 1971.) Manufacturers, wholesalers and other dealers in bulk pharmaceutical supplies were required to register with the Home Office but were not required to introduce any security precautions or to keep any sales or stock records of amphetamine preparations. Only licensed dealers would be able to import amphetamines but this would be under a 'blanket' authority and individual imports would not require specific licences, as was currently the case with drugs controlled under the Dangerous Drugs Act. Logically, since there would have been no records to inspect, no powers of inspection were provided.

These were the 'new and stronger weapons' which, in his speech on the bill's Second Reading on 30 April 1964, the Home Secretary asked the House of Commons to approve, and which his Parliamentary Under-Secretary of State, C. M. Woodhouse, winding up the debate, asserted were necessary to plug a number of existing loopholes including thefts from manufacturers, wholesalers and retailers, forgery and alteration of prescriptions, patients who passed on some of their prescribed supplies to others, and illicit importation.[18] In his speech, Brooke revealed that some months previously he had been out with the police in the West End of London to see for himself some of the problems they were facing. What had most deeply impressed him was 'the danger to teenagers, both boys and girls, if this easy getting and taking of "purple hearts" went on growing and spreading'. What neither he nor Woodhouse explained, nor were they challenged to explain, was how the measures now being proposed would make the obtaining of 'purple hearts', or other amphetamine preparations, more difficult. As the bill's critics complained, the one, and possibly only, benefit was that it would now be easier for the police to deal with those who had successfully obtained 'purple hearts' without a prescription.

The proposals had received a less than enthusiastic welcome from *The Times* newspaper, whose leading article on 1 April 1964, under the heading 'A bill too soon', suggested that a sense of proportion was needed. Emotion was never a sound basis for law-making, particularly by the Home Office. The article asked a number of pertinent questions, none of which were satisfactorily answered during the bill's Parliamentary passage. How much of the current hooliganism was due to 'pep pills' and what evidence was there that 'hastily conceived' legislation would have any effect on the behaviour of restless youngsters? What hard evidence did the Home Office have about the extent of the problem? In many ways the latter was the key question because there were few statistics on which the Home Office could rely, and much of the 'evidence' which had prompted the Home Secretary's hurried response to the Sharpley articles was anecdotal.

The absence of hard evidence was particularly true with respect to the sources of the pills circulating in the West End clubs and elsewhere. With no record-keeping or security requirements, or power of inspection, no one could identify with certainty where the drugs were coming from. As Shapiro has commented:[19]

The question of supply during this period is one that has never been fully investigated. Certainly most of the amphetamines in circulation around the clubs were manufactured drugs, not the product of illicit street laboratories. Nor, in view of the huge number of pills involved, could they simply have been spillage from over-prescribing by doctors. Individual youngsters may have obtained some from the medicine cupboard at home, but not dealers ...

Most of the 'authoritative' statements of the time were little more than guesswork, often reflecting the professional interests of those making them. The Pharmaceutical Society identified thefts from warehouses and supplies in transit, forged prescriptions and supplies brought in from other countries as the main sources but did not mention the opportunities for pilfering by the unqualified staff in pharmacies. Manufacturers' spokesmen, before, during and after the bill became law, were quick to deny there could be any leakage from their premises. Although not an official government spokesman, Lord Balniel, in whose constituency the main manufacturer, Smith, Kline and French (SKF), was located, was satisfied that the company's audit of materials in and out of the premises 'absolutely foolproof'.

In an exchange at a meeting of the Society for the Study of Addiction in September 1966, a Mr Schrire, representing SKF, described as 'nonsense' the suggestion that it was easy for anyone on the production line 'quietly to take a handful and augment their wages by selling them'.[20] And during the House of Lords debate on the bill, it was claimed that most firms imposed 'rather strictly' their right to search employees,[21] which was in contrast with actual practice, as the Inspectorate knew only too well from our visits to Dangerous Drugs licensees. Most of them had a contractual right of search but exercised it sparingly because of trade union sensitivities on the issue. A further red herring was the suggestion that supplies were being imported. Some undoubtedly were, but given that the most popular amphetamine tablets were manufactured in this country and were rarely in short supply, there was little incentive to seek supplies from elsewhere.

If close observers of the 'pill scene' were less than convinced by the industry's defences, they were equally unimpressed by the response of SKF to the specific suggestion that they should change the shape and colour of Drinamyl tablets. As early as August 1959, the Pharmaceutical Society had suggested that preparations should not be identifiable by 'sensory' characteristics such as shape.[22] On 3 February 1964 Ben Parkin was told in the House of Commons that the Home Office had discussed with the manufacturers and the Pharmaceutical Society the possibility of producing Drinamyl in a less recognisable shape but no conclusion had been reached.[23]

Parkin's further question, on 10 March, elicited the information from the Home Secretary that he understood the manufacturers were consulting the British

Medical Association (BMA) before reaching a final decision.[24] Parkin continued to press this issue and in the Second Reading debate on the bill on 30 April, recognising that Lord Balniel had had 'a fairly well-documented brief' representing the manufacturer's position, regretted 'they had dodged the recommendation of deglamourising a pill by altering its shape, its colour and its name'.[25] The question was again raised, during the report stage of the bill on 22 June 1964, when Kenneth Robinson moved an amendment to give the Home Secretary power to require manufacturers to change the appearance of a drug. He had given notice during the Committee examination of the bill that he might do this, as up to that point the manufacturers had been 'unwilling' to make any changes in Drinamyl's appearance.[26]

However, Woodhouse was able to confirm that negotiations between the Home Office and the manufacturers had now been successfully concluded, although he did not think the exact character of that conclusion was best canvassed in public. The amendment was withdrawn and in July SKF announced, in a circular letter, that they would be changing the colour and shape of Drinamyl tablets. On 6 August 1964 *Medical News* disclosed that in future the tablets would be blue in colour and round in shape.

SKF's proffered reasons for making the change were that since there were numerous other round blue tablets on the market, the change would confer a higher degree of anonymity on the product thereby helping materially to combat illegal traffic and misuse. There was a swift response from Professor Stanley Alstead, of the University of Glasgow Department of Materia Medica, who, in a letter to *The Lancet* on 15 August 1964,[27] wondered if the problem was disposed of by this 'curious manoeuvre'. Black marketeers could use other potent blue tablets, such as warfarin, and thus create problems for other manufacturers. Why did the company not go the whole hog and change to a white tablet or offer the ingredients separately? What Professor Alstead failed to anticipate was that after the shape was changed, police would occasionally recover white non-amphetamine tablets that had been soaked in blue ink and which were apparently so effective that the dealers received repeat orders.

The Drugs (Prevention of Misuse) Act came into force on 31 October 1964, by which time the Brain Committee had been reconvened to look at the serious growth in heroin addiction. Although on this occasion 'habit-forming' drugs were excluded from their terms of reference, the Committee nevertheless noted 'with approval the operation of the Drugs (Prevention of Misuse) Act 1964'.[28] Yet, paradoxically, the Committee also expressed concern at 'the large quantity of habit-forming drugs currently in circulation' and the consequent potential danger to the young – a clear indication that the new controls were not making it more difficult for amphetamine tablets to be obtained.

The *British Medical Journal*, on 20 March 1965, commenting on an important decision of the Divisional Court which exposed a serious loophole in the Pharmacy and Poisons Act 1933, had already made a similar point.[29] The Court had ruled that sales of amphetamine by wholesalers to retail dealers who were not 'authorised sellers of poisons', that is, were not registered pharmacists, were perfectly legal, thus opening the way for 'profiteers' to set themselves up as retail dealers. The loophole was closed a year later. The Journal should not have been surprised by the continuing availability of amphetamines outside the usual medical and pharmaceutical channels. By May 1965, the ineffectiveness of the Act had already been recognised in administrative circles in the Home Office and an internal review set in motion. However, it was not until 5 May 1966 that there was any public announcement that the government was looking at the working of the 1964 controls.[30]

Police forces throughout the country had found the new offence of unlawful possession helpful, but those critics who had always maintained the Act would do little to reduce the availability of amphetamine preparations were vindicated by the quantities which some individuals were found to have in their possession. For example, in the three months after the Act came into force, 40 persons had been found in possession of 500 tablets, 11 of more than 2,000, nine of more than 10,000, four of more than 20,000 and one of 63,000, the source of which could not be identified.

But the best illustration of the size and nature of the loophole which Home Office Ministers had succeeded in persuading Parliament the Act would close, was provided by a case in London, involving two men found by the police in possession of 140,000 amphetamine tablets. Enquiries revealed that 60,000 of these had been part of a frustrated export order and the remaining 80,000 had not been missed by the firm concerned.

Although the Drugs Inspectorate was not supposed to show any official interest in amphetamines, we nevertheless took every opportunity on our routine visits to licensees to look at the arrangements for storing them. Only a small number of firms had introduced special security precautions since October 1964 and on most premises amphetamine tablets were stored on open shelves where they were readily accessible to all employees. This easy access was compounded by the unsealed, screw-topped containers in which most tablets were then supplied, and from which it was possible for anyone, provided they were not too greedy, to remove tablets with little fear of detection. The rationale of this approach, as explained by more than one management, was that amphetamines were a popular item on many orders and therefore had to be easily accessible, but also their legitimate cost was so low that it was cheaper to bear the losses through theft, than install expensive security precautions.

It was quite clear that this very serious security loophole would not be closed without statutory authority. This was finally provided, with the passing of the Misuse of Drugs Act 1971, after there had been a detailed examination of the continuing amphetamine problem by a Sub-Committee of the Advisory Committee on Drug Dependence chaired by Baroness Barbara Wootton.[31] The Sub-Committee was assisted by a report, published in 1968 by a BMA working party which had concluded that 'amphetamines have a very small part to play in legitimate medical practice; they should rarely be prescribed and be subject to strict voluntary control'.[32]

## Ineffectiveness of the new controls

There is one question still to be answered. Why did the Home Office waste everyone's time with such a futile piece of legislation as the Drugs (Prevention of Misuse) Act 1964? The answer is not hard to find. This was the first occasion on which 'presentation' entered the drug misuse field. *The Times* newspaper, on 20 April 1964, commented that the bill was initiated by the Home Secretary and did not have the backing of his permanent officials, 'another sign of the government's present sensitivity to public opinion'. A similar point was made by one of the government's back-benchers, Ronald Bell, during the Second Reading debate on the bill. Questioning the need for it, he suggested that 'only too often is this kind of legislation thought up because of some passing need of the moment. People said 'pass a bill. Do something about it. Clean up this mess. Never mind abstract principles'.[33] As Bell appreciated, for the British public, and unfortunately for many of their legislators, the passing of an Act was synonymous with 'action' and very few stopped to consider whether the Drugs (Prevention of Misuse) Act 1964 would achieve the results its title implied. The political response to the Sharpley articles imposed a timetable that did not allow sufficient time for the essential consultations which could have led to a workable and far more effective control scheme.

Despite what was said by ministers, amphetamine could probably have been brought within the scope of the Dangerous Drugs Act 1951, which provided for the control of drugs 'having effects analogous to … cocaine' and it should not have been difficult to obtain the necessary supportive pharmacological evidence. But this approach had been rejected on the grounds that the Dangerous Drugs legislation was concerned only with those drugs which were controlled under international agreements. There was, however, another consideration which Woodhouse disclosed in the Second Reading debate.[34] Dangerous Drugs-type control could not be effectively applied to drugs which were prescribed in 'such large quantities'. This unconvincing argument, which was again to be advanced a few years later as a reason why barbiturates could not be controlled under the Dangerous Drugs legislation, is based on an assumption that because a drug is prescribed widely, it is therefore being prescribed wisely.

If amphetamine had been classified as a dangerous drug in 1964, when its therapeutic value was being seriously questioned and it was being considered for international control, it is probable there would have been a dramatic decrease in the quantities being prescribed. In turn, this would have resulted in fewer tablets being manufactured and therefore fewer in legitimate circulation, weakening still further the argument that the imposition of record-keeping and security requirements would place 'an unacceptably heavy burden' on the industry and professions. As it was, the Drugs (Prevention of Misuse) Act in 1964[35] merely postponed the introduction of stronger controls on amphetamine for another seven years, until the Misuse of Drugs Act 1971 was passed.

# 6

## The better control of prescribing heroin: the second report of the Interdepartmental Committee on Drug Addiction

If there was speculation about why the Interdepartmental Committee on Drug Addiction (the first Brain Committee) was appointed in 1958 there was little doubt that public concern about the continued increase in the number of known young non-therapeutic[1] heroin and cocaine users led to it being reconvened in July 1964. Most commentators have readily accepted that the first Brain Committee had been the victim of a rapidly changing situation but few have been sufficiently uncharitable to point out that the 'new situation'[2] confronting the reconvened Committee was an inevitable consequence of its earlier failure to detect the change in the extent of heroin misuse, which had begun in the early 1950s.

There is, however, some uncertainty about exactly what prompted the Minister of Health to reconvene the Committee when he did. It has been suggested he was responding to pressure from the press and Parliament or the Home Office.[3] It has also been claimed, incorrectly, that the Society for the Study of Addiction had 'some influence on the complex negotiations which surrounded the reconvening of the Brain Committee'.[4]

The facts are really quite simple and straightforward. The complacency of the first report of the Brain Committee and the statement that there was 'no cause to fear that any real increase in addiction was at present occurring',[5] did not equate with the situation the Drugs Inspectorate was seeing on a day-to-day basis or with the experience of others in close contact with the drug scene in London. In order to ensure that the continuing increase in the number of heroin addicts could not be explained away merely as the result of 'intensified activity for its detection and recognition' the Inspectorate made even greater efforts to monitor the situation more closely and to ensure that every heroin addict coming to our notice was recorded in the Addicts Index and hence would be counted in the annual addict statistics.

As a result we were able to produce two reports describing the steadily deteriorating situation. The first, prepared in May 1962 by the then deputy Chief Inspector, Charles Jeffery, was a detailed account of the prescribing of heroin by Lady Isabella Frankau, and the other was yet another review of the nature and extent of heroin addiction in the United Kingdom (UK) which I completed in

November 1963. Although these papers were complementary, it was the latter which triggered the reconvening of the Brain Committee.

## Collecting information on the number of addicts

It must be confessed that some of those we included in the Addicts Index might not have qualified as addicts under a strict interpretation of the World Health Organization (WHO) or the first Brain Committee's definitions of addiction, but there was always some evidence that they used heroin. This might be a report from the doctor of an addict patient, or a pharmacist's record of a prescription for heroin, or an admission of use by a prisoner to a prison medical officer (who under an internal Home Office arrangement reported to the Inspectorate any addicts they saw) or to a police officer by an arrested person found in possession of heroin or injecting equipment. There was, of course, no guarantee that the person whose name (which might be an alias) appeared on a prescription for heroin was addicted, or even required heroin for their own use.

Because we could not then rely on the Metropolitan Police to make frequent and regular inspections of pharmacy records we made arrangements to track supplies of heroin from the two manufacturers to retail pharmacies and hence to individuals in receipt of prescriptions and to their prescribers. In the 1960s heroin was usually prescribed in the form of 1/6 grain (10mgm) hypodermic tablets, popularly known as 'jacks', which the addict then dissolved, hopefully in sterile water, and injected. (Some addicts, probably for commercial rather than therapeutic reasons, insisted on receiving 1/12 grain tablets.) By checking the distribution of these tablets through the wholesalers, we were able to identify the retail pharmacies to which addicts took their prescriptions. Apart from the two 24-hour pharmacies in the West End of London (Boots at Criterion Buildings in Piccadilly Circus, and John Bell and Croyden in Wigmore Street), these were usually located near the addresses of the prescribers. Inspectors (usually me) began to visit these pharmacies at fairly frequent intervals.

These visits allowed us to obtain details of prescriptions dispensed for heroin as well as picking up gossip which helped to build a picture of what was happening. The two 24-hour pharmacies, whose staff were always very helpful, were particularly important in this respect since, as Dr Batt had told the first Brain Committee, they were in effect 'addicts' clubs' where information about new prescribers would be passed on and where it was nearly always possible to find a supply from someone willing to 'help out' a fellow addict. In the days before the police began to take a greater interest, and addicts became more security minded, it was possible to stand at midnight in Piccadilly Circus outside Boots and watch addicts sharing their recently dispensed supplies of heroin, often on the pharmacy steps. At John Bell and Croyden the dispensary was in the centre of the premises with a comfortable waiting area where borrowing, lending or selling of tablets could take place out of the sight of staff. (There was a fish tank in this area into which, it was rumoured, the occasional 'jack' disappeared to give the goldfish a 'buzz'.) But the main market place was always Piccadilly Circus, with Subway 4 of the London Underground Station and the public toilets located there featuring prominently.

## Lady Frankau's prescribing

Jeffery's report of May 1962 confirmed what was obvious to anyone close to the London addict world, that the prescribing of Lady Isabella Frankau, of 32 Wimpole Street London W1, was the mainstay of the flourishing illicit heroin market. She was a psychiatrist (and the wife of Sir Claude Frankau, an eminent surgeon) who had for many years specialised in the treatment of alcoholism in private practice. Lady Frankau's interest in drug addiction had apparently been aroused towards the end of 1957, when Dr Patricia Stanwell, a general practitioner in South Kensington who already had one or two addict patients, persuaded her in the course of a consultation about an alcoholic that she should try her hand with a heroin addict. During the next few months Dr Stanwell accepted an increasing number of addicts on her NHS list and the Inspectorate began to think of her as a potential 'script doctor'. However, enquiry soon revealed that she was prescribing heroin to her addict patients under Lady Frankau's direction, while the latter provided psychotherapy as a preliminary to the addict entering a nursing home for withdrawal under her supervision. Lady Frankau also began prescribing heroin on her own account, initially on NHS prescriptions which she signed 'p.p. Dr Stanwell', but later, as more patients approached her directly, on her own private prescriptions.

In August 1958, after an interview with both doctors, Dyke and Jeffery were satisfied that their motives were unimpeachable and that they were genuinely trying to treat their addict patients. In September 1958 T. C. Green had passed their names to the first Brain Committee secretariat as potential witnesses, pointing out they had been sounded out about giving evidence but had not appeared to be very interested and neither of them responded to an invitation to do so in September 1959.

The preliminary results of the Frankau–Stanwell collaboration in the treatment of heroin addiction were published in December 1960.[6] They described the first phase of their treatment programme as the stabilisation of the patients' drug use by the prescription of 'adequate supplies' of heroin and cocaine so that they would be freed morally and financially from the 'degradation and humiliation of contacting the pedlars', and to make it easier for those who could work to do so. The second phase involved reducing the amount of heroin and cocaine prescribed, with benzodiazepines to control the patients' anxiety and insomnia, and vitamins to improve their physical state and, eventually, withdrawal from all the drugs as an inpatient. Their paper provoked an exchange of correspondence with Dr Ellis Stungo,[7] then Secretary of the Society for the Study of Addiction, who was sceptical of 'their remarkable therapeutic feat in successfully treating 32 out of 51 drug addicts'.

Lady Frankau's rationale for prescribing cocaine, even if the addict had not previously used it, was that it would make it easier to reduce the heroin dosage because, as cocaine produced no withdrawal symptoms, withdrawal from both drugs would be eased. But, in practice, she rarely reduced the dosages of either and seldom attempted withdrawal treatment. The few other doctors in London who treated heroin addicts also began to prescribe them cocaine 'because Lady Frankau told us to'.[8] As a consequence, an illicit market in cocaine developed alongside the already flourishing heroin market.

The Frankau–Stanwell collaboration ended after a period of growing concern on Dr Stanwell's part about Lady Frankau's readiness to increase addicts' dosages of heroin, and on Lady Frankau's at what she saw as Dr Stanwell's too rigid control of the amount she prescribed. The final breach apparently occurred following the suicide of one of their patients in April 1961, which Lady Frankau blamed on Dr Stanwell's too-drastic reduction in his heroin dosage when she took over his prescribing during Lady Frankau's absence on holiday. Dr Stanwell afterwards retained a small number of addict patients on her NHS list over whose heroin dosage she exercised the firm control which had always characterised her dealings with addicts.

It was not until some time after she had parted company with Dr Stanwell that the Inspectorate discovered the extent to which Lady Frankau was accepting addicts as private patients. At first they were of a higher social class than those she saw with Dr Stanwell, including several, as she later frequently reminded me, who were connected to the United States Embassy. She did not prescribe for the latter but supplied them with drugs herself so that their addiction would not be disclosed as a result of their names appearing in pharmacy records. (In November 1962, when I tried to examine her Dangerous Drugs Register, in which the names of these patients should have been recorded, the Register with entries before 1960 was not available because it had been stolen in a burglary at her Wimpole Street address in March 1960.)

Lady Frankau's prescribing of heroin became increasingly bizarre. Not only did she appear to prescribe whatever quantity was requested, but in many cases there was an almost total absence of any regularity or pattern in her issue of prescriptions. It was strongly suspected in a number of cases, and in one confirmed by subsequent enquiries, that the recipients of her prescriptions were not always addicts. She was so certain of her ability to detect whether a patient was telling the truth that she often did not bother to examine new patients to see if they were in fact addicted. (In the course of two telephone calls she made to report new patients while they were in her consulting room I was amazed to hear her, on being asked if their arms showed signs of injections, tell them to roll up their sleeves and show her their arms. She clearly had not intended carrying out this elementary diagnostic procedure.) There were also several instances of her patients receiving dual supplies of heroin because she never bothered to check whether they were already receiving prescriptions from another doctor but simply accepted their statement that they were not.

Even more alarming was her willingness to continue to prescribe extremely large quantities of heroin and cocaine, sometimes providing two or three prescriptions on the same day, despite knowing that the addict was not taking them. For example, in November 1959 she again started to prescribe for HT, her very first patient, who had relapsed following release from prison. The dosage was then 4 grains (240mgm) of heroin with a similar quantity of cocaine per day but by August 1960 this had risen to 10 grains (600mgm) of heroin and 6 grains (360mgm) of cocaine per day. In a little under nine weeks in the early summer of 1961, Lady Frankau's prescriptions had provided HT with around 156 grams of heroin, an average daily amount of 39 grains (2,340mgms), together with 12 grains (720mgms) of cocaine. Suspecting that the patient had been forging or altering her prescriptions, Dyke and Jeffery took them to Lady Frankau who unhesitatingly confirmed their authenticity. Her explanation was, firstly, that in view of the thrombosed state of the patient's veins, she wasted much of each injection, and secondly, the addict with whom the patient was living took much of the heroin from her and 'beat her up' if she tried to refuse, and the extra supplies were to save her from this.

Jeffrey's report of Lady Frankau's prescribing included brief descriptions of 104 patients she had treated, either in collaboration with Dr Stanwell or on her own account, by 31 March 1962. (This number did not include the patients she had personally supplied with heroin.) On that date she was prescribing heroin for 43 addicts. Between 31 March and 21 May 1962 she accepted a further six as patients, had resumed supplies to a further two and transferred two to other doctors on the grounds that they could no longer afford private prescriptions. When Dyke and I saw her in November 1962 she told us she had also seen a number of undergraduates who were 'just playing around with drugs' in the jazz clubs of the West End whom she was able to 'get off drugs' without prescribing or supplying any heroin.

Jeffery's view was that by March 1962 Lady Frankau had already done more harm that any 'script doctor' ever known to the Home Office. The Home Office Legal Adviser, Sir Kenneth Jones, was consulted and his advice embodied what cynics can be forgiven for suspecting is the basic philosophy of bureaucracy, that the problem of Lady Frankau would be resolved 'by the effluxion of time'. As there was little likelihood of this happening in the immediate future, the Ministry of Health was asked to arrange for a Regional Medical Officer visit and in July 1962 Dr Phelps called on Lady Frankau. His assessment of her motivation was:

I gained the impression that she had a strong interest in these people, largely humanitarian, and that she felt safe in her own beliefs and methods. It seems clear that Lady Frankau is quite sincere in her belief that she is in fact doing a great deal towards helping these unfortunate people.

As Dyke and I were to discover when we met her in November 1962 she clearly regarded Dr Phelps's visit as something of a joke: 'If I had not been so busy I would have got on to his chief (Sir George Godber) about him'. In the event, his visit and comments had no effect and she continued her generous heroin and cocaine prescribing.

## Review of heroin addiction in November 1963

In this review I noted that small pockets of heroin users had begun to appear outside London in some provincial cities, and that in 1962, for the first time, there were more persons known to be addicted to heroin than to morphine. The number of new non-therapeutic heroin addicts coming to notice during the year, averaging less than 10 a year between 1955 and 1959, had risen to 24 in 1960 and to 72 in 1962. The number of cocaine addicts, almost all of whom were also known heroin addicts, had also started to rise, from 25 in 1958 with 12 also using heroin, to 112 in 1962 with 105 also using heroin. Since 1959, when the ages of known addicts began to be systematically recorded, the number of non-therapeutic heroin addicts who were aged 34 or younger had risen, from 35 to 126 in 1962, with six aged under 20 coming to notice between 1960 and 1962 including one who came to notice shortly after his 16th birthday and who had clearly been using heroin for some months before.

I also provided an assessment of the quantity of heroin prescribed between January 1962 and June 1963. Neither resources nor time permitted the recovery of every NHS and private prescription for heroin hypodermic tablets issued during this 18-month period, nor, because of the quantities necessarily being held in stock, was it possible to establish an exact relationship between production and consumption. But it was possible to show that at least 80% of the total production of hypodermic tablets of heroin in 1962 had been supplied to addicts. This was equivalent to just over 10 kilograms of heroin and almost as much as the total consumed in all the other countries which still permitted its medical use.

On the basis of the prescriptions which were traced, just under a million tablets of heroin were prescribed for addicts in 1962, with the first six months of 1963 showing a 22% increase on the corresponding period in the previous year. About 60% of these tablets had been supplied on prescriptions issued by Lady Frankau, a fact to which the much quoted statement in the second Brain Report that ' ... in 1962 one doctor alone prescribed almost 600,000 tablets of heroin (i.e.

6 kilograms) for addicts', referred.[9] But it must be remembered that at this time Lady Frankau had by far and away more addict patients than any other doctor.

My review also referred to other doctors treating addicts but who were acquiring their patients at a slower rate than Lady Frankau – and none prescribed heroin in such large quantities. Between March and November 1963 she had accepted 92 new addict patients while by June 1963 Drs Hewetson and Ollendorff had acquired only 35 of the 100 patients they were to describe in the paper circulated to the reconvened Brain Committee and later published.[10] Unlike Lady Frankau, most of the other prescribers accepted they were probably contributing to the surplus of heroin finding its way to the black market, although they did their best not to.

If there had been any doubts about the source of the heroin fuelling the growth in the London addict population, they were resolved by the results of my review. There was still no evidence that heroin was being imported illicitly or of any significant thefts from legitimate manufacturers, wholesalers, hospitals or retail pharmacies. Moreover, there was also much anecdotal evidence from doctors, especially the prison medical service, and from pharmacists, the police,[11] probation officers and others in close contact with addicts, to confirm the existence of a black market in heroin tablets that was considerably larger than it had been in 1955 and fed by addicts who had a very strong motive – financial gain – to seek prescriptions of heroin in excess of their own requirements.

My review also focused on an area of known administrative sensitivity, international opinion. There had been ample evidence over the years of the susceptibility of our delegates to views expressed in the UN Commission on Narcotic Drugs, and in particular, by the United States, that the UK was out of step with the international community over the manufacture and use of heroin. I emphasised that the existence of the gaping loophole in our controls, the inability to deal with doctors who over-prescribed dangerous drugs, was hardly consistent with our international obligations to take all useful steps to prevent drug addiction and to suppress the illicit traffic.

Nor was our international reputation much enhanced by press reports appearing both here and in Canada, describing how easy it was to obtain prescriptions for heroin in London. Although the peak of the influx had passed by 1963, the previous four years had seen the arrival of a steady stream of heroin addicts from Canada, who, having heard of Lady Frankau through the press or from addicts already here, soon found their way to 32 Wimpole Street. Her name was also well known among expatriate American addicts in Paris and in international jazz music circles, with several famous musicians receiving prescriptions from her during their professional engagements in London. In this respect, the prize has to be given to the one who arrived in London from Paris one morning in March 1962, obtained a prescription from her for 15 grains (900mgms) of heroin, 5 grains (300mgms) of cocaine and 100 x 5mgm tablets of methadone, which he had dispensed before returning to Paris the same afternoon. According to Lady Frankau the reason for his visit was 'to explore the situation here with a view to undergoing treatment'.

If the evidence assembled by the Inspectorate showed that the heroin problem could no longer be ignored, there was also a danger, as the 'effluxion of time' comment suggested, that the solution would be seen simply as finding some way of removing Lady Frankau from the scene. Paradoxically, her activities both obscured and highlighted the real problem, which was that it required only one doctor, deliberately or misguidedly, prescribing virtually unlimited quantities of heroin, to do incalculable harm to any attempt to prevent the spread of addiction.

I argued that the substantial demand for heroin which now existed would not disappear with Lady Frankau. It was too easy to hold her solely responsible for the current state of affairs and to forget that she was merely the latest in the long line of 'script doctors' and would, in her turn, be succeeded by others whose motives might be more questionable. Because she charged her addict patients little or no consultation fee, one of the few benefits of her involvement had been the elimination of the old-style 'script doctor' whose financial demands provided addicts with a greater incentive to sell part of their supplies. Given the addicts' talent for finding over-sympathetic, vulnerable or easily manipulated members of the medical profession, other prescribers would certainly (and in fact did) appear in the years to come. We already knew of one potential successor 'waiting in the wings' who had given strong hints to at least two West End pharmacists that he would not be averse to accepting addicts as patients.

The clear message of my review, that we had only ourselves to blame for the present situation, was not well received by Home Office administrators. T. C. Green, who was having his second spell in charge of drugs policy, in his comments on my paper agreed the situation was 'disturbing' but maintained it was not entirely unexpected, as my earlier reports had shown 'a trend towards increasing addiction to heroin' and it had been recognised that 'Lady Frankau's activities were likely to lead to an increase in heroin addiction in London'. However, he did not agree with my conclusion that unless and until we made it far more difficult for an addict in the UK to obtain drugs, heroin addiction would continue to increase.

Nevertheless, Green agreed it would now be a useful time to take stock and deal with the problem before it became worse, and it was important that addiction should continue to be treated primarily as a medical condition and not as a crime. He ruled out any suggestion of prohibiting the manufacture and use of heroin because such a proposal was bound to revive the 'bitter controversy' of 1955, and the United States experience showed clearly 'the most likely result of prohibition here would be to drive addiction underground and lead to an organised traffic in heroin and a general increase in crime'. (The government, via J. H. Walker, had been quite prepared to accept these risks when it had proposed to ban heroin in 1955.)

Green rejected my suggestion for the restoration of the tribunal machinery, on the familiar grounds of difficulty in obtaining the necessary evidence and because such a tribunal 'would be of little use to deal with cases such as that of Lady Frankau'. Like his predecessor, who had made a similar, anonymous, comment on the Hirschman papers in 1936, Green did not explain why he took this view. But he did not rule out the possibility of a modified tribunal to deal with breaches of any new prescribing restrictions, presumably because the issues to be decided would be largely factual, that is, whether a prescriber had complied with statutory requirements rather than clinical judgements. There was, however, little point in proposing a precise scheme of control until there was some idea of what measures would be acceptable to the medical profession, who should be made to take at least some of the responsibility for controlling wayward members.

Green therefore referred the 'new' developments to the Chief Medical Officer, Sir George Godber, who in due course, sought the opinion of Lord Brain. In May 1994 Lord Brain was persuaded to chair a new enquiry by the Interdepartmental Committee on Drug Addiction only on the firm understanding that the enquiry would be brief and restricted to looking into the apparent over-prescribing of heroin and cocaine.

## The meetings of the reconvened Brain Committee[12]

The reconvened Brain Committee, like the first, consisted of eight members including six of the first Committee. The terms of reference were:

> ... to consider whether, in the light of recent experience, the advice they gave in 1961 in relation to the prescribing of addictive drugs by doctors needs revising, and, if so, to make recommendations.

The Report makes it clear that the Committee interpreted its terms of reference as 'to pay particular attention to the part played by medical practitioners in the supply' of addictive drugs and not to 'survey the subject of drug addiction as a whole'.[13]

The Ministry of Health provided the joint secretaries for the Committee, Dr Roy Goulding and A. H. H. Jones. The Home Office officials who attended most of the meetings were T. C. Green, Len Dyke and me. The Committee held eight meetings and by the third was already considering what might be included in the report. The main recommendations were that there should be compulsory notification of addicts, special centres should be created for their treatment, and there should be a restriction of the right of doctors working outside these centres to prescribe heroin and cocaine to patients whose addiction arose other than through treatment for physical illness or injury.[14] How did they come to make these recommendations?

At its first meeting in September 1964 the Committee considered a memorandum prepared by the Home Office. This provided a factual account of the 'new situation', the main features being the steep rise since 1960 in the number of known heroin and cocaine addicts, most of whom were in the age group 20–34 and whose addiction was of non-therapeutic origin. It noted there were also disturbing signs that addiction to heroin and cocaine was spreading outside London; that addicts were being attracted to the UK, particularly from Canada and the United States, as a result of hearing stories of the ease with which heroin could be obtained in London and in many cases knowing the name of a doctor from whom prescriptions were readily available. It concluded that, in the absence of evidence of any growth of organised illicit traffic in heroin, the increase in heroin and cocaine addiction was 'largely due to the prescribing of very large quantities of these drugs by some doctors'. No suggestions were offered as to how the problems identified might be resolved.

Examples of Lady Frankau's prescribing of heroin were included in the memorandum but she was not identified by name or gender. There were also anonymous references to her frequent failure to establish before prescribing that the patient was in fact addicted, or to consult any of their previous doctors, or to seek a second opinion before prescribing over a long period. It was not until she came to give the Committee the benefit of her experience at its third meeting that its members realised the extent to which she was involved.

Unlike its first run over the course in 1958–1960, when oral evidence was only exceptionally taken, doctors with experience of treating addicts were invited to appear before the Committee at its second and third meetings. A distinction was made between 'treaters' and 'prescribers' with the latter invited 'to give them a chance to explain their ideas', suggesting that even at this early stage prescribing heroin was seen to be incompatible with the treatment of addiction. The names of these witnesses and those who submitted written evidence were not listed in an appendix to the Report, as had been the case with the earlier enquiry, because the Committee wished to avoid possible embarrassment and speculation over the identity of the major prescriber.

In their renewed enthusiasm, the Committee considered interviewing a number of addicts but settled for detailed case histories compiled from Home Office records. They also asked for further information about the extent of the illicit dealing in drugs which, with the co-operation of the Metropolitan and Liverpool City Forces, the Home Office duly provided. From the Ministry of Health the Committee sought information about the existing, and as it transpired wholly inappropriate, machinery for dealing with other forms of excessive prescribing.

## Evidence from 'treaters' and 'prescribers'

At their second meeting, on 29 October 1964, the Committee took evidence from 'treaters', represented by Dr Thomas Bewley of Tooting Bec Hospital, Dr Peter Chapple of West Park Hospital and Sister Patricia, the Mother Superior of Spelthorne St Mary. (Sister Patricia, although not a doctor, had probably acquired over the years more experience of treating female addicts and alcoholics than anyone with whom the Committee was likely to be in contact in the course of their enquiry.) After hearing their evidence, the Committee accepted that it might be necessary to review the need to provide centres for withdrawal treatment and to consider the setting up of 'a register of addicts' and a restriction on the supply of drugs to addicts, all of which they had firmly resisted in their 1961 report. (The suggestion for special centres had surfaced during their previous enquiry in the evidence submitted by the Royal Medico-Psychological Association and by Dr Denis Parr.)

In memoranda supplementing their oral evidence, both Bewley and Chapple described the difficulties of treating addicts under existing arrangements. Bewley noted that in his experience the new heroin addicts were usually treated in local mental hospitals, which were overcrowded and understaffed and unlikely 'to provide adequate follow-up of discharged patients or much attempt at case-finding among contacts'. He thought a special unit or units would be necessary if the addicts were not to continue to drift from hospital to hospital and doctor to doctor without sufficient follow-up.

Chapple, while supporting the establishment of special treatment units, saw the interest of the doctor as the determining factor; some psychiatrists found it impossible to treat patients for whom a combination of permissiveness and discipline was needed. He noted that ambulatory treatment was controversial but there were already more addicts than hospitals could cope with, and the current practice of general practitioners prescribing, and of psychiatrists not doing so, was likely to continue. He thought, in these circumstances, that the essential task was one of co-ordination with the small group of general practitioners who now had considerable experience with addicts. (The jettisoning of this experience, for medico-political rather than clinical reasons, was to be one of the criticisms of the arrangements eventually introduced.)

It was at this meeting that the proposal for a standing committee to keep the drug misuse situation under review originated.[15] In his memorandum Bewley suggested that 'the single most important action that could be taken would be to arrange to keep the matter continuously under review'. (In an expanded version of the memorandum published in April 1965,[16] he referred to 'the need for a body' to undertake this task.) Chapple went further by suggesting that the Ministry of Health should set up a permanent committee with powers to investigate all aspects of drug misuse, with funds for research, keeping in touch with international developments, holding conferences on particular subjects and making recommendations.

At the third meeting, on 4 December 1964, it was the turn of the 'prescribers', to address the Committee. They were represented by three general practitioners, Drs A. J. Hawes, J. C. Hewetson and R. H. V. Ollendorff (who was also a psychiatrist at the Paddington Clinic and Day Hospital), with Dr G. G. Gray being unable to attend as arranged, and Lady Frankau.

As had the earlier medical witnesses, the general practitioners also fully supported the depressing picture of the current situation which had been presented by the Home Office, and were in agreement about the need for some form of notification of addicts. They described the difficulties they faced in trying to deal with addict patients (as one put it, 'of acting as barkeeper and prohibitionist at the same time') and drew attention to the inadequacy of existing treatment facilities.

In a separate memorandum Ollendorff suggested that all general practitioners in London should be contacted in an attempt to persuade more to accept 'at least a few drug addicts', that there should be an increase in the number of psychiatric outpatient clinics willing to accept, prescribe for and attempt therapy with addicts, with a central clinic in London where addicts could be seen, assessed, and receive prescriptions where appropriate. At this central clinic there would also be facilities for eventual rehabilitation on day hospital lines and for inpatient treatment.

The Committee's response to the 'prescribers' is most accurately reflected in a comment by Lord Brain after Lady Frankau had completed her evidence rather than by the laconic record in the minutes. Looking over his glasses to the officials sitting at the end of the table, he remarked, 'Well gentlemen, I think your problem can be summed up in two words, Lady Frankau'. The minutes of the meeting merely record that:

> The Committee concluded that the doctors in question, although meaning well, had under-estimated the complexity of the problem of drug addiction. One in particular seemed far too ready to believe addicts.

This blanket dismissal of the very obvious genuine concern of the general practitioners about the developing situation, the lack of support available to them and their suggestions of ways to tackle the problem, was grossly unfair. It was also arrogant because no member of the Committee could offer any comparable practical experience of 'the complexity of the problem' – including Dr Maurice Partridge, the psychiatrist who was a member of both Brain Committees. (In October 1966 he was to admit that all he had learned of drug addiction, he had learned in the United States.[17])

At this third meeting, after hearing from both 'treaters' and 'prescribers', the Committee began to consider its recommendations. There was agreement in principle that, having devised a definition of an addict, it would recommend that addicts should be notified to a central agency. The Home Office and the Ministry of Health were asked to advise on which would be the most appropriate site of the agency. (After the Committee's report was published it was agreed that notifications should be made to the government's Chief Medical Officer at the Home Office. The British Medical Association's working party on drug addiction, reporting in January 1966, had recommended that the Home Office should be the central authority.[18])

The Committee then turned its attention to the problem of over-prescribing, and identified, for future detailed consideration, two possible solutions: drugs could be available to addicts only from a few central clinics, or the present arrangements allowing any doctor to prescribe to them should continue but with the provision of a medical tribunal which 'could discipline doctors prescribing too freely by withdrawing their right to prescribe dangerous drugs to addicts'. The possibility of a total ban on the use of cocaine was also put on the agenda, but the suggestion was later rejected when the Ministry of Health's Consultant Adviser on Ear, Nose and Throat Surgery advised that the drug was still essential in that field.

## Home Office opposition to medical tribunals

The revival of a proposal for tribunals, which they had successfully defeated when the first Brain Committee considered it, saw the re-mustering of opposition within the Home Office. Having heard from A. H. H. Jones, one of the Committee secretaries, that Lord Brain appeared to be moving towards tribunals as a possible answer to the problem of the over-prescriber, Green (who, although he retained his involvement with the Committee, had by now moved to the Charity Commission) wrote to his successor, Peter Beedle, on 20 January 1965, arguing:

> That if one has a case which is good enough to take to court, there is no need for a tribunal but, if the case is not good enough to be tried by a court there is little advantage in referring it to a tribunal which requires much the same kind of evidence as a court.

By suggesting that, in some circumstances, a doctor's prescribing might lend itself to criminal charges Green showed that he still did not understand the problem which had troubled Delevingne in 1924, and the Inspectorate since 1953 when the tribunal provisions were dropped from the Dangerous Drugs Regulations. It was not for the criminal courts to decide medical issues, as Mr Raphael had made clear some ten years earlier, when the Director of Public Prosecutions felt he had a 'good enough case' against Rourke. It was for precisely this reason that the Rolleston Committee had proposed the tribunal solution.

At the same time as he wrote to Beedle, Green wrote to Jones expressing considerable doubts about the usefulness of tribunals, a view, which Jones' reply indicated, was shared by Dr Roy Goulding, his joint secretary. Even though Lord Brain was 'heavily in favour', it was not certain the rest of the Committee were wholeheartedly with him. Some members were believed to favour the alternative of confining the prescribing of drugs to addicts at special centres and if the medical profession was to be confronted with a simple choice between these alternatives, it was not at all certain it would opt for tribunals. Beedle wrote to Jones on 26 January 1965 enclosing a copy of the memorandum on tribunals that had been prepared for the first Brain Committee, and requested that the difficulties inherent in the proposal should be understood by the Committee members before the forthcoming meeting.

## Lord Brain's memorandum

The fourth meeting of the Committee, on 3 February 1965, was primarily concerned, as were all subsequent meetings, with the preparation of its report and recommendations. On this occasion the deliberations were very much guided by a memorandum from Lord Brain in which he set out his personal thoughts on the evidence and the various possible solutions.

Lord Brain noted that it had already been agreed that addicts should be notified and he saw no practical difficulty in defining or recognising a drug addict for the purpose. (The secretariat was later instructed to draw up a definition of addiction based on the Committee's discussion and the one adopted by the Rolleston Committee. The WHO's definition was considered to be too broad for the purpose of notification.)

He also noted that, as present arrangements for inpatient treatment of addicts were haphazard and unsatisfactory, the Committee was in general agreement on the need to recommend treatment centres. His suggestion was for one centre for all London addicts, either at, or related to, a mental hospital or at a large non-teaching hospital, such as the Central Middlesex Hospital, where addicts could be dealt with by experienced doctors and nurses.

Lord Brain doubted if the present law would allow for the compulsory detention of addicts for treatment against their will. He argued that, while there would probably be public support for any necessary new powers, compulsion militated against psychological treatment, and it was likely that patients would soon relapse on discharge if supplies of drugs were readily available. (It was agreed at the 5th meeting of the Committee that there was no need to recommend an extension of powers for the compulsory detention of addicts, and doctors should be encouraged to use the provisions of the 1959 Mental Health Act.)

Lord Brain also doubted whether it would be practicable to compel an addict to attend a treatment centre by making it illegal for a doctor to treat a notified addict for more than a specified period without referring them to a treatment centre because the addict could simply go to another doctor after the period had elapsed. He pointed out that, in any case, this would not deal with the 'reckless prescriber' who might justify prescriptions for large amounts of heroin on medical grounds. Nor would banning heroin solve the problem of dealing with addicts because 'it might merely shift its centre of gravity from the reckless prescriber to the smuggler'. He suggested it would be both unnecessary and undesirable to restrict the prescribing powers of doctors in general in order to control the small number of 'reckless prescribers' and there seemed no alternative to the establishment of some disciplinary procedure to deal with them.

After a lengthy discussion, the Committee agreed that the choice of a procedure to deal with 'reckless prescribers' lay between the establishment of a medical tribunal or some form of restriction on the prescribing of dangerous drugs to addicts other than at specially designated centres. The effect of the exchanges between the Home Office and Committee's secretariat on tribunals is shown by the minutes of the meeting as:

> In favour of a tribunal it was argued that it was the most reasonable course to follow in view of the very small number of doctors involved. However, it was pointed out that there would be great difficulty in obtaining reliable evidence for such tribunals, as addicts were notoriously unreliable as witnesses. Moreover, by the time the offending doctor had been brought before the tribunal, the damage would already have been done. It was agreed that it would be preferable to recommend some form of restriction on the prescribing of dangerous drugs to addicts.

The Committee agreed that, whatever measure it recommended to deal with excessive prescribers, it was essential also to recommend the establishment of treatment centres. These would have to be two types: 'a few special research centres for study and intensive treatment', which would be mostly in the London area, and 'a large number of more general units over the country as a whole' in designated units or beds in local psychiatric hospitals reserved for the treatment of drug addiction.

## Practicality of the proposed recommendations

Most of the remaining four meetings were taken up with discussion of the practicalities and legality of what the Committee was intending to recommend, and the drafting of the report. At the 5th meeting, on 3 March 1965, there was a lengthy and inconclusive discussion of the practical application of the proposed recommendation that a doctor would only be able to prescribe heroin for a 'notified' addict. One major difficulty had to be resolved; if it was found that a doctor had prescribed drugs to an addict and had not notified the addict, how could it be shown that the patient was in fact an addict? The possible solutions considered included seeking powers to acquire the relevant medical records (touching on the fundamental and sensitive issue of confidentiality) or compelling the patient to undergo an independent medical examination.

The outcome of the discussion was an instruction to the secretariat to revise the relevant paragraphs of the draft report and show them to the lawyers. The lawyers' advice with regard to compulsory medical examination was not encouraging, pointing out that there were a number of circumstances under which a person could be medically examined without his agreement but most required the prior authority of a court. Could such a serious interference with the freedom of the individual be justified, especially as it was only likely to be used in very exceptional circumstances? When he reported this advice to the Committee at the 6th meeting, on 31 March 1965, R. F. Tyas of the Ministry of Health, was asked to prepare, in consultation with the Home Office, a paper which set out alternative ways around the difficulties for consideration at the next meeting.

The problem that the Tyas paper was intended to resolve arose from the disinclination of the Committee to support their proposal to link prescribing heroin to notification as an addict with the means to enforce it. They showed no desire to recommend that there should be some power or authority to obtain from a doctor information showing whether or not a patient should have been notified.

One of Lord Brain's main concerns was how were those doctors who tried to evade the new arrangements to be dealt with? He could see no other way of preventing the existing abuses other than, having made addiction notifiable, forbidding the treatment of drug addicts by general practitioners except in special emergencies. The Committee could not escape suggesting some way of dealing with a doctor who did not act in good faith, who, for example, did not notify or continued to prescribe on the grounds that the patient was not an addict. These would be difficult issues for the courts or a tribunal and Lord Brain was anxious that any new offences should turn on matters of fact, whether the doctor prescribed more than a certain amount in a given period or had failed to obtain a recommended second opinion.

Following a meeting with the Inspectorate, and in the light of an *aide memoire* from Lord Brain in which he set out his concerns, Tyas suggested that, in the light of the current situation, the case might now be stronger than it was in 1961, when the Committee rejected the restoration of the Rolleston tribunals, for introducing some professional control or supervision over the prescribing or supplying of certain dangerous drugs to addicts.

Tyas suggested that, rather than involving the courts or setting up a special tribunal, the Committee might wish to consider, in consultation with the General Medical Council, recommending an extension of the Council's powers to permit it to review a doctor's suitability to remain a person authorised to possess, supply and prescribe dangerous drugs. Reference to the Council would be by the Home Secretary and could relate to a doctor who had prescribed 'restricted' drugs to an addict without consulting an approved consultant or treatment centre, or who had failed to check with the central authority about the addict's previous history or where there were doubts about the therapeutic justification for the continuing supplies. In the event, the Committee agreed with this suggestion.[19]

The Committee's last formal meeting was on 20 May 1965 when the Tyas paper was discussed in detail and various amendments proposed to the report. A further draft of the report was circulated early in June and, after interdepartmental discussions which resulted in additional changes, was agreed and signed by members and formally submitted to the Minister of Health on 31 July 1965. In view of what was to happen over the next two years, it is worth noting what Lord Brain said in the covering letter he sent to the Minister of Health, from his holiday home in Ireland:

> You will appreciate when you read the report why we regard the matter as one of urgency and the Committee has asked me to express the hope that you will arrange for the publication of the report with the least possible delay.

The report of the second Brain Committee was published on 25 November 1965.

## Immediate responses to the second Brain Report

The medical press gave the report's recommendations a cautious welcome. The *British Medical Journal*[20] saw the recommendation for limiting the prescribing of heroin and cocaine to addicts to doctors on the staff of the proposed treatment centres as a restriction 'for the first time' on a doctor's right to prescribe 'because of the weakness or worse of a handful of doctors'. It argued that this recommendation could be altered so that all doctors could continue to prescribe heroin and cocaine to addicts so long as they did so only in consultation with a recognised expert. This would:

> ... maintain two essential medical principles; the right to treat disease, and the Committee insist that addiction is a disease, and the linked obligation to consult colleagues where this is necessary or needed.

The British Medical Association (BMA) issued a statement on the publication of the Report, agreeing that the situation it disclosed was 'most disturbing' and required 'adequate remedial measures' and announcing it had set up a working party to examine the recommendations.

A leading article in *The Lancet*[21] was also critical of the proposed restriction on doctors' prescribing of heroin and cocaine but suggested the profession might be wise to accept such a limitation which was 'likely to save it much frustration in an area where therapy by non-specialists is virtually impossible'. It suggested that the Committee 'might have encouraged practitioners to refer suspected addicts immediately to the nearest psychiatric department, and psychiatrists to institute appropriate local arrangements'. This was the first shot in the successful campaign by psychiatry to establish a monopoly in the field.

As in 1961, the Society for the Study of Addiction was permitted a preview of the Brain Committee's report. The Society's meeting took place on 16 November 1965 and was addressed by Dr Henry Matthew, a new and forceful member of the reconvened Committee. I attended the meeting and, in general, the report was well received, although there was disappointment that the narrow terms of reference had prevented the Committee from considering the misuse of amphetamines, and there were differences of opinion about the continued prescribing of heroin. The proposal to set up treatment centres attracted some cynical comment, with one doctor doubting whether they would ever come into existence in the lifetime of anyone present, and another commenting, 'it's glib to talk about centres without knowing what they are to be'. At the Society's Annual General Meeting in March 1966 one member called the report 'a sledgehammer to crack a nut'.[22]

How did 'the prescribers' react to the Committee's report? Lady Frankau's response was entirely predictable: the Committee did not understand drug addiction and had no idea how to treat addicts. Whether she realised she was their main target, or had simply put it to the back of her mind, I cannot say, as she never mentioned it in any of our subsequent conversations. But in an interview published in the *Sunday Times* newspaper on 20 February 1966[23] she commented:

> If the Brain Committee thinks it's going to get effective treatment in centres, jolly good luck to them. But if you know anything about these people, you know just how scared and silly they are about society in any form. And what really infuriates me about the Report is that they made all these terrible accusations against us, but I myself only had twenty-five minutes giving evidence.

The response of the other doctors who gave evidence to the Committee was mixed, ranging from relief that they would no longer be able to prescribe heroin or cocaine to addicts, to disappointment, tinged with resignation, that their efforts to plug the holes in the dyke had been summarily dismissed as arising from 'a sense of duty' because of the inadequacy of other treatment facilities.[24] In a letter to *The Lancet* in December 1995 Dr Hawes[25] suggested:

The few general practitioners who have to do with drug addicts on the National Health Service must jump for joy at the recommendation of the Brain report that they should be prohibited from prescribing for cocaine and heroin addicts.

Another doctor, who did not give evidence to the Committee, but who continued to treat addicts after April 1968, commented in a recent letter to me that 'the best thing that could have happened was taking away the right to prescribe heroin for the junkies. We resented it a lot at first but soon saw how much it helped us to get closer to them. One large barrier had been removed'.

The comments of Dr Hewetson and Dr Ollendorf appeared in publications of more limited circulation than *The Lancet* and, as a result, have received little attention. Like Dr Hawes they demonstrated an understanding of both the ways of addicts and the wider issues, so noticeably lacking among many of those who were to be given the task of implementing the Committee's recommendations. Dr Hewetson[26] complained that 'the problem is not to be understood or solved by hasty blame on those who are doing most of the work'. Dr Ollendorff made no secret of his opinion that the 'report of Lord Brain's Commission [sic] … is a total failure'[27] commenting:

> They have neither understood the problem nor obviously are able to provide an answer … to take drugs out of experienced medical hands seems retrogressive and senseless.

He argued that with better liaison between general practitioners, hospitals and the Home Office, and 'with a Central Assessment Clinic for easy self-referral on an outpatient or inpatient basis' the number of addicts 'could be kept at a comparatively reasonable level, curbing, as much as humanly possible, youngsters from entering the group'.

It was an editorial in *The Times* newspaper, on 25 November 1965, which homed in on the real problem, that there was now 'an increasing social contamination' and convincing evidence of a change for the worse in public attitudes about drug taking. It noted that as far as the Committee's proposals were concerned, the Minister of Health and the medical profession would have to argue out the principles involved in the proposed substantial inroad into the independence of the profession with the onus of defence placed on doctors, although it had to be accepted that 'individual members of the profession have striven conscientiously to deal with the growing evil'. Tragically, history shows that the comment that the Committee's report and recommendations should be 'a spur for early action' requiring Parliament to take remedial action 'now' was extremely optimistic.

## Misinterpretations and myths

It is clear that with publication of the Brain Committee's second report the foundations were laid of much of the current mythology about drug addiction in the UK in the 1960s. The reconvened Committee did not, nor was required to, offer any explanation for the heroin problem it confronted. Nevertheless, it was the thinly disguised implication of its Report that the increasing demand had been created by 'a very few doctors who have prescribed excessively for addicts'.[28] But the question remains why addicts in the UK, who had always been able to obtain drugs from doctors, had not exploited that facility to the same extent, or in so many instances for such blatantly commercial motives, as they began to do in the late 1950s when none of the 1960s prescribers were involved.

Explanations have included proselytism by the Canadian addicts who began to arrive in London in the late 1950s,[29] the development of a hedonistic youth culture,[30] 'transatlantic cultural influence' transmitted by an interest in jazz music and the writings of Kerouac and Burroughs[31] and 'the development of an American-style heroin sub-culture'.[32]

### Were 'not more than six doctors' responsible for the increase in heroin addiction?

The statement in the Brain report that 'not more than six doctors' had prescribed very large amounts of heroin[33] is incorrect. The Home Office memorandum to the Committee mentioned, anonymously, only four doctors prescribing heroin to appreciable numbers of addicts but Lady Frankau was the only one consistently prescribing at an extraordinarily high level. With the exception of an NHS doctor who issued a prescription for 1,000 tablets of heroin to one of his veteran Canadian addicts to cover a lengthy absence from London, she was the prescriber in the other extreme examples quoted in the report. The first draft of the Report referred to 'extremely few' doctors, but this later became 'less than ten' and finally 'not more than six'. This last figure was based on an answer I gave to a member of the Committee when I said I thought that at the time there were about six doctors who were prescribing for more than the occasional addict.

Independent confirmation of the difficulty in stating the exact number of prescribers was provided by the Reverend Kenneth Leech:[34]

> ... there never was a static group of six. At any one time between 1960 and 1968, you could identify between six to twelve doctors in the inner London area who were prescribing significant amounts of heroin for non-therapeutic purposes – that is, for addicts. The group changed from time to time, though some doctors remained constant throughout the period. In almost every case, the doctors were well known to the Home Office Drugs Branch before the press discovered them.

Although the Brain Committee made no comment, mythology has it that the prescribers were all in private practice, and by implication, were motivated by greed. The Home Office memorandum emphasised that 'there is no suggestion that in any of these cases is the doctor giving prescriptions to addicts for financial gain'. Apart from Lady Frankau, all the prescribers who gave evidence to the Brain Committee were NHS general practitioners with busy, well-established practices and were not, as has been uncharitably and incorrectly stated, 'the more fringe members of the medical profession'.[35] None of them treated addicts as private patients as the Committee were told at its first meeting. Their attitude to this sensitive question was fairly expressed by Dr Hawes[36] as 'To have accepted any as private patients would have laid one open to the charge of having a vested interest in addiction'.

Contrary to popular belief, money played no part in how Lady Frankau responded to her addict patients. As she always explained when allegations that she was financially motivated were put to her, these usually emanated from patients she had 'thrown out', those who objected to the number of Canadian addicts she was accepting for treatment, or fellow practitioners, some of considerable eminence, who could think of no other reason why someone of her medical standing should devote so much time and effort to such undeserving patients. Her addiction work, as she often told me, was subsidised by her non-addict practice and it was a frequent occurrence at West End pharmacies to see her prescriptions endorsed 'charge to my account'.

Yet having been perfectly prepared in the early days to sign NHS prescriptions 'pp Dr Stanwell', Lady Frankau told the Brain Committee in December 1964 that it was important to avoid handing out free drugs to addicts. In her interview published in the *Sunday Times* newspaper she reaffirmed this:

> They have to pay for drugs. I think it gives them a bit of self-respect – and anyway, as a taxpayer, I object to paying for other people's pleasures. For consultation, I let them pay what they can which is mostly nothing.

If the prescribers were not financially motivated, why had they become involved in treating addicts? Several of them besides Lady Frankau were interviewed for the article in the *Sunday Times* and the anonymous interviewers' conclusion may provide some explanation:

> All of these doctors have some unusual quality about them – some element of the 'outsider' in their make-up; strong political opinions; the status of the exile; or perhaps an unusual degree of professional compassion. And it is possible as a result of this that they succeed in acting as a link between the outcast addicts and normal society.

In 1970 Charles Jeffery set out the Inspectorate's view of most of the prescribers in a rarely quoted article:[37]

> Surprisingly enough, however, by 1960, when the major increase in addiction began, the problem was no longer mainly related to the activities of 'script doctors', but rather to those of a few newcomers in the field whose motives were unimpeachable. These were dedicated practitioners, who felt that the young addicts presented a challenge which the rest of the profession was refusing to take up, and who were prepared to put themselves to endless trouble on behalf of the addicts. Inevitably this attitude made them all too ready to give their addicted patients the benefit of the doubt when presented with demands for higher dosage, and the addicts (who are expert manipulators) were quick to take advantage of this ... Moreover, the fact that only a handful of practitioners was involved meant that as the numbers of addicts increased each began to carry an excessive caseload, and was even less able to devote the necessary time to deciding which were reasonable demands and which were not ...

Given the reluctance of most doctors to have anything to do with addicts, it is not altogether surprising that the defence of the prescribers, Lady Frankau excepted, should come from non-medical sources. But it was not only in the Home Office that the reality of what they were trying to do was recognised. Speaking in a debate in the House of Commons on 8 May 1968, William Deedes[38] commented:

> Goodness knows, we are not over-endowed with reputable enthusiasts in this field ... they have been filling for some time an essential gap while we have been deciding rather slowly what to do. It is imprudent that under these Regulations these people should be driven out of business and we should then have to draft 500 or so doctors, the work of few of whom has lain regularly in this field, and most of whom are reluctant soldiers, into this business ...

Even Kenneth Robinson, the Minister of Health at the time, paid them a compliment, although it is unlikely he appreciated the real significance of what he was saying:[39]

> ... the Regulations (to restrict prescribing) do not reflect adversely on those general practitioners who have undertaken the difficult and unrewarding task of treating heroin addicts and discharged it in a responsible manner.

Nor is it surprising that the myth of 'the six' persists. The existence of a few easily identifiable scapegoats provides a convenient salve to the collective conscience of a medical profession which had been quite content to let them shoulder the burden largely unaided and to criticise from the safety of their ivory towers. Of course they made mistakes, they were operating in what Leech[40] has succinctly described as 'a vacuum of medical care', with little or no support from the hospital services normally available to general practitioners for the treatment of their patients.

Jeffrey's profile of the prescribers as 'dedicated practitioners' fitted Lady Frankau as well as the NHS general practitioners. The trouble was that her willingness to give patients the benefit of any doubt far exceeded that of the other prescribers. But if it is easy to criticise her prescribing, it is very difficult, if not impossible, to explain it. In her *Sunday Times* interview she expressed the philosophy which guided her:

> The first thing you've got to do with an addict is to give him security, and to him, that means drugs. So that's what I give them, and in the first phase with me I tend to step them up. You have to give them what they need before you start talking about withdrawal.

Unfortunately many of her patients never succeeded in passing beyond this 'first phase' and the high dosages she prescribed appeared to be based on the addict's assessment of their needs, which she accepted because of her unshakeable, and often repeated, conviction that she could always tell when one of her patients was lying.

But more than anything it was her inability to think ill of her patients, except when they transferred to another doctor, allied to her extreme gullibility and capacity for self-deception, which distorted her own sense of values. This was the basis for the eccentricities in her prescribing which had led to the reconvening of the Brain Committee and ultimately to the establishment of the 'treatment centres'. Why should she tell the Brain Committee that she refused to prescribe cocaine, when virtually single-handed she had restored the popularity of this drug within the addict community, often prescribing it to addicts who had never previously taken it? Yet a further example of her capacity for self-deception is her statement, again to Lord Brain and his colleagues, that while the black market was supplied by addicts who obtained from their doctors a greater supply of drugs than they needed, it was comparatively 'small and spasmodic' and did not involve her patients as they were 'too tightly controlled to sell drugs on the black market'.

Yet, as she explained in a letter to *The Lancet* in August 1964[41] it was always her practice to inform the Inspectorate about new patients, and to tell the patient it was necessary for their 'protection' that the Home Office should have their names on record as soon as possible. Her letter had been prompted by a suggestion that all addicts should be issued with 'drug passports'. This she strongly opposed, as addicts would be deterred from seeking medical attention, and employers, friends and associates might find out the person was addicted, which could expose them to the risk of blackmail.

From our point of view her co-operation was very welcome. The only trouble was that the personal particulars she provided of her patients were not always reliable. For example, there was Mr A, whose name I had noted on a pharmacy visit, but when I asked Lady Frankau her for more details she could recall nothing about him, saying 'as you know I don't take a full history until they have come a few times but he must have come with someone reliable'.

The exact number of addicts who came under Lady Frankau's care will never be known. When she gave evidence to the Brain Committee in December 1964 she put the total in the period from 1958 to 1964 at just over 500, although each year this included a small number of undergraduates and young persons from 'the higher social groups', who she described as 'on the fringe of becoming addicted'. In a list of her patients she gave me for a follow-up study, which, because of her death in 1967, was never completed, there were 374 names.

### The Canadian addicts

But if most of our problems with heroin in the early 1960s could be laid at Lady Frankau's door, there is one which cannot. The myth persists that she was responsible for encouraging the influx of about 100 Canadian addicts between 1959 and 1964 and that they were responsible for encouraging the spread of heroin misuse and addiction. In 1970 Imlah[42] gave this version of their influence:

> In Britain heroin became available after a small group of intelligent Canadian heroin addicts came to the country towards the end of the nineteen fifties, paid large amounts of money for heroin prescriptions and began to distribute this heroin among young people who were already dependent on, or experimenting with, drugs. This began a spread which had created some two thousand heroin addicts by the time new legislation was introduced in 1968.

Some 20 years later Strang[43] kept the myth alive by writing:

> It was not until the 1960s that the 'British system' was actually put to the test, with the arrival of several hundred injecting addicts from the US and Canada, and with the subsequent growth of an injecting drug sub-culture, especially in the London area.

The history and influence of the Canadian 'invasion' on the domestic heroin addict population has been described in two papers published in 1971.[44] There never were 'several hundred' addicts from the United States and Canada in the early 1960s. In all, 71 Canadian addicts were known to the Home Office between 1958 and 1964 with a further 20 known between 1965 and 1969. At the height of the 'invasion' a visiting senior officer of the Royal Canadian Mounted Police predicted that around 60 Canadian addicts would arrive and he was not far wrong. The number might have been affected by the Commonwealth Immigrants Act 1962 under which Commonwealth citizens could be refused entry to the UK or deported if they got into trouble, and by 1970 ten of the Canadians had been deported. As for heroin addicts from the United States, by the time of my November 1963 review only 31 had come to Home Office notice. The majority of them were transients, including some well-known musicians who took the opportunity provided by the 'British system' to sample the effects of pharmaceutically pure heroin.

The first Canadian addicts arrived here not knowing of Lady Frankau's existence but once her name, and gullibility, became known, the information was swiftly transmitted back to Canada over the addicts' very effective grapevine. Later arrivals, instead of 'reporting' to the Home Office, as many of the early ones had done, had little difficulty in finding their way directly from Heathrow to 32 Wimpole Street. (One of these, whose sister and brother-in-law were already here, was released from prison in Canada, where he had had no drugs for some time, and, as he frequently enjoyed reminding me, walked out of Lady Frankau's consulting room after his first visit, with a prescription for 12 grains (720mgms) of heroin.)

But it is not true, as her critics often suggest, that the visit Lady Frankau made to Niagara Falls in February 1963, to present a paper[45] at a Conference on Narcotic Addiction organised by the Alcoholism and Drug Addiction Research Foundation, was a recruiting drive. The Canadian influx had already peaked in 1962 although her visit undoubtedly attracted publicity, and this, coupled with the articles written in Canadian papers by satisfied patients, ensured that her name was well known in North America.

There may have been some proselytism by the Canadian addicts. Certainly one was active on the heroin black market. But according to a London addict attending the same doctor as many of the Canadians, 'they kept away from us ... the only time we mixed with them was in the waiting room ... they weren't disrespectful, lazy, insincere or scruffy ... they were older than the British addicts'.[46]

## Home Office influence on the Brain Committees

There is one other myth which cannot be allowed to remain unchallenged. In 'an historical case study' of the background to the two Brain reports, and subsequent policy developments, Smart[47] has given the impression that the Home Office had been able to exercise greater influence over the proceedings of the reconvened Brain Committee than it had over the first Committee (1958–1960). Having been denied access by both the Home Office and the Department of Health to their official records of the period, Smart interviewed a number of anonymous Department of Health officials but apparently did not feel it necessary to consult anyone in the Home Office. As a consequence, her scenario is seriously flawed.

For example, if any of her sources had provided a full account of the background to the reconvening of the Committee, it would have been apparent that Lord Brain had insisted on the very narrow terms of reference, and that he exerted a considerable influence over the way in which the Committee approached its task.

Furthermore, Smart failed to appreciate that both the Brain Committees were commissioned by the Minister of Health and the Secretary of State for Scotland and 'interdepartmental' referred to the Department of Health (for England and Wales) and Department of Health for Scotland (later the Scottish Home and Health Department) and were serviced by Ministry of Health officials. Certainly the 'sense of urgency and the need to act' which characterised the reconvened Committee in 1964 originated in the Home Office, but the implication of the statements that 'only the Home Office and a few individual doctors' gave evidence on this occasion, and that 'professional bodies like the BMA were excluded from giving evidence', is misleading. It was for Lord Brain and his colleagues to determine the evidence they needed to confirm, or challenge, what they were being told by the Home Office, and which persons or bodies they needed to consult.

At the first meeting of the reconvened Committee, as the minutes record, it agreed to approach 'for evidence as needed' the BMA, the College of General Practitioners, the Association of Police Surgeons, probation officers, magistrates and coroners. That the Committee did not subsequently feel any such 'need', cannot be laid at the door of the Home Office, directly or by implication. If the Committee saw fit not to consult the BMA until they had decided on their recommendations, that was a matter entirely for them. (The Rolleston Committee had adopted precisely the same tactic 40 years earlier.)

But it is the suggestion that individuals within the Home Office 'had it in for the doctors' and appeared 'to have taken on a moral entrepreneurial role' and were 'determined' that the reconvened Committee would produce 'new concrete policy recommendations', which is the most imaginative of Smart's interpretations. If a determination that the Committee should produce 'new concrete policy recommendations' equates with a determination to obtain a solution to Lady Frankau's eccentric prescribing and its effect on the extent of heroin addiction, then some 'individuals within the Home Office', of which I was one, must plead guilty. The first Brain Committee, with Home Office assistance, had misread the situation in 1960; we wished to ensure that the reconvened Committee could face up to the reality of what was happening.

# 7

# Implementing the recommendations of the second Brain Report: setting up the treatment centres for addicts

Despite the continuing public anxiety and concern about the heroin situation there was to be a interval of two and a half years between the publication of the re-convened Brain Committee's report on 25 November 1965 and the coming into force of the Dangerous Drugs Act 1967, which gave substance to the Committee's major recommendations. It was not until 22 February 1968 that it became a statutory duty for doctors to notify their addict patients to the Chief Medical Officer at the Home Office, and from 16 April 1968 only doctors licensed by the Home Secretary could prescribe heroin or cocaine to addicts. During the interval, not only did the situation deteriorate further, with a 250% increase in the number of known heroin addicts between 1965 and 1967,[1] but there were also profound changes in the character of the problem, including, for the first time in the United Kingdom, the appearance of illicitly imported heroin.

There are two distinct parts to the story of this crucial period. The first was the preparation and subsequent enactment of the Dangerous Drugs Act 1967 for which the Home Office was primarily responsible. The second, the setting up of the treatment centres where most of the licensed doctors were to work, and upon which the success or failure of the second Brain Committee's proposals 'for the better control of prescribing and supplying' of heroin and cocaine so obviously rested, was the responsibility of the Ministry of Health.

## Preparing for the 1967 Dangerous Drugs Act[2]

On 19 November 1965, a few days before the Brain Committee's report was pub-lished, the Home Affairs Committee of the Cabinet approved the drafting of a bill to give effect to those of the Committee's recommendations for which statutory authority would be necessary, except the proposal to introduce compulsory de-tention for addicts under treatment.[3] This approval, which did not guarantee the bill a place in the government's heavy legislative programme, disposes of the sug-gestion that 'the Government was reluctant to act and needed to be pushed into action'.[4] It was the Ministry of Health bureaucracy, the health authorities and the medical profession who had to be imbued with a sense of urgency. Perhaps antic-ipating this, the Cabinet Committee invited a further reference if any problems arose during the consultations with the medical profession.

Details of the Brain Committee's recommendations had been sent to the General Medical Council (GMC) and the British Medical Association (BMA) for consideration before the report was published. The first hint of likely trouble ahead came on 22 November 1965 when Tyas, the responsible Assistant Secretary at the Ministry of Health, learned that the GMC would probably be unwilling to take on the responsibility for disciplining doctors who failed to notify their addict patients or who prescribed heroin and cocaine to an addict when 'not being a recognized member of the medical staff of a treatment centre'.[5] This was contrary to the personal view of the President of the GMC, Lord Cohen, as expressed to the Chief Medical Officer. Lord Cohen had clearly misread the signs. At a formal meeting with senior Ministry of Health officials on 30 November 1965, the GMC representatives declined to accept the responsibility which the Brain Committee had wished to place on them on the grounds that if new statutory offences were to be created these should be dealt with in the courts.

In the meantime the BMA had set up a Working Party to examine the Brain Committee's proposals. The Working Party recommended that notification should apply only to heroin and cocaine addicts rather than to 'all addicts'[6] and rejected any compulsory detention of addicts for treatment. However, both of these recommendations were reversed by the BMA Council after they had been addressed by Lord Brain in January 1966.[7]

The BMA also felt that the limitation of prescribing heroin and cocaine to doctors at treatment centres was too restrictive, a view shared by their colleagues in Scotland, who were 'strongly opposed' to the plan. It considered that what was required was the control of supply, not necessarily its restriction, and doctors with special experience of the problem working outside the treatment centres should also be authorised by the Home Office to prescribe. The note of the meeting between Ministry of Health officials and a deputation from the BMA on 13 January 1966 records that it was agreed there was some merit in the suggestion that doctors outside the treatment centres should be authorised, and provided it could be ensured 'the six don't get on' probably not more than 50–100 would need to be approved.[8] But as later events showed, other, if not necessarily wiser, counsels in which medical politics played an important part, were to prevail and the suggestion was taken no further. It was equally desirable, in the BMA's view, that addicts should be able to travel freely if they wished and to obtain treatment privately, although this was overlooked a decade later when the role of the private practitioner in the treatment of addiction became the focus of much critical attention.

For the BMA, the most controversial of the Brain Committee's proposals was that the GMC should assume responsibility for policing the new arrangements. The Working Party was not convinced the Disciplinary Committee of the Council was the most appropriate body to fulfil this function, nor did they favour a special tribunal – as this could mean that a doctor charged with a statutory offence might not have the right to elect for trial by jury.

Despite the large spanner the GMC had thrown into the works, sending everyone back to the drawing board, by the end of February 1966 Tyas was able to put forward a draft scheme for discussion. It is not clear which side then proposed what was accepted as the eventual solution, a special tribunal to undertake the disciplinary role. After the meeting, the Ministry officials went away to see if any of the existing NHS tribunals offered a basis for this new scheme. As well as interdepartmental consultations it was necessary to seek the views of the Council on tribunals and to take account of the medical interests; and a final draft did not emerge from the Ministry after this inevitably lengthy process until November 1966. In the end, Section 2 of the Dangerous Drugs Act 1967 provided for the setting up of a tribunal to consider cases of failure to notify, and of prescribing heroin to addicts by unlicensed doctors. The procedure was never used but the provisions formed the basis of the tribunal arrangements in the Misuse of Drugs Act 1971, which extended the tribunals' remit to cases in which a doctor was considered to have prescribed any controlled drug 'in an irresponsible manner'.

On 8 September 1966 the Minister of Health, Kenneth Robinson, wrote to Roy Jenkins, who had succeeded Sir Frank Soskice as Home Secretary, to suggest that efforts should be made to include the Dangerous Drugs Bill in the government's main legislative programme. However, Jenkins was not prepared to give it priority over his proposed Gaming Bill. On 21 November, Robinson again wrote to Jenkins expressing his worries about the increasing public concern at the growing heroin problem and the apparent lack of governmental response. A number of members of Parliament were pressing for some action, among whom William Deedes, Bernard Braine and Renee Short were the most persistent. Robinson's letter drew a manuscript comment on the file from Sir Philip Allen, then Permanent Under-Secretary of State at the Home Office, 'The Ministry of Health have not been getting on very fast with the treatment facilities without which legislation would be pretty well useless'.

The reply from the Home Secretary, on 1 December 1966, expanded this point, without specifically commenting on the Ministry's perceived tardiness. Home Office lawyers would do what they could but would have to give current legislation priority over a bill which as yet had no firm place in the legislative programme and for which policies were not finally settled. The letter also referred to the numbers of addicts seeking Drugs Branch help in finding another doctor following the decision of their previous prescriber to withdraw from the field:

... it seems imperative to make arrangements which would allow general practitioners or social workers to refer any new addicts to a special centre. Until this is done we are likely to be faced with a continuing increase in the number of addicts whether or not the other recommendations of the Brain Committee are implemented.

It was to be nearly another year and a half before the Minister of Health could say that adequate treatment facilities were in place and that the relevant provisions of the Dangerous Drugs Act 1967, which had reached the statute book on 27 October 1967 after a six-month Parliamentary passage, could be brought into operation early in 1968.

## Delay in setting up the treatment centres

Why was the dawning of the 'treatment centre era' so long in coming? If history did not require a more detailed explanation, the question could be answered quite simply with the comments of two members of Parliament very much involved at the time, William Deedes and the Minister of Health, Kenneth Robinson. In a speech in the House of Commons on 8 May 1967,[9] almost two years after reconvened Brain Committee's report was signed and 18 months after it was published, Deedes complained:

> I get the strong impression that in some official quarters this is all regarded as a very tiresome, troublesome business which must not be allowed to delay other important matters. It is very tiresome and it is also very dangerous. I suggest that after two years we ought to move a little faster than we are moving. We are dealing with a small virulent plague which is being tackled in many places at walking pace …

That Deedes was right in his assessment was confirmed by Robinson (by then retired and knighted) in an interview in 1982[10] when he said:

> But I don't think that I ever saw it as the sort of problem that could seriously embarrass the Government as long as we could say that we were doing something about it and that initiatives were being taken.

Whether saying the same negative 'something' repeatedly, actually protected the government from embarrassment is debatable. A trawl through Hansard for the years 1965 to 1968 certainly confirms the bureaucrat's ability to draft ministerial statements, speeches, and replies to Parliamentary Questions which gave as little helpful information as possible, leading members of Parliament to complain that Ministers were being 'evasive' and 'fobbing them off' with inadequate replies. It was a period which gave totally new meanings to words like 'immediate', 'urgent' and 'pressing' and saw the overworking of phrases such as, 'we are (still) consulting', 'we are in close touch with' or 'we are keeping the situation under review' – all euphemisms for 'we don't intend to do anything more (or faster) unless forced to do so by public, press, or Parliamentary pressure'.

No clues to the real reasons for the unconscionable delay are to be found in the officially sanctioned accounts written by Phillipson[11] and Glancy[12] in the early 1970s. Nor is the full story likely to be gleaned from the Ministry of Health's papers if they survive and are eventually released for public scrutiny. This is because so much of the delay resulted from what Robinson was to repeat, *ad nauseam*, were 'essential consultations' with the medical profession and the health authorities, the detail and flavour of which will not be recorded by bureaucratic minute-takers. Nevertheless, it is possible, from those who were very much involved, from press and especially Parliamentary reports, and from other published material of the day, and with the additional benefit of hindsight, to reconstruct a reasonably complete picture of the events of the period. It is a picture which casts doubts on the view that the implementation of the Brain Committee's recommendations for treatment centres was 'a remarkable feat of administration and negotiation'.[13] A more objective assessment would see the period 1965 to 1968 as one of muddle and disinformation.

The writings of the Reverend Kenneth Leech[14] capture so accurately the atmosphere of confusion and frustration of those days, typified by the following passage from his by now famous letter published in *The Times* newspaper on 9 November 1966, a few days before the first anniversary of the publication of the second report of the Brain Committee:

> The Minister of Health's notorious statement of August 2 [1966] about treatment centres was received by doctors, social workers and addicts with cynical laughter or with despair. Those who daily face the problems of the young drug-taker are finding the obstacles almost insurmountable; hours and days spent ringing round hospitals for admissions; refusals, evasions, and interminable delays; addicts whose condition deteriorates and parents whose hearts are broken; doctors who refuse to prescribe and doctors who prescribe with almost criminal irresponsibility; and an overwhelming sense of hopelessness and despair among those who know the drug scene closest.

The 'notorious statement' refers to the Minister's reply to a Parliamentary Question about progress in setting up treatment centres that 'there were already centres for the treatment of addicts and more beds could be made available if the demand increased'.[15]

Leech's concern that there should be adequate treatment facilities for addicts has been contemptuously described by Smart[16] as transforming 'a journalists' campaign into a moral crusade'. At St Anne's Church, in the centre of Soho, he was seeing the heroin problem at first-hand and was therefore well-placed to set ministerial statements about the availability of treatment facilities against the practical reality. And it is equally wrong for the journalists to be criticised, if only by implication, for pressing for the introduction of treatment centres. It was not they but the medical profession, through the reconvened Brain Committee, which had 'discredited the existing 'methods' of dealing with addicts' and suggested that the establishment of treatment centres was the answer to the heroin problem. What Kenneth Robinson and his briefing officials seemed not to realise, when they attacked 'reverend gentlemen' and the press for criticising the efforts of the Ministry of Health, was that these criticisms were shared by many in Parliament, in the medical profession, in the social agencies and at very high levels in the Home Office.

For most of the period in which Ministry of Health officials were negotiating with the medical profession and the health authorities about the establishment of the proposed treatment centres, the Home Office was little more than a bystander. Charles Jeffery, then Chief Inspector of the Drugs Branch, did attend a number of the meetings with representatives of the health authorities. Whether he would have done so is doubtful had not Frank Hart, House Governor at Charing Cross Hospital, and very much a leading figure in these discussions, specifically requested the presence of a Home Office representative.

On 29 March 1966 Jeffery and I attended a meeting at the Home Office chaired by R. J. Guppy, then our Assistant Under-Secretary of State, to review progress on drafting the new Dangerous Drugs Act. At this meeting Ministry of Health officials lifted the corner of the veil on their negotiations with the medical profession and the health authorities. They told us that the exact role and number of treatment centres had not yet been decided, but it might be that the doctors in the centres would rarely supply heroin and cocaine and would stabilise addicts on methadone. The source of this advice was not disclosed but as it was not until September 1966 that the Chief Medical Officer, Sir George Godber, widened the consultation process to include selected clinicians with 'experience in the treatment of addiction', it seems likely to have come mainly from his Consultant Advisers on Drug Dependence and Psychiatry, Dr A. B. Monro and Professor W. H. Trethowan.

It was advice with which the Ministry officials appeared well content and they were quite unprepared for our strong reaction. The minutes of the meeting show 'the Home Office were very concerned that this might lead to a black market', an accurate, if not verbatim, record of our response to this revelation. Thirty years on I cannot remember whether Jeffrey or I made the comment which led to a temporary silence around the table, 'in which case, gentlemen, this discussion is purely academic, you won't get any addicts coming to your centres'. As a result there was some rethinking and by the end of May 1966 the Ministry were still 'not yet able to say that the arrangements envisaged for the supply of heroin and cocaine by hospitals will be fully acceptable'.

## Advice to the Ministry of Health from 'doctors experienced in the treatment of addiction'

The Ministry held two meetings of consultant psychiatrists, usually referred to in subsequent Parliamentary exchanges as 'doctors experienced in the treatment of addiction'. The first did not take place until 14 September 1966, more than a year after the reconvened Brain Committee's report had been signed (on 31 July 1965) and Lord Brain's expression of the need to act with urgency; the second took place on 16 December 1966.

The purpose of the meetings, as Sir George Godber explained, was to try 'to reach a consensus of opinion on the role of the hospital service after the implementation of the Brain Committee's recommendations'. He said there were two main aspects to this role, the provision of inpatient treatment and the 'possible' provision of outpatient facilities for the supply of heroin and cocaine to those addicts who, after attempted withdrawal, required maintenance prescribing.

These meetings cannot have been easy for Sir George because, as Dr Philip Connell, who was to have considerable influence on treatment policies and practice over the next 20 years, was keen to place on record in his Dent Memorial Lecture in 1985, 'it was only with considerable reluctance that the profession accepted the notion of the "stabilized addict" and of prescribing heroin and cocaine to addicts'.[17] What Connell did not place on record were the reasons for the profession's reluctance, when they had apparently been quite content with the first Brain Committee's endorsement of the concept of the 'stabilized addict' only four years earlier.[18]

Few of the psychiatrists who attended the meetings had had any practical experience of dealing with the new crop of heroin addicts on an outpatient basis, and among them were at least two influential hardliners, whose inflexible attitude was to dominate the treatment response in two important areas in the country for many years to come. The recently published views of Sir George's Consultant Adviser on Psychiatry, Professor W. H. Trethowan, were hardly encouraging. In an article in *The Birmingham Post*, on 14 August 1966, Trethowan had questioned the wisdom of treating addicts in special centres, since they might well attract 'those who come not to be cured but in the hope of a ready legalised supply by proclaiming themselves to be incurable'.

Since it was the advice of these doctors that provided the Ministry of Health with the basis for Hospital Memorandum H.M.(67)16 on 'The Treatment and Supervision of Heroin Addiction', issued on 8 March 1967, which set out how the Brain Committee's recommendations for treatment centres were to be implemented, it is worthwhile recalling their main conclusions.

There was general agreement that there was unlikely to be a large demand for inpatient treatment but, when there was, it would be best for addicts to be treated in mental hospitals in small groups of not more than 12. It was right in principle to expect NHS hospital outpatient departments to accept those addicts who could not be induced to accept inpatient treatment and, where necessary and appropriate, to supply them with heroin. But uniformity of treatment was essential and a standard code of practice might be drawn up for the use of the medical staff. The main practical problem, which contributed significantly to the further year it was to take before the treatment centres were up and running, was logistical. How could outpatient departments already working to capacity take on the additional work entailed in caring for addicts?

## Parliamentary pressure to open the treatment centres

When, on 25 November 1965, Kenneth Robinson announced the publication of the reconvened Brain Committee's report to the House of Commons he promised to make a statement as soon as possible when the consultations with the medical profession, already in progress, were complete. Four days later he gave an assurance that the consultations were being treated 'as a matter of urgency' and he hoped to make a statement early in the New Year.[19]

But when Bernard Braine made the first of his many interventions, on 31 January 1966, asking the Minister if the consultations had been completed and what action the government proposed to take on the Brain Committee's recommendations, he was told the discussions with the General Medical Council and the profession, were not yet complete, although it was already clear there was a considerable measure of agreement. Action was being taken on two proposals which did not require legislation: the establishment of treatment centres, about which the Ministry was consulting health boards and which would 'be pressed forward'; and the setting up of a standing advisory committee to keep drug dependence under 'constant review'. The recommendations which would require legislation, included the question of taking power for the compulsory detention of addicts undergoing treatment, and the method of enforcing the proposed limitation of the prescribing of certain drugs, were the subject of further study.[20] What the Minister did not disclose was that the recommendation for compulsory detention had already been rejected by the Cabinet Home Affairs Committee and that the GMC had declined to accept responsibility for policing the proposed notification and prescribing arrangements.

Further probing by Braine on 14 February 1966 [21] and William Deedes on 28 April[22] met with similar responses. Everything was being done with a view to introducing legislation 'as soon as Parliamentary time permits' (a neat attempt to divert responsibility to the Home Office in the event of any future untoward delay) and the provision of treatment facilities were now 'under review'. On 5 May Braine again raised the delay in implementing the Brain Committee's recommendations with Alice Bacon, Minister of State at the Home Office, who had been answering an oral question addressed to the Home Secretary by Renee Short about the steps he intended to take to eliminate drug taking among young people. The reply he received, that 'some of the recommendations need agreement on an international level in respect of certain drugs', must take the prize for sheer inventiveness.[23]

Both Braine and Deedes returned to the attack on 9 May 1966[24] in oral exchanges which drew from the Minister of Health the assurance that he was not dragging his feet but these were serious matters requiring extensive consultations, as 'professional interests' were involved. It was during these exchanges that he mentioned for the first time the current availability of treatment facilities – 'treatment for addicts is already available at a number of hospitals' – a claim which was to cause him considerable difficulty and embarrassment in the future.

In view of Robinson's disclosure that there were treatment facilities 'already available' it was not altogether surprising that he should now be pressed for details. On 20 June 1966 Deedes asked how many establishments under the NHS were available for the treatment of drug addiction and how many addicts were receiving such treatment. Neither question received particularly helpful replies. He was told that treatment had been given at about 160 hospitals in 1965, and in 1964 there had been 1,138 admissions to NHS psychiatric hospitals and units for treatment for dependence on drugs.[25] But it was Deedes' further question on 4 July 1966 about the steps that were being taken to establish in the London area the special institutions recommended by the Brain Committee which brought forth from Robinson the first of the many ambiguous and misleading statements which were to emanate from his Ministry over the next 18 months. He replied that hospital facilities for the treatment of drug addiction already included some specialist units and the extent to which these needed to be supplemented was being discussed with hospital authorities in relation to other relevant recommendations in the Brain Committee's report.[26]

With the long Parliamentary recess looming, Robinson was anxious to make a statement on progress and he did this on 2 August 1966 in reply to a Question from A. J. Wellbeloved when he repeated that there were already centres for the treatment of addicts and more beds could be made available if the demand increased. He went on to say that a conference of doctors 'experienced in the treatment of drug addiction' was being convened (the meeting on 14 September 1966) in order to pool the medical knowledge of the subject, and steps were being taken to set up a unit in which research into the problems of drug dependence could be undertaken. Legislation providing for the notification of addiction and the restrictions on prescribing was being planned, details of which would be discussed with the medical profession, but it had been decided not to provide for the compulsory detention of addicts, although this would be reconsidered should experience show it to be desirable.[27] As this was an arranged Question, for the express purpose of providing the Minister with an opportunity to give a progress report on the action taken so far to implement the Brain Committee's recommendations, it is amazing that Ministry of Health officials, when challenged by Kenneth Leech, 'were quick to point out that in this statement the Minister was not referring to any action that had been taken following the second report of the Brain Committee'.[28]

That the Minister's Answer did little to mollify his critics became apparent the next day, 3 August, when in an adjournment debate, Renee Short expressed the grave concern of many members, and those working in the field, at the apparent lack of activity on the part of the government. During her speech, she produced six 'jacks' of heroin, recently acquired in the West End of London, to show how readily available these now were.[29]

November 1966 saw the publication of Kenneth Leech's letter to *The Times* newspaper which prompted considerable media interest. This was not his first tilt at the 'pernicious and misleading' aspects of the Minister of Health's statement of 2 August. He had already drawn attention to the seriousness of the current situation and the possible consequences of the government's apparent inactivity in an article in the *Tribune* on 19 August 1966.

On 5 December 1966, when Renee Short suggested that a pilot scheme for treating addicts might be set up, she was told that a further meeting of the 'conference of experts' was to be held the following week.[30] What the Minister was almost certainly not briefed to say was that such a scheme, involving inpatient withdrawal and an outpatient prescribing clinic with general practitioners on the staff, had already been set up at St John's Hospital in Battersea by Dr Peter Chapple but had been swiftly closed down by the Regional Hospital Board on the grounds that it was 'premature'. Chapple was, however, allowed to open a prescribing clinic at St George's Hospital.[31]

In another adjournment debate, on 30 January 1967, the government was accused by William Deedes of 'inexcusable tardiness' and warned of the sharp deterioration in the heroin situation since the reconvened Brain Committee reported.[32] He urged the speedy provision of 'institutional means of replacing supplies for which some general practitioners have hitherto been the major source, before filling that gap becomes a major racket' and, if this was not done, the ground lost would be very hard to regain. In a particularly prophetic concluding passage, he added:

But at last perhaps we can contain (the heroin problem) – if we properly use the help of social workers, teachers, police, doctors, church and other services. But it will call for a major effort, it will call for a bigger and more costly effort than many now realise. It will call for more clearly defined Ministerial responsibility, for a sharper sense of urgency and for much clearer directions from the government than any we have yet had.

Robinson's reply was very much the mixture as before. The government recognised the need for 'speedy decisions and urgent action' to implement the Brain Committee recommendations. It was necessary to consult the medical profession in order that its professional experience could be brought to bear in devising a scheme of action, and also that doctors should participate willingly in its execution. This had now been achieved but it had taken longer than expected and he rejected the accusation of tardiness. There had been a recent announcement by the Home Secretary that the government would be introducing a short bill in the current session of Parliament to deal with those proposals for which new statutory powers were needed. This decision had clearly been greatly helped by the intervention of Quintin Hogg (later Lord Hailsham) during Question Time on 26 January 1967 to say that it might help the Home Secretary to know that the Opposition would be sympathetic to a request for Parliamentary time for the bill.[33]

Kenneth Robinson went on to say that the Brain Committee had envisaged there would be inpatient treatment for those addicts willing to accept withdrawal from drugs, followed by rehabilitation and outpatient treatment, with supervision for those who were not prepared to enter hospital. Treatment of the first kind was fairly widely available, a statement Renee Short was quick to dispute. Robinson had previously told her there were 19 hospitals in the South West Metropolitan Hospital Board Region able to deal with addicts, whereas her enquiries revealed that only three were prepared to do so, and she had reports from social workers of the difficulties they were experiencing in getting addicts admitted to hospital.

Robinson also disclosed, for the first time, that in London outpatient treatment for addicts would be provided mainly by the psychiatric departments of the teaching hospitals. A number of questions, including methods of assessing an addict's dosage, the need for special precautions against over-prescribing and a system of identification linked with the proposed new central record, could not be solved by 'government edict' and had required advice from the 'doctors with special experience in the treatment of addiction'. He would shortly be issuing the necessary guidance to the hospital authorities. However, as the problem was largely in London the hospital authorities there had been asked to take immediate action to deal with the existing and potential demand for treatment, along the lines suggested by the 'experts'.

## Hospital Memorandum H.M.(67)16

The Ministry's guidance was issued on 7 March 1967 as Hospital Memorandum H.M.(67)16. It is interesting to contrast it with the guidance in Hospital Memorandum H.M.(61)42 issued after the publication of the first Brain Committee's Report in 1961. Then, NHS hospital boards had merely been asked 'to select hospitals appropriate for giving initial treatment and long-term supervision respectively, and to arrange for any cases of drug addiction which come to attention of the hospital service to be referred to them'.

H.M.(67)16 repeated much of what Robinson had said in the House of Commons in January. It showed that of the 659 heroin addicts known to the Home Office in January 1967, 86% gave addresses in the London postal district and the area covered by the four metropolitan regional hospital boards, with the next highest concentrations being in Birmingham and Wessex. The treatment and supervision of addicts would be demanding and time consuming and where the demand was likely to be high, as in London, the load should be shared by hospitals for the mentally ill and psychiatric departments of general hospitals, both teaching and non-teaching. Accordingly, the metropolitan regional hospital boards, and the boards of governors of hospitals with psychiatric departments in the London area were asked to introduce outpatient services 'immediately on a small scale' which should be linked with beds at the same hospital if possible. Plans should be made to expand these services 'at short notice' if an increased demand followed the introduction of the proposed legislation prohibiting the prescribing of heroin and cocaine by general practitioners.

Hospital boards outside London were asked to take similar steps where 'it seems warranted by the number of known addicts' and authorities both in and out of London were to inform the Ministry (as well as local health authorities and NHS executive councils in their areas) within one month, of the outpatient and inpatient services they were providing for heroin addicts and of their plans for expansion of these should the need arise. (Those aspects of the Memorandum dealing with treatment issues are discussed in Chapter 9.)

The second reading debate on the Dangerous Drugs Bill on 6 April 1967,[34] offered Robinson another opportunity to reveal how the plans for the treatment centres were progressing. There were outpatient facilities 'to a limited extent' in two London teaching hospitals but he hoped he would not be pressed for their names as this might mean that addicts would concentrate on them and the load would not be spread evenly. Four other teaching hospitals would be introducing a service but could not start until the necessary accommodation had been built.

## Still no treatment centres: continuing Parliamentary concern

There was to follow a period of high farce, justifiably described by Leech as 'The strange case of the missing treatment centres'.[35] It started with the debate on the Dangerous Drugs Bill in the House of Lords on 20 June 1967 when, after dealing with the Home Office aspects, Lord Stonham left it to Lady Phillips, in her winding-up speech for the Ministry of Health, to outline the government's plans for setting up treatment centres. He was probably as surprised as everyone else to discover that she was 'not certain at this stage that it would be something your Lordships would particularly want to know', and accordingly declined to set out the Ministry's plans.[36] A few days later, in exchanges in the House of Commons, Kenneth Robinson claimed that outpatient treatment was available at nine hospitals in central London, with other clinics opening in due course, and that about 30 hospitals in the London area already provided inpatient treatment for addicts of all types.[37]

The nine hospitals had been named four days earlier in a letter from the Ministry to Dr A. J. Hawes, who, facing increasing demands from addicts following Lady Frankau's death, had written on 31 May 1967 asking for information about available treatment facilities.[38] Hawes then contacted the named hospitals only to discover that the majority denied having any facilities other than 'the normal provisions of casualty departments and general psychiatric wards'. The Minister's incorrect information was based on an early list provided 'in good faith' by the North-East Metropolitan Hospital Board but this did not deter him from continuing to attempt to equate treatment available in busy casualty departments with the outpatient treatment envisaged by the Brain Committee.

Renee Short returned to the attack on 3 July and asked the Minister what response there had been to Hospital Memorandum H.M. (67)16 by the regional hospital boards. She was told that inpatient treatment for heroin addicts was available in all regional hospital board areas, and outpatient treatment in 12, with the need for expansion being kept under review. Mrs Short pressed for the names of the hospitals, producing the even more unhelpful reply that most mental hospitals and psychiatric units had treatment facilities for addicts to one or more types of drug. She retorted that while this might be correct in theory it did not work in practice as hospitals were unwilling to take addicts on for treatment. Would the Minister therefore see that proper centres were set up in every regional hospital board area with round-the-clock facilities available?

Digging deep into his background briefing material, and avoiding any reference to 'treatment centres' as proposed by the Brain Committee (a significant omission in the light of what was to follow a little later) Robinson rejected Mrs Short's assertion. Figures in his possession showed that in 1966 inpatient treatment for 360 heroin addicts was given at 78 hospitals and units in England and Wales, of which 45 were in the Metropolitan Police District.[39]

On 5 July Lady Phillips apologised to the House of Lords for her earlier failure to provide details of the available treatment facilities.[40] She said there were
now 11 outpatient clinics in London (two more than Robinson had told the
House of Commons on 26 June) and before the end of the month Ministry of
Health spokesmen in both Houses had increased this number to 13. On 19 July in
a Written Answer to Lord Sandford, who had also wanted to know what progress
had been made following the issue of H.M. (67)16, Lord Beswick prefaced his
reply with the familiar qualification that, as services were still being developed, it
would not be in the interests of addicts to publish the names of the 13 hospitals.
At six hospitals the service was provided in the casualty (now called Accident and
Emergency) department on a 24-hour basis; in three others the service was available five days a week; and in the remaining four 'less frequently'. He conceded
that the staff providing these services were not exclusively concerned with addicts.[41] Only five days earlier, on 14 July, Lord Beswick had told Lord Sandford in
an Oral Answer that there would be 14 outpatient clinics in London by the end
of the year while outside London treatment would be available at most mental
hospitals.[42]

Opening a debate on drug addiction clinics on 25 July 1967[43] William Deedes
admitted to some confusion. When the Dangerous Drugs Bill had left the House
of Commons he thought he had understood the position regarding the clinics but
in view of what had been said recently 'in another place' (a reference to Lady
Phillips' comments in the House of Lords) it appeared there were now 11 outpatient clinics, with plans for four more under urgent discussion. Where were they?
Where did they fit into the pattern, as he had not heard of them before? Were they
outpatient clinics in London teaching hospitals or were they private? What was
their eventual role?

Deedes then referred Robinson to a confidential memorandum sent to his
Ministry by London teaching hospital administrators, which he should have seen,
in which the administrators had made their misgivings abundantly clear and
asked a number of disquieting questions. The hospitals had three main areas of
concern: the difficulties of assessing addicts' drug needs, liaison between centres,
and the provision of a 24-hour service. It was generally accepted that for a reasonably accurate assessment to be made of an addict's dosage it would be necessary to
admit the addict as an inpatient for 48 hours, and this could not be done without
extensive use of beds. The administrators were not happy about the sort of intelligence system which would have to be created if there was to be good liaison between the treatment centres and the centre where addict notifications were to be
received. There was a shortage of staff who were both expert and enthusiastic, and
hospitals feared they would have difficulty in finding suitable people. The provision of a 24-hour service would pose even greater problems. Hospitals were being
asked to take on 'a disagreeable and difficult job which will have disruptive effects

on their own regimes' and their views were therefore entitled to be considered by the Ministry.

Whether it was the early hour – the debate had started at 7.34 a.m. – or simply irritation at the continuing criticism, Robinson's reply reached new heights of equivocation and procrastination. Although for the most part it was a rehash of much that had gone before, there were two particularly noteworthy revelations. The first was that despite having told the House in January 1967 that the task of establishing special 'treatment centres' was being 'pressed forward', he now appeared to be questioning the 'treatment centre' concept put forward by the Brain Committee. This was a clear indication that progress in the negotiations was being dictated not by the Ministry of Health, but by those with whom the Ministry was negotiating, confirming what many by now suspected.

In an apparent attempt to rewrite the Brain Committee's recommendation for the establishment, at least in London, of 'specialised institutions for the treatment of addiction', Robinson suggested:[44]

> ... the expression treatment centre is ambiguous. It could be used to mean part of a hospital given over exclusively to the treatment of addicts, or any hospital that provides specialist treatment, whether or not it gives it in a unit that treats addicts exclusively. It may also be used to refer to the new out-patient services for heroin addicts which are being developed or to both in-patient and out-patient services combined. The organisation of hospital treatment facilities for addicts depends on several factors such as the local prevalence of addiction, the scale of current and potential demand for treatment, the resources – staff and accommodation – that can be provided and the views of hospital boards, taking account of medical advice, on the best way to organise treatment. It follows that treatment facilities are provided in different ways and that there is no standard package called a 'treatment centre'.

In the light of this clear indication of the difficulties the Ministry of Health was having in interpreting, and implementing, the Brain Committee's recommendations, it was perhaps not surprising that the only outpatient treatment facilities available on 25 July 1967 were being provided by the casualty departments of 13 hospitals in the London area.

Nor is it surprising that the Ministerial speech-writer and advisers should have ignored a letter from Dr Hawes which appeared in *The Lancet* on 22 July 1967[45] three days before the Debate. Hawes, ever the pragmatist, went straight to the heart of Robinson's dilemma and offered an interim solution. He wrote:

> When referring to these centres our official rulers in medical matters seem to put on solemn faces as if such centres have to be housed in special buildings needing much time, money and forethought. Several have been in existence for years, run by so-called

Junkie doctors, of whom I have the doubtful honour of being one. As we Junkie doctors are general practitioners, our treatment centres have consisted of what the ordinary general practitioner has to offer – stripped to the barest essentials, a consulting and waiting room and the usual clinical paraphernalia. These simple things and the doctor himself are all that is needed ... It is surely useless to pretend that a hospital – any hospital – cannot provide as good a service as the general practitioner. The service really consists of a simplified casualty department. The doctor is not on full-time duty, but he must be available any time of the day or night. So let us have done with the nonsense that any hospital whatever cannot provide a couple of rooms and the work shared among the junior staff – say, half an hour a day apiece. If ordinary GPs have been doing it for years, then any hospital in the country can do as well and better ... I see not the slightest reason why addict clinics should not be set up in every hospital in London and all large cities – and that within a week. The trimmings can come later.

If the Brain Committee had emphasised that their proposals were 'dependent on such treatment facilities being readily available at short notice', there were few signs in Robinson's reply to the debate to indicate that any sense of urgency had yet permeated the corridors of the Ministry of Health. Hospital authorities had been 'asked to plan' to provide facilities but appeared to have been set no deadline. As the lack of space on hospital sites ruled out the possibility of new buildings, except as a relatively long-term measure, Ministry officials were considering with each teaching hospital and regional hospital board what existing buildings could be used with minor adaptations. Yet only three months earlier, during the second reading debate on the Dangerous Drugs Bill, Robinson had announced that four more teaching hospitals would introduce an outpatient service once the necessary accommodation had been built.[46]

But the clearest confirmation that the lack of enthusiasm detected by William Deedes among some hospital administrators was shared by some of their medical colleagues, was provided by the Minister's comment that staffing could only be tackled hospital-by-hospital, in the light of the additional time each consultant psychiatrist was 'able to spare', and each consultant's views on the way in which he or she preferred to treat patients. Therefore, in practice, arrangements were likely to vary and there would not be a string of identical units each run and staffed in an identical way. The differing views of psychiatrists about methods of treatment, and the need for greater experience in this field, made it unlikely that a standard pattern of treatment would emerge in the immediate future (although it would not be long before attempts would be made to bring this about).

The memorandum to which Deedes had referred on 25 July, and which Robinson admitted he had not seen, had been prepared by Frank Hart of Charing Cross Hospital, one of the hospital administrators 'anxious to play a part', as demonstrated by the early opening of the Charing Cross clinic in the autumn of 1967. In it he raised a number of important practical issues which H.M.(67)16 had not addressed and he concluded that 'the Ministry is taking a grave risk in launching the scheme on the lines contemplated'. Hart proposed an alternative of four fully staffed units, offering an 18–24-hour service, whose running costs would probably be no greater than what was currently being suggested. But this received little serious attention as the general policy had been agreed at the consultants' conferences in September and December 1966 and it was now too late to change. However, Hart's memorandum led to the establishment of a working group, on which, he had insisted, the Home Office should be represented, as he was concerned about the apparent divided responsibilities of the two departments.

In addition to the practical problems identified in Hart's paper, the administrators' main worry was about the likely caseload for which they were being asked to make provision. On 25 July 1967 Robinson had told the House of Commons that, after consultation with the Home Office, the Ministry was working on an estimate that 1,000 addicts might seek treatment when general practitioners could no longer prescribe heroin. But the December 1966 meeting of 'experts' had been told that it was likely between 200 and 300 heroin addicts might need to be looked after by the outpatient clinics in central London. This was an estimate based on enquiries by Regional Medical Officers, who had contacted doctors known to be dealing with addicts. (The small total suggests Lady Frankau was not contacted.) The number of heroin addicts known to the Home Office in 1965 was 521 and the projected figure for 1966 was 900; the final total was 899.

The discrepancy greatly troubled Frank Hart, who saw that if there was only one unknown addict for every one who was known, the clinics could be facing a caseload of some 2,000 patients. At this point the Home Office was asked to explain the basis of its 'estimate', which was a record of the number of different heroin addicts who had come to notice at some time during the year in question and represented the minimum number of addicts who might come forward for treatment. The Ministry of Health was using as the base from which the new service would start 'the number of addicts getting heroin on prescriptions from general practitioners' and officials thought there was no reason to suppose this was rising – indeed it might well fall off with the imminent legislation. This was an extraordinary comment given that one of the objects of the exercise was to encourage as many addicts as possible to seek treatment.

The search for 'treatment centres' continued through 1967 and into 1968 in the press, by social workers and others trying desperately to place addicts in treatment, and also in the Home Office. At one point the Home Office Assistant Under-Secretary of State, Neil Cairncross, was moved to ask for a briefing as 'the exact state of affairs is not too easily discovered from the Ministry of Health reports'.

This was not altogether surprising as Jeffery discovered when he attended a meeting with health authority representatives and Ministry officials two weeks before the debate of 25 July 1967. It then emerged, 'to the consternation' of the officials, that only Westminster Hospital had outpatient facilities operating on a regular basis, with a clinic up and running for five days a week from 9.30 a.m. to 5 p.m. and it was planning shortly to open a similar one at Queen Mary's Hospital, Roehampton. The Charing Cross Hospital clinic was due to open in October and intending to operate for five days a week and for slightly longer hours, from 9 a.m. to 9 p.m. University College Hospital and West Middlesex Hospital were just coming into the picture 'on a limited scale'. The Maudsley Hospital clinic would also open in October with eight outpatient half-day sessions, four for narcotic and four for non-narcotic users.

A variety of excuses, but no convincing reasons, were available to explain this depressing lack of progress. Excuses included lack of space until new accommodation was built, the need to appoint additional medical staff and, confirming the 'reluctant' acceptance by the Ministry's 'experts in the treatment of addiction' to undertake maintenance treatment, the refusal by the consultants at three hospitals to do so. (One of the three hospitals was St George's, on whose staff was Dr Maurice Partridge, the consultant psychiatrist who served on both Brain Committees.) But the underlying reason was, as the Advisory Council on the Misuse of Drugs[47] was later to say, because of local health authority:

> ... unwillingness to use capital and revenue funds for this purpose since diversion of money would mean that other services would have to suffer and there was little enthusiasm for providing services for such an unpopular group of patients.

Questions in Parliament about the funding of the proposed 'treatment centres' had received much the same response as the attempts to discover when and where they would be established. When first asked about the financial arrangements by William Deedes on 25 January 1967, Robinson said he did not expect the cost to be 'very large in relation to the total cost of hospital provision' and all hospitals were given extra money each year not earmarked for special purposes.[48]

On 13 February 1967 Bernard Braine tried another tack, when in addition to a request for an estimate of the cost of setting up treatment centres, he asked if there would be additional Exchequer money or if cuts would have to be made in other parts of the NHS. He was told, once more, it was too early for an estimate of the cost but no cuts in other parts of the service were anticipated.[49] This was to be the standard reply until the second reading debate on the Dangerous Drugs Bill, on 6 April 1967, when Deedes again raised the matter. Reminding Robinson of his earlier reply in January he now asked what additional resources were to be allocated to the problem.[50]

The reply gave the first hint of the 'special relationship' which the London teaching hospitals were to have with the Ministry of Health over the next few years, a relationship, not entirely confined to resources, which the Ministry was to come to regret. Robinson repeated that all hospital boards were given development money each year from which these new treatment facilities should be financed, but he now accepted it might be difficult for the teaching hospitals to absorb the costs from their development money. Should this prove to be the case he was prepared to make sufficient money available out of a small contingency fund held by the Ministry of Health.[51]

The promise that there could be special financial provision for the teaching hospitals did not impress some medical members of Parliament, who had clearly been there before. Sir John Vaughan Morgan was quick to point out that hospitals had had experience of being given a special job by the Ministry of Health for one year, and a special allowance, only to discover in the following year they were required to finance it out of normal revenue.[52] Similar scepticism was voiced by Lord Amulree in the House of Lords on 20 June 1967, when Lady Phillips made a similar disclosure.[53] However, all attempts to obtain similar financial assistance for non-teaching hospitals were unsuccessful, the explanation for the preferential treatment of the teaching hospitals being that their proposed expenditure on drug addiction was much greater in relation to their total budget.

## The Advisory Committee on Drug Dependence

Not all the critics' fire was directed at the perceived delay in setting up the treatment centres. The Brain Committee's proposal for 'a standing advisory committee to survey the whole field and to call attention to any development that might be cause for concern worthy of further study' was not overlooked and also attracted justifiable criticism for the delay in its implementation. Even before the publication of the Committee's report it had been agreed that the appointment of such a body would not require legislation, and, in his first statement of the government's response to the Committee's proposals, in January 1966, Kenneth Robinson had announced in the House of Commons that a standing committee would be set up.

The terms of reference of what was to become known as the Advisory Committee on Drug Dependence, were finally announced to the House of Commons in a Written Answer on 26 July 1966.[54] It would be chaired by Lord Brain (who had accepted the invitation on the clear understanding that his Committee's recommendations would be implemented), with the names of the members to follow as soon as possible. The Committee would be required:

To keep under review the misuse of narcotic and other drugs which are likely to produce dependence and to advise on remedial measures that might be taken or on any other related matters which Ministers may refer to it.

The full membership was announced on 31 October but the Advisory Committee did not meet for some time, due mainly to the illness and subsequent death of Lord Brain. However, before this, on 4 July, Hector Hughes asked Kenneth Robinson if steps would be taken to ensure that members of the Committee were 'neither addicts nor partial to addiction' and 'free from this secret vice' otherwise 'their work will be ludicrous, futile and held up to public ridicule'. To this Robinson gave the not unreasonable reply that 'If he is right in that it is a secret vice it would be difficult to give the proof he requires'.[55]

There was, of course, a very important issue hidden behind Hughes' question. Given the low level of experience of drug misuse in 1966, how were members of the Advisory Committee to be chosen? Should they come from among the very few who did have some real experience of what was happening on the street, or should they be chosen from the ranks of 'the great and the good' nominated by their professional organisations more for their experience of committee procedure than for any special expertise in the field with which the Advisory Committee was concerned? Or should there be a balance between the two? In the event, precedent was followed and the middle choice adopted.

By 1970 the Advisory Committee on Drug Dependence, which first met on 12 January 1967, had rapidly prepared and published four important reports, now rarely mentioned but which contained between them a wealth of common sense, vision and proposals for action which, if acted upon, would have guaranteed a higher state of preparedness for the re-appearance of the heroin problem in the early 1980s.[56]

## Comments on progress in the medical press

On 25 November 1967, the second anniversary of the publication of the reconvened Brain Committee's report, leading articles in the *British Medical Journal* and *The Lancet* delivered scathing attacks on the Ministry's 'paper schemes' for implementing the Committee's proposals. H.M.(67)16 had recently been joined by H.M.(67)83, dealing with the rehabilitation and aftercare of heroin addicts. Both articles described the content of the two memoranda as 'admirable' but, as the *British Medical Journal*[57] commented:

> The trouble comes when turning from the Ministry's memoranda to the realities. Those in Alexander Fleming House seem to have some of the characteristics of the kind of student who writes alpha papers but muffs the practicals.

After posing a number of important practical questions, such as where the consultant sessions for the new treatment centres were to be found, whether new psychiatrists were to be 'manufactured' or withdrawn from other services and what training courses had been arranged, the *British Medical Journal* conceded that it would not be fair to put all the blame for the delay on the Ministry of Health, because to a large extent the solution to the problem rested with local health authorities, but it was not unreasonable 'to ask for more practical action and more evidence of a sense of urgency'. The article ended with a prophetic warning: 'With a situation as threatening as this today's minor blunders, procrastination, or meanness are the stuff of which tomorrow's disasters are likely to be made.'

*The Lancet,*[58] noting there would now 'apparently be co-operation between all branches of the health services, including local authorities, mental hospitals, treatment clinics and general practitioners', then shattered the illusion by reminding its readers that 'such a degree of co-operation has not been very manifest in the past and that it will occur in the future is a pious hope' and the treatment of addiction was 'the graveyard of pious hopes'.

## The treatment centres named

On 30 January 1968, in a Written Answer, Robinson at last disclosed the long-awaited names of the hospitals where the new outpatient clinics would be established. There were 15, with extra clinics to be provided shortly at some hospitals already offering a service, and four new ones to be opened in the next few weeks. But even now his officials could not resist the temptation to include facilities which did not equate to the treatment centres proposed by the Brain Committee. Thus, included in the 15 was one hospital where addicts would be seen by appointment only, one where they would be seen in the general psychiatric outpatient clinic, and another in the casualty department, with 'emergency only' treatment available at four others.[59]

In January 1968 Regional Medical Officers had again contacted those general practitioners known still to be in touch with heroin addicts. (Lady Frankau had died and Dr John Petro, who had taken on some of her patients, as well as many of his own, and who was to be another notorious 'script doctor', could not be reached.) This survey revealed that 21 doctors were seeing 344 addicts, a larger number than in December 1966, although over half of these were attending Drs Chapple and Gray, and most of them were not receiving heroin. Despite a minor worry caused by the discovery of small pockets of heroin addiction in Crawley and Welwyn Garden City, it was felt adequate facilities would shortly exist and that the restrictions on the prescribing of heroin and cocaine to addicts could now be introduced.

On 6 May 1968 William Deedes 'prayed' against the Dangerous Drugs (Supply to Addicts) Regulations 1968, which had come into effect on 16 April 1968. (He was using a Parliamentary procedure by which he could initiate a debate about the Regulations. In January he had also 'prayed' against the Dangerous Drugs (Notification of Addicts) Regulations, 1968.) In his speech he regretted that the size of London did not lend itself to the adoption of the system[60] '... which Birmingham enjoys, by which all agencies, police, chemists, social workers and the hospitals co-operate sympathetically to get addicts into the right hands.'

In the light of what has happened over the subsequent 25 years, it is Deedes' perception in 1968 that the present scheme could only be 'an emergency measure', which should be remembered. As time went on it would be necessary to move away from the formal arrangements involving NHS hospitals, towards *ad hoc* institutions placing far greater emphasis than was then the case, on the social factors involved in addiction.

For his part, Kenneth Robinson took the opportunity to reply to some of the criticism directed at him and his department over the previous two years. He said there had been a consistent campaign of denigration of the government's efforts, waged by some newspapers and a few people concerned with the problem of addiction mainly in a voluntary capacity, who were 'hostile to the whole concept of hospital treatment for addicts'. One inevitable side effect of this was damage to the addicts' confidence in hospital treatment and made them less likely to seek it. The transfer of addicts from general practitioners to the treatment centres had been accomplished in a remarkably orderly fashion but it was too much to expect this to be publicly acknowledged in those journals which had confidently predicted chaos.[61]

But was Robinson being fair to his critics? Why should he assume that complaints about the lack of facilities from people with first-hand experience of the difficulties of trying to obtain hospital treatment for willing addicts, indicated hostility to the whole concept? So much of the criticism aimed at the Ministry of Health was inevitable, given the picture of lethargy, incompetence and muddle painted by his statements in Parliament and the comments of his officials. At a time when the situation was being described in the medical press as an 'epidemic', and by Williams Deedes in Parliament as 'a small virulent plague', it was not unreasonable that concerned individuals should have expected rather more urgency and determination than his Ministry had shown. There cannot be many epidemics in our recent history which have been allowed to spread unchecked for such a long time before a viable response emerged.

The key question, which Robinson dared not answer, except by vague references to the complexities of the consultations with health authorities, was whether those consultation processes could have been speeded up and adequate services to replace those provided by general practitioners put in place much earlier than 16 April 1968. Some delay was inevitable because the Brain Committee had provided little guidance about how the treatment centres should operate beyond the suggestion that they should have facilities for medical treatment and laboratory investigation with provision for research, and that they might be linked to a psychiatric hospital.[62] Yet it was not until September 1966, two months before the first anniversary of the publication of the Brain Committee's Report, when the first meeting of the 'experts in the treatment of addiction' took place, that there was evidence of any serious planning for the centres by the Ministry of Health.

## Why did it take so long to open the treatment centres?

So what went wrong and why did it take so long to adopt the reconvened Brain Committee's solution to the heroin problem? Why did the Minister of Health allow himself to become the target of such persistent criticism, verging at times on ridicule. The Committee may have failed to provide a detailed blueprint for their ideal treatment centre, but they clearly intended that in addition to bringing the medical supply of heroin under more stringent control, the treatment centres would be part of an integrated service with proper facilities for the long-term psychological and physical rehabilitation of the addict.

It cannot be that Ministry of Health officials did not understand what they were being asked to provide; the Committee's joint secretaries were Ministry officials and the direction in which the Committee were moving was known long in advance of the publication of its report. Yet in Parliamentary Answer after Answer, and in speech after speech, from quite an early stage, the impression was given by the Minister of Health that there were plenty of treatment facilities available, if only addicts, and by implication, their doctors, would bother to use them. This reached the height of absurdity with the pretence that casualty departments in several London hospitals were performing the functions of the 'Brain treatment centres'.

Leaving aside the now unanswerable question of the extent to which outside influences may have contributed to this period of 'disinformation' and confusion, there are, I suspect, a number of factors which may have affected the Ministry's response. These include their lack of experience with the problem of drug addiction, and the deference, often bordering on subservience, which officials seemed to show to medical opinion and medical administrators; so it was hardly surprising that the Ministry lost control of the negotiations. The inevitable result was a failure to appreciate the urgency of the task, and a fundamental lack of will and understanding of the need to put the national interest above narrow professional interests and ambitions.

Apart from not knowing what treatment facilities were available, Ministry of Health officials allowed the priorities which the Brain Committee had set out very clearly to be changed. No longer was it their most important task to get the addicts away from those doctors whose prescribing was giving rise for concern and into the care of experts whose 'duty' would be to treat and, if thought necessary, to provide the addict with drugs. Instead, they saw the most pressing need was to provide these new hospital-based 'experts' with all the necessary facilities, including adequate accommodation and funding, and special urine testing arrangements (a diagnostic tool not readily available to the general practitioners) without which they could not possibly be expected to accept this new responsibility.

If this appears unduly critical of the Ministry of Health officials it has to be said, in their defence, that apart from setting up and servicing the Rolleston Committee, they had had little reason to take an administrative interest in drug addiction since 1919, when Sir Malcolm Delevingne had ensured that the primary responsibility for drug control would rest with the Home Office and not with the newly created Ministry of Health. The main contact between the two departments over the intervening years had been through the Regional Medical Officer Service about individual cases of addiction.

As evidence of the lack of experience of Ministry officials, no copy of the Rolleston Report was readily available in 1958 at a meeting with the Home Office to discuss the appointment of the first Brain Committee and nor could any of the medical administrators present recall ever having seen a copy of DD 101, the advisory Memorandum to Doctors and Dentists. The Home Office had to put forward the names of individual doctors who could be approached to give evidence to the Committee. There had been no alarm signals from Alexander Fleming House (where the Ministry was then housed) about the developing heroin situation which led to the reconvening of the Committee in 1964. But why should the Ministry have taken any special interest or devoted resources to what the first Brain Committee had told them in 1961 was a non-existent problem? Hospital Memorandum H.M.(61)42 had been issued in 1961 urging health authorities to provide facilities for the treatment of addicts and presumably, and not unreasonably, this was assumed to be an adequate response to the Committee's report.

Although there was 'no central departmental expertise' upon which to draw[63] there is another more cogent explanation for the poor showing of the Ministry of Health. In an interview published in 1990, Dr A. A. Baker, who in 1967 had assumed responsibility for setting up the new treatment service although he was not a career civil servant, laid bare the basic philosophy of his senior ministry administrative colleagues at the time, saying:[64]

> I was told my first duty was to protect the Minister, i.e. to make sure that any advice, anything the Minister said, was in keeping with accepted policies and would not lead to criticism in Parliament … the Department wasn't primarily a planning organisation. It didn't see the need to solve problems of the future in the way I did; it was more concerned with covering the day-to-day problems.

174

In 1982 the Treatment and Rehabilitation working group of the Advisory Council on the Misuse of Drugs was more forthright in commenting on the development of the treatment centres:[65]

> ... there was no central plan advising how they should be set up, what facilities were needed and what the staffing structure should be. In fact, the problem had developed so rapidly that very few doctors or other professional staff had the training, experience or interest to respond in other than an ad hoc manner.

# 8

# Implementing the recommendations of the Second Brain Report: the notification of addicts

The notification of addicts was a vital brick in the second Brain Committee's new defences against the spread of heroin and cocaine addiction. The Committee provided a definition of an addict[1] and recommended[2] that:

> All addicts ... should be formally 'notified' to a central authority and this authority should keep an up-to-date list of such addicts with relevant particulars.

In making this recommendation, the Committee drew an analogy with the Public Health Act, which requires doctors to notify patients suffering from infectious diseases, saying '... addiction is after all a socially infectious condition and its notification may offer a means for epidemiological assessment and control'.

The Committee noted, as it had in its first report[3] that it 'would object to any attempt to equate the term 'notification' with 'registration', which 'might seem to imply that the addict is officially recognized as having the right to an approved quantity of dangerous drugs'.[4]

To emphasise the importance it attached to notification, the Committee went on to recommend that failure by a doctor 'to notify an addict (as defined) with whom he has come into a professional relationship and who is not already notified'[5] should become an offence to be dealt with by an 'appropriate tribunal', which it suggested should be the Disciplinary Committee of the General Medical Council.[6]

The recommendation for compulsory notification of addicts was greeted with approval by the medical press. The *British Medical Journal*[7] was enthusiastic about the analogy between addiction and an infectious disease, commenting:

> Notification of addicts is the basis – sound and acceptable – of the committee's proposals. Drug addiction is a disease, and a disease which spreads by contagion in a community. Once a disease is notifiable a number of consequences follow, of which the statutory provision of treatment centres is one ...

*The Lancet*[8] had some reservations:

The nature and site of the proposed central authority for notification is perhaps deliberately left vague. On the one hand, the Home Office has done well for a long time with the overseeing of this exceedingly difficult problem; on the other, it does use policemen for the purpose.

The working party set up by the British Medical Association (BMA) to examine the Committee's report did not accept that a case had been made for the notification of addicts to 'all dangerous drugs'. It thought this would be unacceptable to the profession because it would be impracticable, and suggested that notification should be limited to patients addicted to heroin and cocaine. However, after a discussion at the meeting addressed by Lord Brain, the BMA Council approved the working party's recommendation that all addicts should be notified, with the Home Office as the central authority.[9]

The BMA working party also suggested that records of the normal sources of supply of notified addicts should be kept by the Home Office (already a long-established procedure by the Drugs Inspectorate) and that all prescriptions for (heroin and cocaine) should be sent by the chemist to the central authority immediately after dispensing. The latter was a totally impracticable suggestion, because, apart from the staff resources that would be needed, it would have seriously disrupted NHS pricing arrangements.

## The introduction of statutory notification of addicts

The central authority to which addicts were to be notified was named as the Chief Medical Officer at the Home Office in the Dangerous Drugs (Notification of Addicts) Regulations 1968. In 1985 the House of Commons Social Services Committee wondered whether addicts might be discouraged from seeking treatment because they feared that notification to the Home Office carried 'a stigma of criminality'. John Patten, then a junior minister in the Department of Health and Social Security, commented that although 'there might be some logic in transferring it (the Addicts Index) to my Department... it was not worth the upheaval... we should leave well alone'.[10]

The index of addicts which had been maintained by the Drugs Inspectorate since 1934 (see Chapter 2) was adapted to accommodate the increased flow of information which formal notification would bring, and in order to produce statistical material more quickly to meet the unprecedented interest in drug addiction which the publicity given to the Committee's report was stimulating.

The notification of addicts was given statutory force by a Regulation made under the Dangerous Drugs Act 1967 with the definition of an addict as:

A person shall be regarded as being addicted to a drug if, and only if, he has as a result of repeated administration become so dependent upon the drug that he has an over-whelming desire for the administration of it to be continued.

The Regulation came into force on 22 February 1968. After that date any medical practitioner who came into a professional relationship with a patient he knew or suspected to be addicted to any drug in Part 1 of the Schedule to the 1965 Dangerous Drugs Act was required to notify certain details of that patient to the Chief Medical Officer at the Home Office. The drugs included heroin and morphine, cocaine and cannabis and all other drugs brought under the strictest control by the 1961 United Nations Single Convention on Narcotic Drugs.

The 'certain details' the doctor was required to provide when notifying an addict patient included the person's name, date of birth, national insurance number, the date of attendance, and the name of the drug or drugs to which they were addicted. Although not required to do so, doctors usually also volunteered the details of the drugs, if any, they had prescribed at the attendance.

Since the General Medical Council had declined to accept the disciplinary role envisaged by the Brain Committee (see Chapter 7), the Act allowed for doctors who failed to notify an addict to be referred to a specially constituted tribunal consisting of four doctors and a legal assessor.

The notification procedure was retained under the Misuse of Drugs Act 1971, and the Misuse of Drugs (Notification of and Supply to Addicts) Regulations 1973 came into force in July of that year. These Regulations applied to 14 of the drugs most strictly controlled by the Act (Class A drugs) including cocaine, diamorphine (heroin), dextromoramide, dipipanone (Diconal), hydrmorphone, levorphanol, methadone (Physeptone), morphine, opium, oxycodone, pethidine and phenazocine. The Home Secretary, after receiving advice from the Advisory Council on the Misuse of Drugs, could amend the Regulations and add or remove drugs from the list to which they applied. In 1991 the Council considered, but rejected, a proposal to add amphetamines to the list of notifiable drugs.[11]

## Reasons for notifying addicts

In 1924 the Home Office had asked the Rolleston Committee to suggest some means of dealing with 'the very difficult case of the addict who goes to several doctors at once and obtains treatment from them all'.[12] In responding to this request, the Committee[13] considered the possibility of notifying such cases to the Home Office, saying:

> The primary object of a system of notification would be to enable the Home Office more readily to detect cases in which patients were obtaining drugs of addiction from

two or more doctors concurrently … A requirement for notification would no doubt tend to diminish doubtfully justifiable supplying or ordering of the drugs … [and] assist practitioners to exercise firmer control over their patients … [and] would tend to relieve practitioners … from the liability to irksome inquiries, which at present are unavoidable.

In the event, the Rolleston Committee did not recommend notification because it believed that the benefits were outweighed by the disadvantage of impairing the confidential relationship between doctor and patient, and because the Home Office took the view that notification 'is not essential for detecting persons who obtain drugs of addiction from more than one doctor at a time'.[14] Nevertheless, the Committee thought:

> … every practitioner prescribing morphine or heroin for the first time to a patient who does not require the drugs except for the treatment of symptoms produced by addiction will be well advised … to make inquiries of that patient as to the sources from which he had obtained, or is at the time, obtaining, the drugs in question, and as to the names and address of practitioners under whose care he is, or has been.

Compulsory notification had been considered, and rejected, by the first Brain Committee for reasons which did not receive any mention in its report, although a question about the desirability of making addiction compulsorily notifiable appeared in the questionnaire sent to potential witnesses by the Committee secretariat. Doctors' responses had varied, with some, like Dr Denis Parr who had experience of treating addicts, in favour and others opposing, usually on grounds of principle rather than practicality. The Committee made only an oblique reference in its report to notification as a means of identifying addicts when it noted that 'While there is … no system of registration of addicts … the Departmental arrangements ensure that nearly all addicts to dangerous drugs are known'.[15]

In my 1963 review of the heroin situation I had advocated compulsory notification to try to make certain the Drugs Inspectorate knew of all addicts who approached doctors and to be able to confirm their identity, because several examples of addicts using aliases had come to light. I suggested notification would make it easier for us to identify new addicts, to discover those who receiving dual supplies of drugs and, most importantly, to detect 'script doctors'.

At an early stage in their deliberations the reconvened Brain Committee decided that notification would be desirable, and reached this conclusion without any prompting from the Home Office. The Committee saw the purpose of the notification, given a workable definition of addiction, as the means of ensuring that a patient, who was not suffering from painful injury or disease, for whom a doctor might consider prescribing heroin or cocaine, was in fact, an addict (see Chapter 6).

## Concerns about the confidentiality of notifications

The introduction of statutory notification brought with it a number of ethical and practical problems, but by far and away the most important issue was that of confidentiality. How could the Home Office, so closely identified with the police in the public mind, be entrusted with medical information? These fears were understandable although they were unnecessary – the Notification Regulations did not exempt the Drugs Inspectorate from their obligations under the protective provisions of the Official Secrets Acts. In any case, the Home Office had been collecting information about drug addicts for nearly 50 years, and had been recording this on individual personal files with no complaints. Yet because this rather hit-and-miss arrangement was now to be formalised, it was apparently assumed that the practices and safeguards of previous decades were to be abandoned.

Procedures put into place to ensure that information about individuals in the Addicts Index was held in strictest medical confidence included checking the names and addresses of inquirers in the Register of the General Medical Council before returning telephone calls to say whether or not an individual had been notified and the name of the doctor who most recently notified them. Any further information about addicts and their medical management was exchanged on a doctor-to-doctor basis.

The main reason for the concern about confidentiality was probably that, for the first time, the vital role played by the police in the monitoring of the legitimate use of drugs was realised. What this concern failed to take into account was that the information doctors were now required to provide under the Notification Regulations differed very little from that which pharmacists had been recording in their Dangerous Drugs Registers since 1921, including the name of the person receiving the prescription and that of the prescribing doctor, to which the police had always had access. Nevertheless, assurances were given during the passage of the Dangerous Drugs Act 1967 through Parliament that, although it would be necessary to pass the names of notified addicts to the police so they could help the Inspectorate monitor the effectiveness of the Notification Regulations, the information would be used for this purpose and no other. This practice ceased in 1975 after complaints from a number of doctors that some police officers had used the information to assist them in criminal investigations. In any case, the specialist inspecting police officers were perfectly capable of correctly interpreting the entries they saw in the pharmacists' registers and did not need to be told that someone receiving regular supplies of methadone was probably an addict.

As I pointed out in 1991 in the SCODA Newsletter,[16] when confidentiality resurfaced as an issue, there are many potential sources of information other than the police, particularly in rural areas. Some years ago one of the original West End addicts turned up in my home town in Cornwall and my parents, who neither used the pharmacy to which he took his prescriptions, nor had any contacts in the local constabulary, were able to tell me far more about him than was recorded in either his Home Office or Scotland Yard files. Nor should it be overlooked that the addiction of some of the very well-known, notified, personalities become known to the general public as a result of press, and not Home Office or police, action.

## Uses of the Addicts Index

As described in Chapter 2, an index of addicts coming to their notice was started by the Drugs Inspectorate in 1934. The primary value of the Inspectorate's index was the monitoring of the legitimate use of dangerous drugs when almost all addicts obtained their supplies on prescriptions, and to prepare the annual drug addiction statistics until that task was taken over by the Home Office Statistics Branch in 1968. The subsequent changes in the nature of the opiate misuse problem when the majority of addicts usually became dependent on illicitly imported heroin, saw the decline of the utility of the addicts Index as a control tool. Also, for this reason the addict statistics told us less about the true extent and nature of the heroin problem than they had in the past.

When I joined the Inspectorate in 1952 brief details of all addicts coming to Home Office notice were noted on 5" x 3" cards and stored in a small wooden cabinet. There were separate sections for current, 'cured', and professional addicts, with a large 'suspense' section into which the cards of 'cured' addicts were supposed to be transferred five years after the last report of their receipt of a prescription for a dangerous drug. In addition, there was an index of genuine 'medical necessity' cases, and a geographical index, based on police force areas, in which were recorded the names of supplying pharmacies and the names of addicts and persons receiving regular supplies of drugs. The purpose of this was to enable Inspectors quickly to link supplies noted on visits to wholesalers with likely recipients. In those days the information we had on individual addicts was very limited, often no more than their name and the name of their prescriber, the drug and rate of supply (updated periodically where possible) and the date on which the case had come to notice and had been investigated.

This information on individual addicts was sufficient to meet the statistical requirements of the League of Nations but when, in the 1950s, the United Nations sought additional information, such as whether the origin of the addiction was therapeutic or non-therapeutic and the ages of the addicts, the inadequacy of our procedures both for collecting and storing information about addicts was exposed. As a result the old wooden cabinet and its contents were retired and replaced by a Kardex system, which was still the basis of the Addicts Index until 1986, when, after the failure of an earlier attempt, it was successfully computerized.

## Detecting addicts receiving dual supplies

One of the many practical problems which the staff of the treatment centres realised they would face, as had the general practitioners before them, was the possibility of addicts attending more than one treatment centre under different identities and receiving prescriptions from each. To counter this, the Ministry of Health produced a special form for notifications from hospitals which, in addition to the information required by the 1968 Notification Regulations, provided space for a physical description of the patient which attempted to identify individuals by their personal appearance as well as by name or alias, gender and date of birth. Notifiers were asked to indicate the addict's height, build, complexion, colour of hair and eyes, and any distinguishing features such as scars or tattoos. From this information the staff of the Addicts Index were supposed to identify likely 'duals'. Since a great many addicts were males, 5'10" in height, with brown hair, brown eyes and pale complexions but no distinguishing marks, we soon realised, although not before a considerable amount of scarce staff resources had been expended, that this was a particularly futile exercise. When it was discovered that the measured height of an individual addict, as recorded by two different notifiers, could vary by as much as 3" the procedure was abandoned.

## 24-hour check on notifications

If the Inspectorate did at least give the identification scheme a fair trial, we never took seriously the proposal of the Brain Committee[17] that doctors should be able to consult the Index 'at any hour of the day or night if there is a need to check whether or not a particular addict has been notified, or to obtain further particulars about an addict's history'.

The expectation that the Home Office would be able to provide up-to-date information about an individual addict's prescribed drug dosage, as many doctors were encouraged to believe, was quite impractical. Notifying doctors were not required to supply any details of which drugs, and the dose, they were prescribing. When carrying out their inspections of pharmacy Dangerous Drugs Registers, the police usually recorded the name of the pharmacy dispensing the prescription, the name of the prescribing doctor and the name and dose of the drug/s prescribed during 'the past three months'. But, as the inspections were carried out at irregular intervals, usually no more than once or twice a year, the most recent information available could be up to a year old. All we could do was to provide the name of the addict's last notifier to the enquiring doctor so that he could discuss the case if he wished.

As none of the treatment centres were open on a 24-hour basis, and some were not even open daily, there was obviously no reason for us to provide a round-the-clock service. Nevertheless, in the early days of the new regime out-of-hours enquiries were common, doubtless as a result of the advice in the Ministry of Health memoranda explaining the new arrangements to the medical profession, which made it clear that the Home Office could be contacted for information at any time. Hardly a weekend went by without one or other of us, usually me, getting a call from the Home Office Duty Officer asking me to ring a doctor from a hospital casualty department, often from outside London, who, faced with an addict who had run out of supplies for any one of an infinite variety of ingenious reasons, wanted to know whether or not the addict had been previously notified.

In any case, an addict approaching a doctor, or casualty department, outside normal hours, could be treated as an emergency case. Whether the addict had or had not been notified to the Home Office in no way limited doctors' absolute discretion to treat an addict patient as they saw fit – except that to prescribe heroin or cocaine or, since 1985, dipipanone, the doctor would have to be licensed.

## Statistics of notified addicts

The Addicts Index, or according to Smart,[18] 'The National Addicts' Index', acquired a certain mystical status. Statistics of the annual number of known addicts derived from the Index figure prominently in almost all the post-1968 descriptions of the history and development of the British opiate problem. The limitations of these statistics, and of the notification procedure, were usually the subject of much detailed comment which, in reality, told us more about the authors' misunderstanding, and in some cases complete ignorance, of both the origins and the practical purpose of the Index. The statistics were no more or no less than an accounting of the number of addicts known to the Home Office during the year and much intellectual effort has been spent on their detailed analysis and interpretation.[19] Statistics which are unsupported by qualitative comment, as the addict figures were until the 1980s, have a limited value and can be interpreted in many ways. Unwelcome rises can be attributed to better compliance by doctors with the Regulations and decreases, or very small rises, as a sign that the worst may be over.

According to Edwards, 'the key question' about the annually published addict statistics was 'whether what is being counted is a small and inconstant fraction of the true prevalence, or a fairly accurate reflection of the truth'.[20] But this question is totally irrelevant; the Index was never intended to provide the 'true' extent of opiate addiction in the United Kingdom (UK). It always was merely the repository for information about those opiate addicts coming to the notice of the Home Office, rather haphazardly prior to 1968 and later through doctors' notifications.

The relationship of the 'true' addict population to the total 'notifiable' population depended very much on the effectiveness of the machinery for bringing such cases to official notice. In the pre-war period, when, according to one of those involved at the time, the Home Office addict records were 'a complete shambles', the statistics probably bore little relationship to the total number of addicts receiving prescriptions for dangerous drugs. The main reason why little reliance can be placed on the early statistics has already been mentioned. It was not until 1939 that the police, who since 1921 had been responsible for the routine inspection of retail pharmacy records, were asked to report to the Home Office, for further investigation, any regular or large supplies of drugs to individuals. While this undoubtedly improved the flow of information, the overall cover provided by these inspections did not reach acceptable standards until some 40 years later when most police forces had been persuaded to appoint specialist officers to undertake this work. It was by no means uncommon, as late as the reconvened Brain Committee's enquiry, to discover therapeutic addicts whose supplies had remained unreported for up to 20 years.

Another factor contributing to the unreliability of the early statistics was the practice of retaining addict cards in the 'live' section of the Index for up to 10 years after the most recent information about them, except, of course, when they had died. This practice was discontinued in 1945 and in future an addict's card was to be removed one year after the addict had been reported as 'cured', or had dropped out of sight. The immediate effect of this was a substantial drop in the known addict population, from 559 in 1944 to 367 in 1945, a reduction which has been used as testimony to the effectiveness of the 'British System'. There are, however, good grounds for believing that the new procedure was not strictly followed and that cases were counted as 'live' long after they should have been removed from the Index.

The statistics were hardly more reliable for much of the post-war period prior to 1968, except in relation to heroin, and did not merit the confidence of the first Brain Committee that 'the arrangements for recording manufacture and supply, and for inspection, continue to ensure that nearly all addicts are known to the Home Office, to the Ministry of Health and to the Department of Health for Scotland'.[21] The Home Office memorandum to the Committee had described the methods of collecting information about the number of addicts as 'chancy'.[22]

In any case, the Committee's statement was not only inaccurate, since neither of the two Health Departments it mentioned were involved directly in the 'arrangements', it also ignored the obvious fact that addicts receiving supplies entirely from illicit sources would not be brought to light by inspections of legitimate suppliers. More importantly, in 1960 inspections by the police of retail pharmacy records were at best haphazard and at worst almost non-existent.

Nor was notification an unqualified success in improving the 'truth' of the statistics. As Mott has noted, 'there has been evidence of poor compliance ever since the Regulations were introduced'.[23] (Whether compliance would have been improved, if, as originally considered, a fee was payable, is an interesting, if cynical, thought.) Misunderstanding of the Notification Regulations persisted and was not helped by the impression that notification was necessary only if an addict had been accepted for treatment or if a prescription had been issued.[24] This was a serious misinterpretation of the Regulations which placed the onus of notification on any doctor who 'attends' a patient 'he considers, or suspects, to be addicted'. 'Attends' had not been defined by either a tribunal or in the courts but in my time in the Home Office it was always taken to mean that a doctor had been consulted professionally by an addict, whether about an addiction or any other condition; it certainly would not apply to the doctor who once asked me if he was required to notify all the cocaine addicts he was meeting socially.

The other major loophole in the notification procedure arose from the definition of addiction in the Regulations. A doctor who believed his patient did not fall within that definition would not be required to notify and although his opinion could be tested by reference to a tribunal, the likelihood that this would be done, other than in exceptional cases, was, in my experience, remote. The second Brain Committee anticipated that from time to time there might be doubts about whether a patient was an addict according to the definition, although they had no doubts about the easy diagnosis of the new breed of addict with which they were primarily concerned. As Lord Brain commented in his memorandum to the Committee:

> I do not think there is any practical difficulty in defining or recognising a drug addict. None of the witnesses we have heard have suggested that they were doing anything other than treat addicts, and in practice, the only people other than drug addicts who need large doses of drugs of addiction are suffering from incurable diseases which are easily recognised.

But to meet any doubts which might arise in respect of the latter group, the Committee proposed that a doctor in such difficulty should be able to obtain a further professional opinion from a member of 'an officially recognised panel of doctors covering the country'.[25] Although a number of consultants in a variety of specialities were nominated to provide this further advice, they were very rarely called upon to do so and the procedure was eventually abandoned, but not before it had prompted an interesting exchange of correspondence in *The Lancet*. In a letter of 16 March 1968 Dr Hugh Freeman,[26] of the Salford Royal Infirmary, saw the absence of psychiatrists from the panels to assess doubtful cases as another example of psychiatrists being treated as 'second class citizens'. The presence of 23 surgeons and 65 physicians on the list was 'nothing short of ludicrous'. He was answered the following week by Dr A. G. Fullerton[27] who, after explaining that the function of panel members was to give a decision in cases in which the physical condition of the patient warranted the continued supply of heroin or similar drugs and in which any addiction was iatrogenic and therapeutically justified, suggested the absence of psychiatrists from the list was 'probably to allow them to get on with the job of treating addicts'.

The first year of statutory notification, 1968, saw a 61% increase in the total number of addicts known to the Home Office to 1,729, from 1,053 in 1967 – an increase not entirely due to the increasing problem, or to the success, of the new treatment centres in flushing out a large number of addicts who had previously chosen to maintain their addiction with illicit supplies. Many of those who were notified in 1968 did not reappear in the following years, suggesting that some notifiers, perhaps wishing to play safe, had been rather over-zealous in notifying people whose drug use did not meet the Regulation definition of addiction, or as I think more likely, that there was a considerable amount of market research by the addicts themselves, often using multiple identities, to see which clinic was likely to offer the best deal, and in a number of instances deciding that they preferred the often simpler conditions of the illicit market place.

If for these and other reasons there were some addicts whose names did not reach the Index, there were a number whose inclusion was not justified, as was shown in respect of notifications from prison medical officers in 1969.[28] Similarly, in the period before notification was introduced, when the decision to include a case in the Index was taken by an Inspector, on the basis of an assessment by the prescriber or the Regional Medical Officer, mistakes were undoubtedly made. But they did not really matter as long as the bulk of our addict population had become addicted as a result of medical misadventure, a situation which obtained until the early 1960s. International drug control legislation has never been interpreted in the UK as preventing doctors from using opiates to relieve suffering, even if there was a risk that some patients would become addicts. Iatrogenic or therapeutic addicts are not, or should not be, the concern of combatants in the 'drug wars' of today.

The 1968 and 1973 Notification of Addicts Regulations did not require the occupation of the addict to be recorded. As a consequence 'professional' addicts (people working in medical and allied professions) who, for many years represented almost 20% of the known addict population, were no longer counted separately in the addict statistics. As it would have been an impossible task to check every name against the Medical Register, there was no way of knowing, whether doctors were one of the under-notified groups or if 'professional' addiction was a greater or lesser problem than in earlier days.

Nevertheless, despite all its flaws and limitations, the Index was of value to *bona fide* researchers. That it was not much used before 1968 was not, as *The Lancet*'s anonymous reviewer of Edwin Schur's *Narcotic Addiction in Britain and America* commented in 1964[29] because 'official policy still prevents the research worker from making the best use of the material available about Britain's addicts'. This is another of the totally unfounded 'authoritative' statements which remain on the record for posterity; the reality is that drug research did not become fashionable until after the reconvened Brain Committee had focused attention on what was happening and by so doing had opened the doors to funding which earlier would probably have been unavailable. That until the late 1960s very few were interested in researching drug problems cannot be explained on the grounds of official hostility, nor can the quite reasonable, and necessary, conditions under which access was allowed to personal confidential material in the Index be described as obstruction.

It is unfortunate that so many of the descriptions of the Addicts Index showed a lack of understanding of its origins and functions and its relationship to the notification system. So many commentators persist in seeing the Index as they would like it to be rather than as the simple database it really was. The notification system was not 'an attempt to maintain a basic central data collection system to monitor important aspects of a country's more serious drug problems'.[30] Notification was seen by the reconvened Brain Committee as essentially a control measure to help us deal with the situation as it existed in 1965, although they suggested it 'may offer a means for epidemiological assessment and control'.[31]

## Editor's note: The end of notification

On 22 March 1997 it was announced that the Home Secretary intended to revoke the Notification Regulations and the requirement for doctors to notify their addict patients was omitted from the Misuse of Drugs (Supply to Addicts) Regulations 1997 which came into effect in May 1997. The reasons for dispensing with the notification procedure included the restricted range of drugs to which it applied and the high cost of the resources needed to maintain 'a recording system which either needed to be completely overhauled or dropped'.[32] Further, given that more and newer drugs had become popular with drug misusers, the utility of the procedure in providing 'a means for epidemiological assessment and control' as envisaged by the Brain Committee had waned.

The information collected by Regional Drugs Misuse Databases set up by the Department of Health in England in 1990, and similar databases in Scotland and Wales, is intended to remedy this shortcoming of the notification procedure. In that year the medical and drug treatment agencies were invited to provide the Drug Misuse Databases with anonymized information about their patients or clients irrespective of the drugs they misuse, including alcohol, and whether or not they met the criteria for notification as addicts.

With the demise of the notification procedure, the Home Office involvement in the collection of statistics on drug addicts, which began in 1934, came to an end. From January 1997 the six-monthly statistics of 'individuals starting agency episodes in Great Britain' produced by the Department of Health from information supplied by the Regional Drug Misuse Databases became the major indicator of the extent of heroin and other drug dependence in Britain.

# 9

# The challenge to the practice of medicine: the operation of the treatment centres

The physical establishment of the treatment centres for heroin and cocaine addicts is only a minor part of the story. Of far greater importance, especially in view of the reluctance with which the medical profession had agreed to participate, is how the centres were to operate and the clinical policies and practices they were to follow. What was the state of clinical experience for the treatment of heroin addiction in 1965 and how was the initial clinical response developed? These key questions are particularly relevant to any consideration of whether the treatment centres, sometimes called drug dependency clinics, or Drug Dependency Units (DDUs) as they were later to become officially known, succeeded or failed in their original purpose.

But these are questions which, to a large extent, have been glossed over since the dawning of the 'treatment centre era' on 16 April 1968, with the result that the original purpose of the treatment centres has been misrepresented and rejected. It is therefore worth recalling some of the early clinical responses to what Dr Philip Connell[1] described as 'a challenge to the practice of medicine' and before the thinly disguised attempt was made to impose, by stealth rather than with any scientific rationale, the orthodoxy which *The Lancet* had warned about in November 1967 when, in an Annotation criticising the Ministry of Health's 'paper schemes', it pointed out that it seemed unwise to rely on any single approach to the treatment of addiction because there was 'a hazard that orthodoxy will develop before even the superficial premises have been explored'.[2]

## The London teaching hospitals and psychiatry take over

One of the first decisions of the Ministry of Health was to choose the London teaching hospitals and psychiatrists to play the leading roles in setting up the treatment centres. The main reason for involving these hospitals was that they were mostly located in central London where the heroin problem was most serious at the time and where treatment facilities were most urgently needed.

But there were undoubtedly also other considerations, for instance, the influence of medical politicians, which can be detected behind much of the negotiation on the implementation of the Brain proposals, and the assumption by Ministry officials that the teaching hospitals were the repositories of all knowledge and wisdom.

Another possible consideration was that the medical staff of the hospitals had not previously been involved in the treatment of addicts and so could be presented as offering a total break with the events, which had not reflected too well on the profession, that led to the reconvening of the Brain Committee. It would be good for the profession's public image if the medical establishment, in the form of the teaching hospitals, was now seen to be playing a major part in tackling this new threat to the youth of the nation. But whatever the reason, or reasons, the decision to site the treatment centres in the teaching hospitals contributed greatly to the delay in translating the reconvened Brain Committee's recommendations into practice.

The involvement of psychiatry was probably inevitable, as the first Brain Committee had been in no doubt that 'addiction should be regarded as an expression of mental disorder rather than a form of criminal behaviour'.[3] It was, however, quite wrong in prefacing this statement in the report with the words 'like the Rolleston Committee'. The Rolleston Committee, while regarding addiction to morphine and heroin as 'a manifestation of disease and not as a mere form of vicious indulgence', had been very careful to point out that 'addiction may be acquired by injudicious use of the drug in a person who has not previously shown any manifestation of nervous or mental instability'.[4]

To the reconvened Brain Committee the addict was 'a sick person'[5] and although its report referred to 'doctors', not psychiatrists, working in the treatment centres, it suggested that these centres might 'form part of a psychiatric hospital or of the psychiatric wing of a general hospital.[6] Lord Brain apparently had no doubt that heroin addiction was a 'mental disorder'; he was reported in 1966 as telling the British Medical Association (BMA) Council:[7]

> There are some addicts who are basically normal people who had, as it were, accidentally become addicts through the opportunity of taking heroin ... but that was not true of the vast majority ... Drug addiction was basically a complex psychiatric problem made all the more complex by the coexistence of physiological disturbances. Only an experienced psychiatrist could assess the psychological factors in each individual contributing to the addiction.

If there were some very psychiatrically disturbed individuals among the 1960s addict population, there were also significant numbers whose only 'problem' was that they used heroin for non-medical purposes. As one of the general practitioners of the period recently recalled to me, 'perhaps some of my patients needed a little psychiatric help but the majority did not'. In view of his key role in the Ministry of Health in setting up the treatment centres, the most revealing comment has come from Dr A. A. Baker, who said he had always believed that drug addiction was 'primarily a social problem with some medical complications, rather than primarily a medical one'.[8]

However, the die had been cast and the treatment of drug addiction, drug dependence, drug misuse, and later, of the 'problem drug taker', became the fiefdom of the consultant psychiatrist. As a result, although no one realised it at the time, narrow medical parameters would dominate treatment responses for the foreseeable future. Even in 1982 the Advisory Council on the Misuse of Drugs, while advocating 'a multi-disciplinary response to the needs of problem drug takers', gave the primary role to hospital-based services led by consultant psychiatrists.[9]

The hopes for a comprehensive, integrated treatment and rehabilitation service frequently expressed in the medical journals and in Parliament, and recommended by the Advisory Committee on Drug Dependence[10] would not be fulfilled when the treatment centres opened in 1968. And, just as Dr Vincent Dole had found in the United States (US), there would be 'an obsession with the chemical' rather than a concern for the interests of the individual or society in general, and a philosophy would prevail that addiction was 'evidence of a psychological defect or weakness and that the only acceptable goal of treatment is total abstinence'.[11]

If there is by now some acceptance of the more limited contribution to be made by psychiatry, and medicine in general, in dealing with addiction, this has been slow to develop. If clinics run by consultant psychiatrists were the medical profession's answer to the problems presented to the reconvened Brain Committee so be it. Yet in 1965 psychiatrists were quite unprepared for the responsibility about to be placed upon them. But why should they have been prepared? In 1961 the first Brain Committee had told them there was no cause to fear that any real increase in addiction was occurring, hardly an encouragement to any ambitious psychiatrist seeking a field in which to specialise. Moreover, the Committee had felt obliged to offer, in Appendix III of their Report, notes on treatment based on US experience from Dr Harris Isbell of the National Institute of Health Addiction Research Centre at Lexington, because 'only a few doctors in Great Britain have any great personal experience' of treating addiction'.[12] This point was underscored in 1966 by Dr Maurice Partridge, the consultant psychiatrist who sat on both Brain Committees, when he told the New York Medical College[13] that in the United Kingdom:

> Until recently drug addiction hardly existed. The amount of case material was so small that there was not even one person with enough experience to speak with any sort of authority on this unsalubrious subject.

## Who were the 'doctors experienced in the treatment of addiction'?

If by 1966 there were so few doctors with personal experience of treating addicts, how had the Ministry of Health been able to find 25 'doctors experienced in the treatment of addiction' to attend the meetings in September and December 1966, and to provide the advice upon which the Ministry relied so heavily in planning the new treatment service? Kenneth Robinson's repeated references to the advice he was seeking and receiving from these 'experienced' clinicians undoubtedly helped create an impression that there was an untapped reservoir of expertise which would ensure that from now on addicts would be treated 'properly' and the mistakes of the general practitioners who had (allegedly) created the present situation, would not be repeated.

Where had these 'experts' been in the period between the two Brain Committee reports? As most of the 25 were based at London hospitals there should surely have been adequate treatment facilities in existence prior to April 1968, as Kenneth Robinson kept insisting. So why had those trying to find professional help for addicts encountered such difficulty? The most charitable answer to these questions is that whoever drafted the phrase 'experienced in the treatment of addiction' for Robinson was confusing academic knowledge, and perhaps some limited and mostly inpatient contact with the middle-aged therapeutic and professional addicts who for so long had made up the bulk of the British addict population, with experience of the problems presented by the new young non-conformist, hedonistic heroin addicts.

If popular mythology has it that 'not more than six' general practitioners were supposed to have caused the problem to which the reconvened Brain committee was asked to direct its attention, the truth is that in 1965 there were probably no more than six psychiatrists in the country who had shown sufficient interest in drug addiction to be regarded as 'experts'. Furthermore, on the evidence of 'contributions to the literature' there was very little medical interest in addiction in Britain at the time. Neither the *British Medical Journal* nor *The Lancet* published more than the occasional reference to it while the most important paper about heroin addiction to appear in the *British Journal of Addiction* by 1964 was contributed by two general practitioners, John Hewetson and Robert Ollendorff.[14]

At the Chief Medical Officer's first meeting with 'doctors experienced in the treatment of addiction' on 14 September 1966, the list of those attending read like a Who's Who of the London psychiatric establishment. Yet there were only three consultant psychiatrists in the country who could call on much experience of dealing with the new generation of heroin addicts on an outpatient basis. They were Dale Beckett, John Owens and Julius Merry, with Merry the only one of the three to be present at the subsequent meeting in December.

Beckett, in addition to his inpatient Salter Unit at Cane Hill Hospital (later to be closed because of staff hostility to addicts, rather than on clinical grounds), had been treating addicts at his outpatient clinic at Norwood Hospital since 1965. Most of these had failed the rigorous admission procedure for the Salter Unit, administered by the Unit's current patients, and he felt morally obliged to help them. Merry had been involved in addict treatment at Lambeth and West Park Hospitals for a similar period, with the bulk of the outpatient work at the latter hospital in 1966 being undertaken by his Senior House Officer, Peter Chapple.[15] Chapple had been treating addicts at Cane Hill Hospital since 1964 and had given evidence to the reconvened Brain Committee, but because he was not of consultant status he could not be invited to the Chief Medical Officer's meetings. His work as 'an outstanding innovator and activist in the treatment of drug dependency'[16] deserves to be recognised in any history of this period.

Similarly, the pioneering work of John Owens, the consultant psychiatrist at All Saints Hospital in Birmingham has not received acknowledgement from post-1968 policy analysts and commentators. Owens' problem, in addition to being a provincial psychiatrist, was that he was a forthright Scot who believed that those who could treat did so while those who could not, or were disinclined to, contributed papers to the literature. Beckett, Chapple and Owens shared a common failing: their thinking and their approach to what Owens called 'this contagious disease of adolescence' was out of tune with current mainstream psychiatric opinion in which their concept of social rehabilitation before detoxification found only limited support.

There was, of course, the wealth of experience of the much-criticised general practitioners, but they were the untouchables to the medical establishment and to those others who had no direct knowledge of their work. It would therefore have been unthinkable for the new 'experts' to be seen to be availing themselves of the experience of even those general practitioners who, as Kenneth Robinson conceded on 6 May 1968, had undertaken 'the difficult and unrewarding task of treating heroin addicts and discharged it in a responsible manner'.[17] They had faced, and to a large extent overcome, the same problems the treatment centre doctors would meet and they had done so without the benefit of the sophisticated diagnostic aids and purpose-built accommodation now considered to be essential before the new approach could be implemented. Despite the widely held view that all general practitioners grossly over-prescribed, most of those who had attracted Robinson's grudging acknowledgement were, by 1966, more than a match for the most wily addict and could have offered useful practical advice to those who would be succeeding them. But these general practitioners were not consulted.

## Clinical guidance for the treatment of heroin addiction from the Ministry of Health in 1967

As Smart[18] has asserted that 'the clinics symbolized rather a rationalization of treatment, bringing treatment practices under a more centralized influence', it is important to be clear how, and by whom, that central influence was exercised. The Brain Committee had been reconvened, just as the Rolleston Committee had been set up 40 years earlier, to consider a control problem on which the government needed medical advice. That advice was then accepted by the government and the medical profession. However, the reconvened Brain Committee had not provided any answers to the clinical questions arising from their proposals. How these were to be resolved was one of the items on the agenda of the two meetings of 'doctors experienced in the treatment of addiction' held in 1966, from which emerged the clinical guidance and advice contained in Hospital Memorandum H.M.(67)16 'The Treatment and Supervision of Heroin Addiction' issued by the Ministry of Health on 7 March 1967.

The basic aims of the new approach were set out in paragraph 8 of this memorandum:

> ... Some addicts will not accept withdrawal treatment, at any rate to start with, and complete refusal of supplies will not cure their addiction – it will merely throw them on the black market and encourage the development of an organized illicit traffic on a scale hitherto unknown in this country (paragraph 15 of the second Brain Report). *The aim is to contain the spread of heroin by continuing to supply this drug in minimum quantities where this is necessary in the opinion of the doctor, and where possible to persuade addicts to accept withdrawal treatment.* For these purposes the medical supervision of addicts is necessary; this will include attention to those physical illnesses to which addicts are prone and the maintenance of a therapeutic relationship which may at any time render withdrawal treatment acceptable to the patient ...

The key sentence, in my italics, has been the subject of much retrospective comment and analysis, particularly in the context of whether containment of the spread of heroin use was ever a realistic aim for the treatment centres and if so, whether they succeeded or failed to achieve it. The abandonment of this aim within a few years, without any serious scientific evaluation, has been justified on the grounds that experience had shown it was impossible for the centres to combine a social control function with their primary therapeutic role and, moreover, that they should not have been expected to perform this dual role. This criticism of the reconvened Brain Committee, and the 'doctors experienced in the treatment of addiction', did not surface until the initial enthusiasm with which the centres had approached this task had worn off and been replaced by the realities of dealing with patients stubbornly resistant to all attempts to change their lifestyle.

That H.M.(67)16 referred to 'continuing to supply heroin' was not surprising. There was no reference to prohibiting the therapeutic use of heroin in the formal evidence submitted by the Home Office and Ministry of Health in 1958 to the first Brain Committee. As it had been only three years since the abortive attempt to ban it, T. C. Green, the administrator responsible for drugs matters in the Home Office, was naturally reluctant to revive the controversy. Nevertheless, he proposed to mention the possibility of prohibition to the secretariat for them 'to work it in'. Whether he ever did so, and if so with what result, is not clear from the surviving Home Office papers. The Committee's report contains no reference to a possible ban.

Nor was the subject mentioned in the report of the reconvened Brain Committee. Prohibiting the prescribing of heroin was one of the options considered, but informal soundings of the profession suggested that although the new synthetic analgesics were probably now more readily acceptable, there was still strong support for the use of heroin in the treatment of certain conditions. In the circumstances, the Committee agreed with Lord Brain that, while from one point of view a ban would simplify their problem, it might merely shift its centre of gravity from the reckless prescriber to the smuggler, and would undoubtedly meet with much the same opposition as the 1955 proposal had done. Demonstrating a remarkable *volte face* from his position of a few years earlier, Lord Brain told the Council of the BMA in January 1966:[19]

> We of course considered this [abandoning the use of heroin altogether] but our enquiries convinced us, if we were not convinced already, that in certain circumstances, there is no satisfactory substitute for heroin, and we thought it quite wrong that doctors and patients should be deprived of an essential drug because it is abused by drug addicts and the few doctors who supply them.

The publication of H.M.(67)16 did see a brief re-run of the 1955 controversy. It was provoked by a proposal from Dr J. A. R. Bickford and colleagues[20] in Leeds for a total heroin ban. In a letter to the *British Medical Journal* on 18 March 1967, they suggested that H.M.(67)16 'did not go far enough' and that the government should immediately ban heroin, as there were now adequate substitutes. The increase in addiction was a situation of such gravity that it required the surrender of doctors' traditional rights and independence of prescribing. However, Dr M. Dales, also of Leeds, pointed out there were only two known heroin addicts in the city and invited evidence that there were adequate substitutes for heroin.[21] Dr Heber, from New South Wales, also took issue with Dr Bickford saying heroin had been banned in Australia for a number of years but this had not hindered illegal trafficking and had merely increased the price on the black market. In Dr Heber's view the real tragedy was that its unavailability meant that there was now a new generation of doctors who were unaware of its merits and knew only of its dangers, as described in the Sunday newspapers.[22]

## Treatment centres or prescribing centres?

What post-1968 critics of the aim expressed in H.M.(67)16, to contain the spread of heroin addictionby prescribing it, have failed to ask is, how did the very situation feared in 1965 by *The Lancet*,[23] that the term 'treatment centre' would merely be a euphemism for 'prescribing centre', come about? First though, because of the belief that the centres' policy on prescribing heroin was being dictated by the Home Office, some comment on the Home Office role, and expectations, is required. This belief, that clinicians were confined in some form of bureaucratic straitjacket, is shown by the remarks of clinic staff in the 1970s quoted by Stimson and Oppenheimer[24] 'we were told you will prescribe', and there had to be prescribing because this was 'what the Home Office wanted'.

As far as I am aware the source of these 'instructions' to prescribe heroin has never been identified but it was certainly not the Home Office. This does not mean that there was no concern there about the possibility of an entirely illicit market in heroin developing or that the Ministry of Health had not been made aware of that concern. The much quoted paragraph 15 of the second Brain Report, expressing the dilemma that insufficient control over the prescribing of heroin could lead to the spread of addiction as was then occurring, while too severe restrictions could deter addicts from seeking supplies from legitimate sources, had been drafted by T. C. Green. The Assistant Under-Secretary of State, R. J. Guppy, had made known his anxiety that the implementation of the Committee's recommendations should not lead to an increase in crime, which was also the view of the Home Secretary of the day, Roy Jenkins, as he confirmed in an interview with Horace Judson in 1973.[25]

The Home Office anxiety was well founded. By 1965 there were unmistakable signs of changing public attitudes to the use of drugs and of increasing organisation in the illicit cannabis traffic. It was not unreasonable to assume that these traffickers might be attracted by the higher profits which successful importation of heroin would bring. Ten years earlier, when the government attempted to prohibit the legitimate use of heroin, Dr J. A. Hobson of the Middlesex Hospital, who was then probably the only consultant with any first-hand experience of the new wave of addicts, warned[26] that, 'All the heroin addicts I have seen in the last few months have told me they are assured that if heroin is banned there will still be supplies, but probably they will be more expensive'.

If the 54 known heroin addicts in 1954 could be assured that future illicit supplies would be available, how much more likely was it that the 521 known in 1965 would be similarly reassured? That we were right to hold these concerns was not long in coming. In a letter to the *British Medical Journal* on 3 June 1967,[27] Dr John Hawes reported that some of his patients had told him that 'powdered heroin has for the first time appeared in the black market instead of the usual sixth of a grain tablets'. The first samples of this substance, to become known as Chinese heroin, came into the possession of the Metropolitan Police in September 1967.

If the Home Office anxiety to avoid the creation of an organised illicit traffic in heroin had persuaded the Ministry of Health to seek advice from a wider range of medical opinion in September and December 1966, it was almost certainly mentioned by Sir George Godber, when he sought, at these meetings with the 'doctors experienced in the treatment of addiction', to overcome their 'considerable reluctance' to co-operate in the new approach. But Sir George's success in securing a measure of agreement, could not guarantee that the reconvened Brain Committee's intentions, any more than the Rolleston philosophy in which they were firmly rooted, would be fully understood or fairly implemented.

The signs that the Rolleston spirit would have a short life expectancy were there for all to see but were not recognised. From the outset there was confusion over 'maintenance', a term which does not appear in the Rolleston Report, the second Brain Report or in H.M.(67)16. Yet within a few months, and before the issue of the Memorandum, the Brain 'treatment centres' were referred to as 'maintenance centres' by Dr Philip Connell.[28]

There was an obsession with the dangers of over-prescribing, and an ethical, rather than therapeutic, objection to the use of heroin, which in part reflected a susceptibility to transatlantic influences not always relevant to the British situation. One of the well-known addicts of the time, the late Alexander Trocchi, predicted that energies which should have been brought to bear on the real problem would be dissipated as doctors engaged in a battle of wits to ensure that addicts received the smallest possible amount of heroin. It was Trocchi's 'battle of wits' which was to dominate the early years of the 'treatment centre era'.

Another early threat to the traditional British flexible approach was the indecent haste with which some sought to establish a 'uniformity' of practice which meant that the individual doctor's right to complete clinical freedom would be subordinated to medico-political views, for which there was often no scientific evidence. It is here, in the way in which the second Brain Committee's intentions were interpreted and implemented, rather than in the Committee's basic approach or the aims set out in H.M.(67)16, that clues to the origins of the 'social control versus treatment' dilemma, and to many of the other changes over the next decade, are to be found.

## How were the treatment centres to meet 'the challenge to the practice of medicine'?

On 20 May 1967, two months after H.M.(67)16 appeared, the *British Medical Journal* published four short papers which discussed, on the basis of the authors' personal experiences, some of the problems of providing treatment for addicts in special centres. The authors were Dr Thomas Bewley[29] and Dr Philip Connell,[30] both London hospital-based consultant psychiatrists, who for varying periods over the next 20 years were to hold the post of Consultant Adviser on Drug Dependence to the Chief Medical Officer; Dr Peter Chapple,[31] in the role of a general practitioner in London; and Dr John Owens.[32]

As an expression of the 'current thinking', these papers are important as they do much to explain the course of subsequent developments. There was a striking contrast between the orthodox, and rather academic, views of Bewley and Connell on the one hand, and those of Chapple and Owens on the other. Lart[33] has suggested that 'the gap between the perception of the two specialists and that of the general practitioner reflects that between the perceptions of "hospital medicine" and "biographical medicine". This would have been an acceptable thesis had she not overlooked Owens' important contribution and also been unaware that Chapple held a psychiatric qualification and had first come into contact with addicts while working in a hospital setting. The gap in perception had therefore little to do with the direction from which the contributors had entered the field. The vision, and understanding of the problem, shown by Chapple and Owens derived from their close involvement with the treatment in the community of addicts over the previous two years.

In his contribution, Chapple went straight to what he considered 'the real problem', and described what later became called harm minimisation:

> Institutional treatment of addiction has been an almost complete failure (except for a few special units still on trial) throughout the world, because it has created a situation where the patient finds himself in conflict with his doctors – often being forced to relinquish drugs against his will – but also because it fails to address the real problem, which is that of teaching the addicted patient to live in society without using drugs, or, if he must use some drugs, to use those which are as lightly addicting as possible, and to use the oral route in preference to the intravenous route.

Owens directed his initial comments to what he considered were the two fundamental errors in current thought about narcotic addiction in the United Kingdom:

> Firstly, there is the implicit assumption that heroin addiction is an entity in itself – in pure culture as if it were uncontaminated by other drug-taking – and, secondly, there is the notion that narcotic addiction is exclusively a medical matter. These two misconceptions dominate and thus distort all thinking and planning about this phenomenon – this contagious disease of adolescence. They cause, I believe, clinicians to take up a denervating position and to indulge in sterile controversy.

He went on to say that 'rather than fighting colleagues in medical administration' clinicians should make 'a determined effort to study the local problem and consider how the treatment centre idea can be modified and applied in terms of local circumstances'. He feared that the treatment centres 'will merely become prescribing centres' by 'transferring the prescribing to unskilled hospital staff, possibly junior medical staff delegated to this chore and possibly poorly motivated'.

To anyone who has watched the medical manoeuvring over the years it will be no surprise that Owens' views found little favour in influential establishment medical circles and were summarily dismissed. The accompanying leading article in the *British Medical Journal* merely noted 'some interesting data from Birmingham which suggests that measures to stop the spread of addiction there are proving effectual', with Chapple's contribution being seen as arguing that there was a place for the general practitioner in the treatment of addiction.[34] But the Journal's initiative in commissioning these papers has been ignored in almost all the serious commentaries on the period.

In April 1968 Connell[35] summarised the rationale of the new approach, which saw the addict as a sick person and 'properly within the ambit of medical practice' and embraced 'the concept of prescribing heroin to addicts who do not wish to be withdrawn from the drug', while noting the dangers inherent in that approach and the safeguards needed to prevent 'untoward developments'. As Connell was then the Chief Medical Officer's Consultant Adviser on Drug Dependence, his paper has been seen as the official elaboration of the meagre guidance which had appeared in the second Brain Report and in H.M.(67)16. (This interpretation is supported by a further memorandum, which he submitted to a meeting of treatment centre consultants at the Department of Health in September 1969,[36] in which he summarised the 'informal agreements' reached by the consultants at earlier meetings, many of which were included in his April 1968 paper.)

Connell described the rationale under 12 main headings, including the need for the prescribing of heroin to addicts to be under tighter control than hitherto and to prescribe 'more closely to the actual dose taken by the addict' so that there would be less 'circulating to ... uncommitted individuals'. He suggested that 'Hospital clinics staffed by "experts" are much less likely to overprescribe' and, in case they did, a licence to prescribe heroin (and cocaine) to addicts could be withdrawn. He was much concerned with avoiding the development of a criminally organised black market if the prescribing of heroin to addicts was abruptly ceased, and the consequent likelihood that the addict would be driven 'into criminal activities in order to obtain the money to maintain his dependence and to avoid withdrawal symptoms', while heroin provided free by the treatment centres meant that addicts would not need to commit crimes to obtain money to pay for the drug. Furthermore, prescribing 'pure British-made heroin' rather 'than the impure material which circulates in a criminally organized supply system' would reduce health complications and death. He noted that 'the treatment centres will be oriented towards eventual withdrawal of the patient from the drugs and would be backed with special inpatient units' and he rejected 'punitive detention' and compulsory detention in hospitals as treatment options.

Connell saw dangers in the new approach. It required only a small number of over-prescribing doctors to 'encourage an epidemic of drug-taking where a socio-cultural demand expresses itself', and the experts in the special centres would not be infallible and had no accurate tools to assess an addict's dosage. Moreover, all professions had their share of 'weaker brethren' and there would now be more doctors in London prescribing heroin than there had been before 1965. It would therefore be necessary for 'careful evaluation and careful practice', if the situation was not to become much worse than it had been in the days when general practitioners had been free to prescribe.

He suggested there were two main safeguards against such dangers, illustrating the emphasis which was being placed from the outset on prescribing and uniformity of practice. Once the clinics were 'working smoothly and preferably on an appointed day' there could be an agreement that all clinics 'will reduce the amount of heroin prescribed over a period of, say, a month to about a half'. It 'must' also be agreed that 'no heroin addict will ever receive a dose higher than that considered to be necessary during the first few attendances at the clinic'. Among the other measures he considered essential to enable a close watch to be kept on future developments, were some so basic it is not immediately obvious why they had to be detailed. For example, there would have to be careful records of the quantities of drugs prescribed in each centre and 'agreement that after 16 April 1968 no addict will be prescribed heroin until it has been established that he is in fact taking heroin, and until attempts have been made to evaluate the smallest dose which will prevent withdrawal symptoms'.

He saw the present situation as presenting a number of challenges: to physicians in the treatment centres to work together in a reasonably uniform manner; to biochemists, pharmacologists and chemical pathologists to produce urgently qualitative and quantitative methods that would assist the clinician in determining which drugs, and the dosage, the patient was taking; to physicians to produce 'hard data relating to treatment programmes'; and to epidemiologists and sociologists to produce 'data relating to the causes of drug taking, methods of spread and suggestions relating to prevention'. He concluded that 'it would be a tragedy if the opportunities given to us were lost because of lack of interest, lack of co-ordination, lack of support or rivalries and jealousies'.

It is against the background set out in this important paper, and in similar comments by other influential figures in this formative period of the 'new approach', that the operation and success or failure of the reconvened Brain Committee's proposals have to be judged. Unfortunately, that debate has seldom looked beyond the simple 'social control versus treatment' issue. Far less attention has been given to questions such as whether those proposals, and the Rolleston principles on which they were based, were universally understood and accepted, whether there was ever any realistic hope that the treatment centres would be able to fulfil their intended role, whether the implementation of the 'new approach' was influenced by any of the factors of which Connell was fearful or the extent to which the challenges he identified were taken up.

## United States influence

Another factor, to which there have been few overt references, but which undoubtedly affected the clinical response, was the American experience of the addiction problem. As early as 1965, in his much-quoted paper on the changing pattern of drug addiction in the United Kingdom(UK) Bewley[37] had referred to the American view that 'the maintenance of stable dosage levels in individuals addicted to narcotics is generally inadequate and medically unsound', a contradiction of the Rolleston Committee and the first Brain Committee's acceptance of the concept of the 'stabilised addict'.

Following publication of the second Brain report, a number of those psychiatrists who were to be involved with the new treatment centres visited the US and came back with varying views on the relevance of American experience to the British situation. Their interest mainly centred on the failure of the American prescribing clinics of the 1920s, the use of methadone, and the therapeutic community programmes such as those provided by Synanon and Daytop.

A detailed examination by Dr Griffith Edwards of the relevance of American experience to the British scene appeared in the *British Medical Journal* in August 1967.[38] His important paper was based on an eight-week visit to the US and offered much food for thought for those who were then engaged in planning the British response. But it is in the light of what happened in the years after 16 April 1968, and in the context of any assessment of whether the 'treatment centre era' was a success or failure, that his main conclusions need to be recalled. Firstly, in relation to the role of compulsion in the treatment of the individual patient commented:

> The only way of determining whether in Britain treatment can be successful without compulsion is to try intensive-treatment programmes ... one can predict at the outset that voluntary treatment will appear to be ineffective if the treatment under consideration is lackadaisical, carried out by medical staff with too many other commitments, and unsupported by adequate social work and rehabilitative services ...

Secondly, in relation to the basic philosophy of the reconvened Brain Committee approach, Edwards argued that:

The whole of American experience would suggest that if our new programme is to be other than foredoomed to failure and a prelude to debacle, it must be conducted with vigour and energy, must be a matter of reaching out rather than sitting back in hospitals, must focus on human needs and rehabilitation rather than on drug maintenance or detoxification. Saving of money at this stage may prove a costly economy.

Addicts were unpopular both with doctors, to whom they presented a very poor prognosis, and with the general public, who saw their problems as self-inflicted and therefore undeserving of much sympathy and even less deserving of material resources provided from the public purse. The question of whether the centres would be adequately and properly resourced, for which the omens since November 1965 had not been encouraging, was a recurring theme in leading articles and annotations in the medical journals, and elsewhere. So, too, was the need for sufficient, and appropriate rehabilitation facilities, which would be essential if the earlier work to withdraw addicts from their drugs was not to be undone, as well as for research and the careful and continuing evaluation of the treatment response.

These concerns were summed up by Dr Max Glatt in 1966 in his review of the reconvened Brain Committee's Report.[39] He commented:

> ... everyone recognised the overriding need for a comprehensive, large-scale programme of research, education and prevention, as well as of rehabilitation. It remains to be seen how much money the Treasury would make available for these purposes in view of the competing claims of so many other pressing social and other problems of the time.

The addicts understood the respective roles of treatment, prescribing and maintenance much better than some of those who were well placed to influence the general direction of the clinical response. As Glatt noted in his review, 'one group of addicts suggested the establishment of two types of centres: actual treatment centres and, separate from them, 'maintenance centres', the latter to be staffed by those 'prescribing doctors who might be willing to cooperate'.

## Advice on the operation of the treatment centres from Lord Brain and others

The reconvened Brain Committee has been criticised for its failure to provide a detailed blueprint of how the proposed 'treatment centres' were to operate, but to have done so would have been incompatible with the concept of clinical freedom. The Committee considered that it was for 'the doctors at the treatment centres to determine a course of treatment and, if thought necessary, to provide the addict with drugs'.[40] This was a very clear indication that the Committee considered prescribing heroin as an optional part of treatment, a point reinforced by Lord Brain when he discussed the Committee's proposals with the Council of the British Medical Association in January 1966.[41] In an obvious reference to Lady Frankau, he suggested that those doctors who claimed to treat large numbers of addicts from their consulting rooms were, for the most part, 'not treating their patients at all but merely supplying them with drugs'. No addict could be adequately treated 'without an initial period at a properly equipped and staffed treatment centre'. He was reported as going on to say:

> The success of these centres would depend upon their ability to provide for addicts bet-
> ter treatment than they could get elsewhere. The one or two existing units had shown
> that if good and humane treatment was offered to addicts some would avail themselves
> of it.

Lord Brain's elaboration of his Committee's intentions escaped the notice of the *British Medical Journal*'s leader writer, who, on 11 February 1967,[42] noted that 'one important decision that the government has made is that outpatient clinics shall be set up to offer maintenance prescribing of addictive drugs by specially appointed staff'. This serious misrepresentation of the Committee's intentions was accompanied by the qualification that every effort would be made to persuade the addict 'to proceed from maintenance to withdrawal', and with the comment that if clinics were to offer 'energetic therapy rather than act merely as centres for handing out drugs', they would be expensive to run.

In the leading article accompanying the Bewley, Connell, Chapple and Owens' papers, in May 1967, the *British Medical Journal*[43] offered further thoughts on what was necessary in planning for treatment. Firstly, there was a need for 'tolerance and kindness', with the addict being 'encouraged to attend a clinic and be received there in a friendly way, given his essential supplies, have any physical ills treated, and offered help with his social problems'. Secondly, there should be facilities for 'instant admission' to a special unit when he asked for it, and thirdly, facilities for 'prolonged social rehabilitation'.

Dr Julius Merry had a clear vision of the function of the new outpatient treatment centres.[44] In 1968 he shared the *British Medical Journal*'s concern that there should be 'energetic therapy' and attempted to rebut criticisms that the treatment centres were 'obviously not therapeutic'. He thought the centres would promote a greater awareness of the extent of the addiction problem, and thus a more effective control, as well as:

> … an opportunity for the therapist to build up a relationship with the addict, in the
> hope that at a future date the patient will avail himself of the opportunity to undertake
> withdrawal treatment and the much more difficult process of rehabilitation.

Important implications for the operation of the treatment centres emerged from one of the first studies conducted by researchers from the newly established Addiction Research Unit at the Institute of Psychiatry under the direction of Dr Griffith Edwards. In their 1968 report *Heroin use in a provincial town*[45] they noted that, in general, the addicts they interviewed who had had inpatient withdrawal treatment were back using heroin on the day of their discharge, and suggested this pointed to the inadequacy of physical withdrawal as a sole means of treatment. They considered that heroin use was much more a way of life than merely a habit to be broken, and all too often the addict was coerced into treatment without being convinced of the desirability or possibility of a permanent cure. Therefore, what was needed was help in restructuring the addict's future in a way that was meaningful to the addict, help with problems that remained unsolved and which required extending treatment to enable psychological as well as physical issues to be tackled, and the provision of intensive and prolonged aftercare in the community.

## Staffing the treatment centres

Most of those who had experience of treating addicts recognised that the key factor in the success or failure of the new approach would be the attitude of the doctors working in the treatment centres. Even well-resourced and fully-staffed centres would achieve little if those who set their treatment philosophies and practices were merely 'going through the motions' and had no genuine enthusiasm for what they were being asked to do.

The late Professor Francis Camps (a former President of the Society for the Study of Addiction), writing in 1970, believed the result of the new approach would 'depend a great deal on the intelligence of the approved doctors when dealing with the addicts in the early stages of the exercise and whether they can succeed in obtaining their confidence'.[46] He saw the early stage of the treatment centre approach as 'a holding operation', when it was of vital importance to understand:

> ... that the addict wants his heroin and no amount of theory or clinical prejudice based on the fact that it is not desirable would alter this. Hence, any personal opinions and prejudices held by those in charge of the prescribing must be discarded until all addicts were firmly related to their new supply.

It was an earlier suggestion by Camps for 'an interregnum during which the volunteer doctor would continue to help', which prompted *The Lancet* to return to the issue of 'orthodoxy'. The anonymous writer of an Annotation,[47] on 10 February 1968, asked what would become of all the volunteer effort over previous years, citing as examples Spelthorne St Mary (whose Mother Superior, Sister Patricia, had given evidence to the reconvened Brain Committee), the Chelsea Addiction and Research Centre (run by Dr Peter Chapple and Dr Geoffrey Gray) and the voluntary workers at St Anne's Church in Soho (organised by the Reverend Kenneth Leech). It suggested that their future was:

> … uncertain not because their treatment was uncertain but because the Ministry of Health might not 'recognise' such establishments, since they do not conform to the orthodoxy which has curiously evolved out of the Brain report.

The writer went on to argue that if it was admitted there was no agreed treatment for addiction to heroin, cocaine or methylamphetamine (which was by then beginning to cause concern), 'the need for insistence on orthodoxy would then disappear'. The proposed solution was 'to call urgently a national inter-disciplinary conference to clear up some of the vast confusion and to hammer out policy'. Not surprisingly, *The Lancet*'s plea for 'the volunteer effort' had little effect. There had been an earlier indication, in May 1967, that at least one of the Ministry's senior medical advisers, Dr Philip Connell, doubted whether 'such people' could be sufficiently objective to deal with individuals who were past masters 'at manipulating those who are emotionally involved'.[48]

But Camps was not the only one to understand, and accept, the need to retain the hard won experience of the handful of doctors who, virtually unaided, had previously carried the burden of treating addicts. In a letter to *The Lancet* on 18 December 1965 Dr Patrick Mullin[49] of the Southern General Hospital, Glasgow, who was already working in the field, had written:

> … it seems possible that the standard of general medical care required by the addict outside hospital may be underestimated, and if the goodwill of the doctors who have looked after addicts is lost a problem may well occur in the medical management of this small but extremely vulnerable group.

In 1966 Max Glatt[50] had noted that the most experienced practitioners were the 'prescribing doctors'. He supported the involvement of these doctors, who might work in a treatment centre or be responsible for 'supervising the after-care of addicts seen at the centre, including the provision of maintenance supplies to those patients for whom this procedure had been found necessary in inpatient assessment'. He suggested the possibility of limiting the number of addict patients a general practitioner could treat at any one time, and the maximum 'allowable' dose of heroin which could be prescribed without reference back to the centre could also be explored.

The working party appointed by the British Medical Association to examine the Brain Committee's recommendations, had also thought the proposal to limit the prescribing of heroin and cocaine to addicts to doctors on the staff of treatment centres was 'far too restrictive'. Therefore, in addition to the treatment centre doctors, 'panels of doctors with special experience of the problem should be authorized by the Home Office to prescribe drugs for addicts'. This recommendation was accepted and approved by the Council of the Association at their meeting with Lord Brain.[51]

In another call for a comprehensive treatment, preventive and rehabilitation service, Chapple[52] urged that any new legislation should allow the family doctor to participate in treatment, including prescribing for addicts, because it would only be through co-operation between the general practitioner and the psychiatrist that these 'very difficult and demanding patients' could be helped. It was not until the late 1980s, in response to the high level of HIV infection among injecting drug users in Edinburgh, and the lack of local treatment services, that a policy of shared care with general practitioners was pioneered by Dr Judith Greenwood,[53] the local Community Drug Problem Service consultant psychiatrist.

## Licensing doctors to prescribe heroin and cocaine to addicts

During the second reading debate on the Dangerous Drugs Bill in the House of Commons on 6 April 1967[54] Bernard Braine suggested that, because the provision of an adequate number of hospital outpatient treatment centres was proceeding so slowly, doctors in the community should be licensed to prescribe heroin and cocaine to addicts. Kenneth Robinson said that the government, in consultation with the profession, had decided it would be better to restrict licences to doctors working in the treatment centres. On 8 May 1967[55] Braine again raised the matter and pointed out there was nothing in the bill to prevent doctors outside the centres from being licensed, but Robinson reaffirmed his intention not to license doctors who did not work at a treatment centre. The proposal drew strong criticism from Leech and a number of others familiar with the London West End heroin problem, who in a circular letter to all members of Parliament on 18 April 1967 argued that it would seriously jeopardise the relationship between addicts and doctors, as those doctors who knew addicts and 'were trusted by them' would now be excluded and the centres would be staffed by people with no experience of addicts or addiction.

The method agreed for applying the restrictions on prescribing was the adaptation of the licensing procedure used by the Home Office for controlling the commercial manufacture and distribution of dangerous drugs. The statutory authority for licensing doctors provided by Section 1 of the Dangerous Drugs Act 1967 empowered the Secretary of State to make regulations prohibiting any medical practitioner from prescribing or supplying such drugs as were specified in the regulations, 'except under the authority and in accordance with the conditions of a licence issued by the Secretary of State'. Although this would appear to allow the Secretary of State complete discretion to licence whomsoever he chose, and to impose such licence conditions as he considered appropriate, there was an overall qualification, usually overlooked but very important in the context of the licensing policy, which came into operation on 16 April 1968. The power to make regulations was qualified in Section 1 of the Act by the words 'for preventing the improper use of drugs'.

The licences to prescribe heroin and cocaine to addicts were to be issued in the name of the Home Secretary, but the licensing policy was set by the Ministry of Health, the Home Office having made it clear during discussions on the implementation of the reconvened Brain Committee's recommendations that the determination of who should and should not be licensed was primarily a medical matter. The criteria under which licences would be granted were set out in a Memorandum on the Dangerous Drugs (Supply to Addicts) Regulation 1968 distributed by the Ministry of Health on 25 March 1968.

The Memorandum explained that licences would be issued to consultants who treated, or who might be called upon to treat, heroin addicts in psychiatric hospitals or units and who had been nominated by regional hospital boards or hospital boards of governors. Other medical staff, such as medical assistants, senior registrars, registrars and clinical assistants, working under the supervision of licensed consultants would also be eligible for licences. In the case of these 'other grades', the holder of the position should have been in practice for five years since full registration by the General Medical Council, reduced in 1974 to two years because of staffing problems. Given the lack of experience at the time in the treatment of addiction among doctors working in hospitals, those in the junior grades would be working under the supervision of, in most cases, an equally inexperienced consultant. Applications for licences from doctors working outside the NHS would be considered on similar criteria and the institutions should have facilities comparable to those of NHS hospitals treating heroin addicts.

The Drugs Inspectorate did take the precaution of checking the names of the nominated doctors in our records to see if any had previously come to our notice, although a positive result would not necessarily have disqualified the nominee from holding a licence.

For many years the whole procedure was a wasteful farce, as licences had to be issued to doctors, mainly those working in the provinces, who were, at the time, unlikely to see any heroin addicts and to others who had absolutely no intention of ever prescribing heroin to an addict. Initially some 600 licences were issued, renewable annually, a task which placed a heavy burden on the Drugs Branch Licensing Section. By 1986 the number had been reduced, not without difficulty, to around 200 renewable every three years.

The Inspectorate carried out a survey in 1970, which showed that licences had had to be issued to doctors who would not countenance the giving of any dangerous drug to an addict and who were only prepared to offer inpatient withdrawal treatment, and even to some who were reluctant to treat addicts under any circumstances. In some instances the holding of a licence was seen as a matter of prestige and in others as an important means of ensuring that a 'no prescribing' policy prevailed. This was a complete reversal of the normal Home Office practice for the issue of commercial licences, which required the applicant first to establish a genuine need to be licensed.

The Memorandum on the Dangerous Drugs (Supply to Addicts) Regulation 1968 said nothing about a need for the potential licence-holder to have any previous experience in the field. The question of the experience and enthusiasm of the doctors who would now be responsible for addicts' treatment was raised by William Deedes in a Parliamentary debate on 6 May 1968.[56] Referring to the possibility that the Chelsea Addiction and Research Centre might now have to close because the general practitioners who ran it, Peter Chapple and Geoffrey Gray, were not to be licensed, he said:

> Goodness knows we are not over-endowed with reputable enthusiasts in this field and I might ask why are they there anyway? … It is imprudent that under these Regulations these people should be driven out of business and we should then have to draft 500 or so doctors, the work of few of whom has lain regularly in this field and most of whom are reluctant soldiers, into the business.

Robinson was unmoved, as he had been during the protracted interdepartmental discussions following Chapple's application for a prescribing licence. He said it was worth emphasising that:

> … we shall not issue licences for use in general practice. The new system must be applied without exception. This does not, of course, imply that any doctor who has an interest in the treatment of addiction will be prevented from treating his patients. It is only where he considers it necessary to prescribe heroin that he would need to secure for that purpose a suitable hospital post.

No reference was made by Robinson to the fact that Chapple was licensed for a part-time hospital appointment where he was under the supervision of a consultant who was a very recent entrant to the field. This did not escape the attention of Dr A. J. Hawes who, in a characteristic broadside in The Lancet on 27 April 1968,[57] wrote:

> It passes the wit of man to understand why these two doctors [Chapple and Gray] who

are capable and experienced as few others can be, and who are offering a ready-made research and treatment unit free to the Ministry, should be refused [a licence]. Still more mystifying is it when one hears that one of the doctors has been accepted for the treatment of addicts in a large teaching hospital in central London. He is a capable person in one place, but unsuitable in another 3 or 4 miles away.

Robinson could not reveal that medical politics, rather than national or patient interests, had dictated licensing policy and that the exclusion of general practitioners was part of the understanding by which the Ministry of Health had secured the co-operation of the previously reluctant senior clinicians.

## Implications of the refusal to licence general practitioners

In the circles which dictated licensing policy it was believed that if general practitioners were given licences, as the British Medical Association and others were suggesting, there would be the danger of chaos and the possible spread of heroin addiction. In other words, there would be a continuation of the situation that existed before the reconvened Brain Committee reported. What was overlooked was that the licensing system provided much more effective control over prescribing than supervision by inexperienced and often disinterested consultants and Medical Committees. The Secretary of State had complete discretion over the issue of licences and their conditions. Thus, if it were to be found that a licensed general practitioner was prescribing heroin or cocaine in an irresponsible, or generally unacceptable way, the licence could be withdrawn, or more stringent conditions imposed – for example, the number of addicts that a doctor could treat at any one time or the dosage that could be prescribed without obtaining a second independent opinion could be limited. But the 'understanding' between the Ministry of Health and senior clinicians, rather than the specific proposal of the Brain Committee, explains why this was never seriously considered.

If the inflexibility of the licensing policy could be defended on clinical and medico-political grounds, it is doubtful if it could have successfully withstood a challenge in the courts. The lawyers had made it clear at the time of the heroin ban controversy in 1955, that the powers given to the Secretary of State under the Dangerous Drugs Act 1920 were to enable him to prevent the 'improper use of drugs', and 'improper use' was not qualified by the words 'in the opinion of the Secretary of State'. Similarly, the power to make Regulations under Section 1 of the Dangerous Drugs Act 1967 was 'for preventing the improper use of drugs'. Without this qualification the Secretary of State would have had even greater discretion to use his powers on the basis of a personal opinion held in the face of overwhelming contrary evidence.

Moreover, the words 'improper use' recognised there could be 'a proper use' to which the licensing system applied. What the Ministry of Health's 1968 licensing policy was, in effect, saying was that the licensing of any doctor in general practice carried a substantial risk of 'improper use', whereas the licensing of a doctor not previously involved or interested in the treatment of addicts, whose sole qualification was that he occupied a particular psychiatric post and was under the nominal supervision of a consultant, did not. Doctors whose previous prescribing had been suspect, for example, Lady Frankau, would certainly have been refused licences but a refusal, based solely on the grounds that the doctor was a general practitioner, was more doubtful. But above all, the policy was a slur on general practice as a whole, and on those responsible and experienced doctors who had carried the burden of treating addicts before 1968.

## Government influence on treatment policy

Some have seen H.M.(67)16 as a government 'directive', requiring doctors to pursue a pre-determined treatment policy and have ignored the very clear implication of the Memorandum – that the form of treatment, choice of drug and dosage to be prescribed, were matters to remain, as they always had, entirely within the discretion of individual clinicians. Just as the proposal for 'treatment centres' was a medical initiative, so any clinical guidance was to be provided by clinicians. Although licences for doctors to prescribe heroin or cocaine to addicts were granted by the Home Office, it was the Ministry of Health which set the criteria of eligibility. These were concerned with the status of the doctors and their place of work rather than with their experience of the treatment of addicts or, if they had any experience, of their preferred treatment methods. The government could not, and had no desire to, dictate how doctors treated their patients. In April 1967 Kenneth Robinson had told the House of Commons[58] that, 'The form of treatment and the decision whether or not to supply an addict with drugs will rest with the licensed doctor'.

But preservation of the idea that the creation and operation of 'maintenance' clinics was official government policy is an important part of the mythology and misunderstanding which has grown up around the events of the 1960s and has provided fertile soil for policy analysts. A good example of this misunderstanding been provided by Smart,[59] whose 'historical case study' of the development of policy on drug dependence in the 1960s, contains the following passage:

> The Department of Health and Social Service (DHSS) did, however, gradually impose some restrictions on treatment centres. It was able, through close contact with the Home Office, to refuse prescribing licences to doctors whose methods they did not approve and thus effectively to close them. Where treatment methods became too scandalous (in one instance a patient in a unit was able to bring in a shotgun) the units could be closed or responsibility transferred to other consultants.

The reality of the influence government departments exercised over the therapeutic work of the treatment centres has been succinctly described by Stimson and Oppenheimer.[60] They noted that, in the UK, clinical matters are 'left to the discretion of individual clinicians' and 'it would not be accurate to think of clear-cut policy directives emanating from the government'. They did, however, see the close informal links which the Drugs Inspectorate and colleagues in the Department of Health had with clinicians as enabling us to exert a subtle influence on clinic policy but, they emphasise, this 'was not seen by the doctors as a threat to their clinical freedom, or as an interference in their decisions about the treatment of patients'.

For the Inspectorate's part, we felt it was important for the consultants to have a Home Office perspective on what was happening on the street. The only occasions on which we could be said to have exerted any influence was when it became necessary, as it did from time to time, to remind them that nowhere in the Dangerous Drugs Act 1967 or the Misuse of Drugs Act 1971 or the Regulations was it stated that 'these provisions shall apply to everyone except a treatment centre consultant'. These occasions usually arose in connection with the practical application of the Regulations and I recall the considerable difficulty we had in convincing one particular London consultant that he could not prescribe over the telephone, or amend prescriptions already sent to a pharmacy. Failure to notify their addict patients was another problem which sometimes led to a certain amount of pressure having to be exerted. But an insistence on compliance with the requirements of the Regulations is a far cry from government interference in the day-to-day running of the treatment centres.

# 10

# Drug misuse at the start of the treatment centre era

The Dangerous Drugs (Supply to Addicts) Regulations 1968, restricting the prescribing of heroin and cocaine for addicts to licensed doctors, came into effect on 16 April 1968, a date which has acquired a special significance in relation to the British opiate problem, and therefore of the 'British system.' Unfortunately authorities do not always agree on what the 16 April 1968 actually meant in practical terms.

Edwards[1] did not consider it marked any 'abrupt departure from the fundamental ethic of the British system', although the way the system was now to work in practice, was a break with the past. On the other hand Stimson and Oppenheimer[2] saw it as a turning point in British policy towards addiction and 'the end of the "system" that had emerged from Rolleston's interpretation of the first legislation to control drugs in the 1920s'. They, confusing practice and policy, perhaps represent the majority view. It is not one I share. What is more important, and less often emphasised, is that the drug misuse situation facing the treatment centres on 16 April 1968 was not the situation which had been described to Lord Brain and his colleagues three years before, nor was it the same situation upon which the 'doctors experienced in the treatment of addiction' had based their clinical advice to the Ministry of Health.

## Increase in the extent of heroin use

During 1966 and 1967, the two years of consultation and negotiation by the Ministry of Health with the medical profession and the health authorities to set up the treatment centres, four major changes occurred in the drug scene. Firstly, the known heroin addict population increased dramatically, from 342 in 1964, when the Brain Committee was reconvened, to 1,299 in 1967, of whom 745 were new cases. Secondly, and equally worrying, were the signs that heroin addiction was spreading beyond London to other parts of the country where it had not been 'a serious problem' while the Committee were sitting.[3] There were now small groups of addicts in several provincial cities and in towns in south-east England, often centred on one or two established addicts who had returned, or come, from London. Thirdly, by April 1968 a black market in entirely illicit heroin, which everyone had been so anxious to avoid, had been established, although it was small in scale and not yet highly organised. Finally, it was in 1968, with the prescribing of injectable methylamphetamine by Dr John Petro, that the foundations were laid for what Kenneth Leech has described as 'the spread of the needle culture', which saw the coming together of two hitherto distinct groups of drug users – the heroin-using junkies around Piccadilly and the Soho club pill takers; it was also the year when 'the phenomenon of 'fixing' became an integral part of the lives of many young people'.[4]

No one should have been surprised by the deterioration in the overall situation. As Bewley[5] had pointed out in 1965, there was a rising number of young people who had become addicted through contact with other addicts and the rate of increase depended on the number of vulnerable people in the community and the number already addicted. It also depended, of course, on the availability of heroin and, as shown by the stable price of six 'jacks' (1/6 grain hypodermic tablets) for £1, there was clearly sufficient supply to meet the rapidly growing demand, both in London and outside.

Nor was it surprising that illicit sources of supply should eventually appear. There had been several dire warnings that addicts would not await the Ministry of Health's convenience and would look elsewhere to meet their requirements. As early as 15 November 1966, in a letter to *The Times* newspaper, following the departure of a prominent prescriber, Dr Hawes reported that his addict patients were telling him that 'there was plenty of stuff to be had on the black market even though the source from over-prescribing doctors is drying up' and he predicted 'an explosion in the teenage addict population as the months go by'. William Deedes,[6] in the House of Commons debate on 30 January 1967, made the same point when he warned Kenneth Robinson that, as some of the doctors previously involved in prescribing heroin were withdrawing from the scene, there was now a very serious gap into which 'an element, certainly illicit, certainly non-medical, possibly criminal' had begun to enter. In a further letter to *The Times* newspaper, on 27 June 1967, Dr Hawes referred to the appearance on the black market of heroin in powder form, which had never previously been available, and suggested that 'the Ministry of Health does not seem to understand the implications of what they are doing'.

Certainly the Ministry appeared blissfully unaware of the atmosphere of uncertainty and rumour created by their apparent lack of any sense of urgency, and the effect this was having on individuals already disenchanted with most aspects of normal society. Nor did the endless repetition that 'it would be premature and unhelpful to addicts' to give any publicity to the treatment units being planned reassure those worried about what was likely to happen to them in the near future. It was this uncertainty, rather than the 'consistent campaign of denigration of the Government's efforts', as Kenneth Robinson had told Parliament, which did most to damage addicts' confidence in hospital treatment and make them less inclined to seek it.

While illicitly imported heroin was soon to become a permanent feature of the scene, in 1966 and 1967 liberal prescribing was still the mainstay of the black market. Lady Frankau continued to treat and prescribe for addicts, although not as spectacularly as before, until an illness from which she was not to recover compelled her to retire. She died in May 1967. There were some new prescribers who, for the most part have escaped historical attention and whose involvement was, in any event, overshadowed by the sudden and somewhat mysterious appearance (early in 1967) and subsequent activities of Dr John Petro. As Leech noted in his obituary in 1981, from then until the end of 1968 Petro was often 'front-page news in almost all British newspapers' and was to become 'one of the most hated and despised figures in the country'.[7]

The prescriber whose withdrawal from the scene had prompted Hawes' letter of 15 November 1966 was Dr Geoffrey Dymond who also held an appointment as a Metropolitan Police Divisional Surgeon. Between April 1966 and November 1966, when the difficulties of the dual role of police surgeon and prescribing doctor were pointed out to him by a senior Scotland Yard medical officer, Dymond had prescribed heroin privately for over 80 addicts, according to *The Sun* newspaper of 11 November 1966, with many coming from 'Oxford, Chelmsford and other towns out of London'. The gap left by Dymond was partly filled by Dr M. W. Browdy, who had first qualified as a doctor nearly 60 years earlier. Although Browdy was never a lavish prescriber he was a 'soft touch' and particularly vulnerable to addict pressure, both because of his age and because he practised alone from a small upper-floor flat in Shaftesbury Avenue, very close to 'junkies' corner' in Piccadilly Circus. Two other heroin prescribers, Dr A. Cohen and Dr L. J. Wood (who was later to be found guilty by the General Medical Council of prescribing amphetamines otherwise than in the course of *bona fide* treatment[8]) were exposed by the *News of the World* newspaper on 14 January 1968.

It was amphetamine prescribing which was also responsible for the downfall of Dr Christopher Michael Swan, second only to Petro in public notoriety. Swan was less involved with heroin addicts than is generally supposed, but when it was no longer possible for him lawfully to prescribe heroin for them, he opened the East London Addiction Centre, from which vast quantities of amphetamines reached the black market. The events which led to him being sentenced to 15 years imprisonment in 1970, and to the erasure of his name from the Medical Register, were fully covered in the medical press.[9]

## Dr John Petro

It was Dr John Petro who was the dominant figure of the immediate post-Frankau years and whose prescribing was largely responsible for the glut of pharmaceutical heroin on the black market and for the Methedrine (methylamphetamine) epidemic that had such a catastrophic effect on the injecting scene in 1968. But as Leech commented, although Petro had been front page news, his rise and decline and significance in the development of Britain's drug culture had never been adequately documented. With one shining exception, an article 'Who speaks for Petro?' by Dr Margaret Tripp,[10] the few references to him in the various commentaries on the period rarely looked beyond what had appeared in the press. For anyone wishing to understand this confused and confusing period, these two articles are crucial, as are the comments of former patients, some of which were quoted by Stimson and Oppenheimer.[11]

The inadequacies of the 'British system', emasculated by the lack of medical tribunals, the delay in remedying those inadequacies through the reconvened Brain Committee's proposals, and the reluctance of his professional peers to regard what Petro was doing as 'infamous conduct in a professional respect' must all share responsibility for the untold damage resulting from his 18-month period of notoriety.

It is now impossible to be precise about when, how and why Petro became involved in the treatment of heroin addicts. My first knowledge of him was early in 1967 when Lady Frankau became ill and her companion, Mrs Clarke, telephoned me to say that Petro had offered to look after some of Lady Frankau's patients during her illness. Until then, Petro's name was unknown to the Home Office in relation to drugs and drug addiction, although his brother, Alexander, who was in practice in South Kensington, had seen a few of Lady Frankau's patients when emergencies occurred at weekends when she was out of London. This may have provided the link but another, and more plausible, explanation of his sudden appearance was given to me by the late Bill Arnold, one of the veteran Canadian addicts who had come to London a few years earlier. Arnold had met Petro in a gambling club in Shaftesbury Avenue early in 1967 and had introduced him to other Canadian addicts, who were also patients of Lady Frankau. Yet another version, as Leech records, often propagated by Petro himself, was that he had been recommended to Lady Frankau by her husband, Sir Claude Frankau, who had been one of his tutors at St Georges' Hospital Medical School. This, however, is contradicted by Mrs Clarke's considerable misgivings about transferring any but the most hopeless of Lady Frankau's patients to Petro's care.

From the outset, Petro expressed his intention of co-operating fully with the Inspectorate and in the early days telephoned frequently to check on the backgrounds of patients formerly with Lady Frankau and to let us know which of them were now under his care. This co-operation did not last long, as he was soon to enter his peripatetic period, moving from one cheap hotel to another in the West End of London. For a short time until he was asked to leave, he had a consulting room in Wimpole Street. One result of his frequent changes of address was an increase in the number of telephone calls the Drugs Inspectorate received from addicts seeking his whereabouts or the names of other doctors they might approach. We were also telephoned by doctors confronted by addicts who claimed to be Petro's patients but, as we did not have the same close contact with him as we had with most other prescribers, we were usually unable to provide any helpful information.

On 7 July 1967 the *Daily Mail* and *The Sun* newspapers revealed, in front page stories, that Petro's main practice address was the refreshment room at Baker Street Underground station. Overnight he became the centre of very considerable press interest and not surprisingly took careful steps to conceal his subsequent whereabouts, making arrangements by telephone, and sometimes telegram, to meet addicts in cafes, pharmacies and other public places. Unfortunately, while this kept the press at bay, it meant that addicts also had difficulty in finding him and we continued to be bombarded with requests for his address. Early in August 1967 I managed to contact him at the latest of his hotels and as he said he had 'lots to tell', I arranged for him to come to the Home Office on 10 August. Most of the interview was devoted to a detailed account of his recent dealings with the press and the police, who he was convinced were deliberately hounding him and preventing him from carrying on his 'work'. There was little discussion about this 'work' or individual patients but he did promise to let me have a list of his patients to assist us in responding to enquiries from other doctors.

In view of his complaint about the police, I arranged a further meeting at which Detective Sergeant Dave Patrick, of the Metropolitan Police Drugs Squad, was present. This took place on 21 August when we made it clear that there was no official campaign against him and that most of his problems were of his own making. As long as he continued to practice in such an unorthodox fashion, and to attract addicts in such numbers, he was bound to be the focus of press and public interest. When he asked if we thought he was over-prescribing, I told him there was no doubt whatsoever that he was, and Patrick said he knew of a number of people who were actively engaged in selling heroin and cocaine obtained on his prescriptions. Petro accepted that he had caused problems and promised he would be more co-operative in the future.

But although he continued to keep in touch with me by telephone and occasional visits to the Home Office, there was no noticeable improvement in the information we had about his patients. Most of our conversations were about the interesting facts he was discovering about addicts, particularly their distinctive skin conditions, his successful use of daptazole in the withdrawal process, and how the addiction problem should be tackled. From time to time individual addicts were mentioned, but usually in relation to their problems with the police. The promised list of patients did not materialise until November 1967 and contained 130 names of individuals, the majority of whom were receiving heroin and/or cocaine or Methedrine with some receiving only amphetamines in tablet form. Petro admitted this list was incomplete by some 20 names and a few weeks later told me there were probably another 30 or 40 to be added, although these were never forthcoming. As he had never, since the early transfers from Lady Frankau, checked the background of patients before prescribing, most of the names on the list were unknown to us, or could not be readily identified. By this time he had established a base at the Winton Hotel W2, where a sympathetic manager had provided him with a separate entrance so that he could see patients. But he had already made the mistake which was to bring about the end of his heroin and cocaine prescribing and also to precipitate the Methedrine epidemic of 1968.

In October 1967 one of the Metropolitan Police chemists' officers found that Petro had obtained small quantities of heroin, cocaine and methadone on his own signed orders. Details of these, and any supplies which he had made to patients, should have been recorded in his Dangerous Drugs Register but when he was visited by one of our Inspectors and Detective Sergeant Patrick, on 26 October, it was found he had not done so. Other purchases later came to notice and were also found not to have been recorded, as a result of which he appeared before Marylebone Magistrate's Court on 14 February 1968. He was fined £100 on each on 17 charges of failing to keep proper records of his purchases and supplies of dangerous drugs, a very heavy penalty for what most courts tended to regard as minor technical offences. The conviction and fine enabled the Home Secretary to withdraw Petro's authority to possess and supply dangerous drugs, which he did immediately by a Notice in the *London Gazette*.

However, before his conviction, there had been another period of chaos and confusion attracting widespread press coverage. This was started by a report in the *Sunday Express* newspaper on 17 December 1967 that Petro was about to be evicted from the Winton Hotel, and led to an avalanche of telephone calls to the Inspectorate from addicts as they sought his new address. (The address he was showing on his prescriptions at this time was Glenfinart Hotel, Ardentinny, Argyllshire, which he claimed was his only permanent address.) It soon became clear from these calls and the frequent visits he was now making that he was trying to use the Drugs Inspectorate as the agency through which he could maintain contact with his patients. His visits tended to coincide with calls from addicts asking to speak to him and on one occasion he arranged to leave a prescription with us for an addict who claimed to be in desperate need, giving credence to the belief in addict circles that he could always be contacted through the Home Office.

He was told very plainly and firmly that the Home Office was not a post office or contact agency and that he should obtain practice premises and cease his irregular and unorthodox activities. Despite a number of subsequent assurances that he was on the point of securing premises, it was not until shortly after his television appearances on the 'Frost Programme', on 11 and 12 January 1968, that he told us he would now be practising from 15 Tramway Avenue, Stratford, London E15.

This remained his practice address for some time, although we continued to receive calls from addicts complaining that he never seemed to be there.

### Petro's prescribing of Methedrine

Petro's appearance on the scene in 1967 was undoubtedly a significant factor in the further deterioration of the heroin problem, with his liberal and indiscriminate prescribing making a major contribution to the pool of surplus heroin in the West End. As a consequence, its very ready availability tempted many of those on the fringes of addict circles to try its seductive effects. London also became the main source of supply for the small groups of addicts in other parts of the country. But it was his prescribing of injectable methylamphetamine (usually in the proprietary form of 25mgm ampoules of Methedrine, a product of Burroughs Wellcome) which had far more serious consequences for the future course of drug misuse in this country. It was more serious because it established the bridge between the amphetamine pill-takers and the heroin-injecting 'junkies'.

The 'Methedrine epidemic' demonstrated once more the gaping loopholes in our drug control responses, some of which the public had been deluded into believing had been closed with the passing of the Drugs (Prevention of Misuse) Act 1964 which made the unlawful possession of amphetamines an offence. It was an episode which reinforced the need for machinery to control, rapidly and effectively, drugs to which the existing international treaties did not yet apply, as well as machinery to enquire into, and to curtail swiftly, the over-reckless, or simply ill-advised, prescribing of such drugs. It also provided a classic example of the damage which can be wreaked by just one doctor acting in this manner.

By the time the Home Secretary was able to stop Petro from prescribing any dangerous drug, in February 1968, we were aware of a small but increasing use of Methedrine, as a few doctors began to prescribe it in preference to cocaine. When Petro could no longer prescribe heroin he began to prescribe Methedrine with even greater generosity and abandon. This was perfectly lawful as it was not controlled under the Dangerous Drugs Act. Nor was his ability to continue to practice, and therefore prescribe drugs, immediately affected by the decision of the Disciplinary Committee of the General Medical Council on 31 May 1968 to erase his name from the Medical Register, following his February conviction. As the law then stood the doctor had 28 days in which to lodge an appeal against the decision, and if he exercised that right, he could continue to practise until the appeal had been decided by the Privy Council. Not surprisingly, Petro appealed and was therefore able to continue prescribing Methedrine until his appeal was dismissed. His name was finally erased from the Medical Register on 30 October 1968. (This loophole, which Petro used to such effect, has now been closed and the Professional Conduct Committee of the General Medical Council, as the Disciplinary

Committee is now known, can direct that a practitioner's registration to practice to be suspended forthwith.)

But even before the withdrawal of Petro's Authority to prescribe dangerous drugs, the Advisory Committee on Drug Dependence had been alerted to the increasing intravenous use of methylamphetamine. This was at their meeting in November 1967 when they were also told of the British Medical Association's decision to set up a working party to investigate the usefulness or otherwise of amphetamine preparations.[12] The Committee agreed that in due course a sub-committee, which under the chairmanship of Baroness Wootton had been looking into cannabis use, should be asked to undertake a similar examination of amphetamine use and misuse.

However, before this further enquiry began on 18 October 1968, the 'Methedrine problem' exploded in a flurry of media and Parliamentary interest and concern, triggered initially by allegations in December 1967 by Reverend John McNichol, founder of the National Association on Drug Addiction, that some doctors were already switching to Methedrine to evade the impending changes in the law relating to prescribing heroin and cocaine to addicts. If this was not strictly true it ensured that the intravenous use of methylamphetamine was an item on the agenda of the Advisory Committee's next meeting on 9 February 1968. Then the Committee was told by one of their medical members that the proportion of heroin addicts also using Methedrine had risen from 20% at the end of 1966 to 80% at the end of 1967. This was the main reason behind the Committee's subsequent conclusion that intravenous use of methylamphetamine was as serious as the heroin problem and the same controls over prescribing should therefore apply.[13] But this was not possible under existing powers, as the amphetamines were not controlled under the Dangerous Drugs Acts but only under the light control of the Drugs (Prevention of Misuse) Act 1964.

The Home Office and Ministry of Health were therefore asked to consider the introduction of the necessary legislation while, at the same time, the Chief Medical Officer was asked to consult the medical profession about reducing the overall use of amphetamines. This Sir George Godber did and in due course, on 18 March 1968, he wrote to all doctors to alert them to the possibility of heroin addicts switching to Methedrine and of the need to reduce the current widespread use of amphetamines.[14]

By this time Parliamentary interest had also been aroused and in the House of Commons on 6 May 1968, the Minister of Health, Kenneth Robinson, using one of his by now favourite words, announced that the Advisory Committee on Drug Dependence were being asked to look 'urgently' at 'the particularly worrying problem of Methedrine'. The difficulty, he said, was to get the real facts about Methedrine abuse and dependence, and the Committee's expert advice was awaited.[15] Although there was no doubt about the source of most of the

Methedrine now flooding the West End of London, officialdom required some authoritative statement before any action could be proposed, particularly when it involved the medical profession.

The June 1968 meeting of the Advisory Committee was 'inconclusive', with the preference for amending legislation remaining. At this meeting, Sir George Godber disclosed the fact that he had discussed the problem with the manufacturers and had secured their agreement to a voluntary scheme, for one year, confining supplies of Methedrine ampoules to hospital pharmacies. The secretariat were accordingly asked to prepare a paper, setting out possible lines of action and expressing the Committee's deep concern about the problem. The paper was also to highlight the inadequacy of the existing law to control new forms of drug misuse and the inability to deal with doctors who were exploiting individuals' need for drugs.

At the same time the Inspectorate was also seeking 'the facts' and on 24 July, just in time for a meeting of the Advisory Committee, we completed a very hurried survey of the legitimate use of methylamphetamine injections. This was by no means comprehensive, as we had no statutory authority to obtain the information we required, there were no detailed distribution records which could be examined, and for various reasons the details of the insignificant quantities dispensed on NHS prescriptions could not be readily obtained. However, with the customary excellent and willing co-operation of the pharmaceutical profession, we were able to compile a remarkably small list of retail pharmacies, mostly in the London area, to which substantial supplies of methylamphetamine injections were being delivered. Almost all were already well known to us as pharmacies to which heroin addicts were taking their prescriptions and from these we collected all the private prescriptions for methylamphetamine injections dispensed in May 1968, the first full month after the coming into operation of the restrictions limiting the prescribing of heroin to addicts to licensed doctors. The results were startling.

Analysis of the 853 private prescriptions we recovered revealed that the total number of ampoules of methylamphetamine dispensed during the month was 35,248, with Petro and Swan being responsible for just under 90%. Petro had prescribed 24,905 ampoules for 110 patients, over 30 of whom were receiving an average of 10 ampoules per day, the highest being 46 ampoules per day. By comparison Swan's contribution was much more modest, 6,033 ampoules for 84 patients. Browdy, the only other significant prescriber, was responsible for 3,124 ampoules for 59 patients; he told us that, apart from 20–30 'regulars', most of these patients were 'casuals' for whom he prescribed no more than one week's supply at two ampoules per day and usually never saw again. Five other doctors, dealing with a total of 11 patients contributed a further 1,186 ampoules to the total. It is almost certain that further prescriptions were dispensed at pharmacies we were unable to cover in the time available.

Insofar as the names and addresses on the prescriptions were accurate, most of the recipients appeared to live in the London area with a small number giving addresses in Hertfordshire and Essex. An appreciable number had previously come to notice as heroin addicts and almost certainly some, possibly under false identities, were at the same time receiving heroin prescriptions from treatment centres, some of which were also prescribing methylamphetamine as a substitute for cocaine.

## Manufacturers agreement to limit supplies of Methedrine

Confronted with the clear evidence that this was very much a Petro-induced problem, and assured of the willing co-operation of the manufacturers, the Advisory Committee readily agreed to Sir George Godber's voluntary scheme, which was discussed with the British Medical Association and the manufacturers without reference to the Home Office. However, finding and agreeing a solution is one thing, implementing it is quite another – as we discovered at a meeting with the Ministry of Health early in August when it was quite clear that the bureaucracy had taken over. At this meeting Ministry officials explained that before the scheme could be put into operation there were many organisations to be consulted and agreement would have to be reached on the terms on which supplies could be made by hospital pharmacies and the records that would have to be kept (no doubt in anticipation of future Parliamentary Questions). The Ministry was forced to bring forward its plans on learning that the proposals had become public knowledge and that Granada Television was planning a programme on the problem for screening in October. Accordingly, on 2 October 1968 the Ministry of Health issued a Press Notice, together with a corresponding circular to health authorities (F/D 121/45), explaining the arrangements by which, for the next year, doctors could obtain supplies of methylamphetamine injections.

This arrangement with the manufacturers saw the end of the 'Methedrine epidemic'. As information from the prison medical service showed, 'while 400 regular users of intravenous methylamphetamine were admitted to Brixton prison in 1968, there was not a single admission in the whole of 1969'.[16] In one of the two major academic studies of the 'epidemic' de Alarcon reported there had been 'a dramatic fall in the local use of Methedrine' after October 1968 in an area south of London covering one metropolitan borough and one urban and three rural districts.[17] The other study, by Hawks et al.,[18] was concerned mainly with the characteristics of the users. Both studies confirmed the willingness of Methedrine users to take other drugs. Hawks commented on the ease with which they would use heroin if it was available or to use it instead. De Alarcon found his subjects were quite prepared to inject crushed amphetamine tablets or the powder from capsules of barbiturates.

As for Petro, the erasure of his name from the Medical Register meant that he could no longer prescribe scheduled drugs and could not therefore provide his large addict clientele with an acceptable substitute for Methedrine. After serving a short prison sentence for the non-payment of his fine, he became a worker for the Simon Community and virtually disappeared from public view. But he was often to be found in the West End among his former addict patients, ministering to their general medical needs. From time to time he would telephone me and we would meet in one of the coffee bars so familiar to him. The conversation was usually about 'the old days', the current drug scene and his views on how it should be dealt with, and the progress of the autobiography which he never completed. I last saw him, at his request, in the old people's home in West London where he died in 1981. His place in the history of drug misuse in the United Kingdom is assured but he will be remembered more for his media image than for the one positive outcome of his brief reign, the restoration of the tribunal machinery, by the Misuse of Drugs Act 1971, whereby future irresponsible prescribers could be dealt with.

## Methedrine substitutes

Injectable methylphenidate (Ritalin) could have been an acceptable substitute for Methedrine, which other willing doctors might have been induced to prescribe. This was stopped as a result of the unsolicited action of its manufacturers, Ciba, who swiftly announced that they were making the injectable preparation available through hospital pharmacies only.

The withdrawal of the injectable forms of methylamphetamine and methylphenidate from general use was followed by the prescribing of amphetamine powder by a few general practitioners. However, this was effectively terminated by the action of the Pharmaceutical Society, which recommended that pharmacists should not dispense such prescriptions.[19] This initiative was fully supported by the British Medical Association.[20]

## Poly-drug misuse

In the aftermath of the Methedrine epidemic, the West End drug scene could now no longer be divided into 'the junkie' scene at the Piccadilly Circus end, and the 'pillhead' scene north of Shaftesbury Avenue. Leech has noted that not only had these geographical boundaries largely disappeared but multi-drug use had become an established feature of the drug scene.[21] My recollection of the period from 1965 to 1968, which I have checked with others, is that we entered it with a drug scene in London which could be roughly divided into three groups. By far the largest were the cannabis users, closely linked to the 'underground' and the 'alternative society', who were later to embrace LSD and other 'mind-expanding' substances. The next largest were Leech's 'pillheads', and their counterparts in provincial cities, frequenting the all-night clubs and coffee bars. Finally, there were the 'junkies', the heroin and cocaine addicts who were, for the most part, looked upon by the other groups as freaks whose drug use was far more serious and dangerous than their own. By 1968 the dividing lines between the 'pillheads' and the 'junkies' had become very much more blurred and, as Edwards has commented, it would be 'a misreading of events to suppose that multiple drug use only emerged in the 1970s'.[22]

## Heroin moves outside London

When the Brain Committee was reconvened in 1964 there were hardly any non-therapeutic heroin addicts known to the Home Office outside the London area and almost all of these had some connection with the capital. The Liverpool police, consulted by the Home Office on the Committee's behalf, had encountered only three heroin addicts in the previous year, all young women who had returned to the city from London where they had become addicted.

By March 1967, when Hospital Memorandum H.M.16(67) was issued, the picture had changed significantly. The appendix to the Memorandum set out the distribution, by regional hospital board area in England and Wales, of heroin addicts known to the Home Office in January 1967. This showed there were now small pockets of addiction in a number of regions although the vast majority (86%) of the 659 known heroin addicts were in the area covered by the London postal district and the four metropolitan hospital boards. Of the 92 addicts outside London, the largest group (47) was in Birmingham.

Changes were also occurring in the London area, with new addicts now coming to notice in the East End, the south-east, Crawley and Welwyn Garden City. Again it was Kenneth Leech, in November 1966, who was the first to warn publicly of the worsening situation:[23]

> The underworld is spreading to embrace kids on the 'pot and pills' fringe, spreading into new areas geographically, spreading socially and economically through sections of working-class urban delinquency.

It is not being wise after the event to suggest that these developments were hardly surprising. Given the rapidly changing attitudes to drugs among many young people, the prevailing non-conformist atmosphere of the 1960s, and above all, the ready availability of heroin, by courtesy of Lady Frankau and John Petro, the number of addicts was bound to increase. But the rate of increase, if dramatic between 1965 and 1968, appears almost stationary in comparison with what began to happen in the 1980s. A possible explanation for this comparatively slow growth is that heroin in the 1960s almost invariably was used by injection, an important deterrent for many, which survived until heroin smoking became popular in the late 1970s.

The heroin available in the 1960s came from addicts who had successfully persuaded doctors to prescribe them more than they needed. There was no criminal involvement or commercialisation in the heroin supply chain and new addicts were created by what Rathod described as 'convivially motivated spread'.[24] The 'evil pusher', so popular with the media, was virtually unknown. The Addiction Research Unit's study of heroin users in Cambridge in December 1967 and January 1968 could find no evidence of anyone 'pushing' and concluded that heroin became available through 'a cooperative rota system rather than a commercial enterprise' with someone going to London to 'score' from addicts.[25] This study provides independent support for the concern being expressed about the delay in bringing the prescribing of heroin under firm control. Of the 37 heroin users studied, most had first started using heroin in 1966/1967, prompting the authors to repeat the fundamental truth, which had been evident since at least the early 1950s, that 'a person will not end up using heroin if it is not available'.

Further confirmation that non-addicted 'pushers' were not then a major factor in the distribution of heroin, was provided in 1970 by MacSweeny and Parr.[26] They had difficulty in discovering heroin 'pushers' (defined as someone making a profit of £15 a week from selling heroin), and concluded:

It seems to be in the make-up of the young narcotic addict to buy, sell, borrow or... lend small quantities to and from other users ... most claimed to have sold only to known users but a minority of five had on occasion sold to non-users with little concern for the consequences.

If the return of addicts from London was a major factor in the development of small pockets of addiction in the provinces, and if London was the main source of heroin for them, in a few places opiate use was fuelled by the theft of drugs from hospitals or pharmacies, as in Manchester where, in 1965, there was 'a considerable school of young morphine takers', a number of whom later switched to heroin.[27] Similarly in Glasgow in 1966, a break-in at a large pharmacy resulted in morphine circulating among a small group of friends, some of whom, when supplies ran out, sought help from local hospitals, with others moving to London.[28] Over-prescribing was never a serious problem in these areas and there was very little pressure on local general practitioners. As a former Manchester addict recently told me, it was much easier to obtain supplies from London, and in the days when Petro and Swan were operating boxes of 'speed' were brought back to Manchester.

The spread in south-east England was, however, more closely linked with what was happening in the clubs in the West End of London. The outbreak in Crawley took everyone by surprise, and although there were some who inclined to the view that many of those involved were not truly addicted, the sudden appearance of a significant number of young heroin injectors was disturbing. Fortunately, as a result of the local community response led by Dr Raj Rathod, who was in charge of psychiatric services in Crawley and Horsham, and the late Dr Richard de Alarcon, the situation was largely contained.[29] The pioneering work of these doctors has not received the recognition it deserves; indeed the Crawley outbreak and its significance are now rarely mentioned in commentaries on the period, although their published papers still stand as a major contribution to the understanding of the mode of spread of drug misuse.[30]

The influence of the London drug scene, and the activities of John Petro in particular, were also keenly felt in Welwyn Garden City.[31] Although a treatment centre was opened by the Regional Hospital Board, local general practitioners had still not been told officially of its existence nine weeks later. Their enquiries to the Board received replies that 'it was not policy to inform general practitioners', prompting a protest from the local branch of the British Medical Association.[32] This was one of the very few treatment centres outside central London, but dealt only with addicts living in the town. This meant that addicts living outside its catchment area were forced to seek help from London treatment centres, as did addicts from other areas on the periphery of the capital where treatment provision was lacking. This added to the caseloads of the London centres and provided an excuse for delaying the provision of adequate local treatment facilities.

## Heroin use and treatment in Birmingham

As the appendix to H.M.16(67) showed, in January 1967 there were more heroin addicts in the Birmingham Hospital Board Region than anywhere else outside London. *The Birmingham Post* newspaper pointed out, on 25 November 1965 in a comment on the second Brain report, that heroin addicts were being treated at All Saints' Hospital in Winson Green long before the report was published. The All Saints Unit was opened in the autumn of 1964 initially to treat alcoholics although it was a designated 'addiction unit' as it was thought that addiction to other substances might emerge from the city's large minority ethnic population. In the spring of 1965 a young heroin addict arrived from London and within a short time the Unit was seeing around 12 new addicts a month. This sudden and unexpected influx of extremely demanding individuals seeking 'help', which really meant a free supply of drugs, prompted the director of the Unit, Dr John Owens, and his colleagues to look again at the traditional attitudes and responses to the problem, many of which they decided to abandon in favour of a 'community treatment programme' and a team approach.[33] The basic framework and principles of their response offer an interesting comparison with the thinking shortly to emerge in

London from which, for the most part, the word 'community' was conspicuously absent.

The All Saints' Unit programme was developed to contain the heroin problem. The treatment of established addicts was not aimed primarily at withdrawal of the drug, but rather to improve their health and social functioning and establish a working relationship with them, while in some cases it was accepted that maintenance prescriptions would be the only realistic treatment given their life situation. If this differed very little from the aims set out later in H.M.(67)16, the Birmingham team had some less orthodox thoughts on how these aims might be achieved.

The Unit was prepared to take self-referrals, as well as referrals from doctors, probation officers and the police. A worker from any social agency who had a meaningful relationship with the patient would become part of the therapeutic team. As a general principle patients were always involved in decision-making about their social behaviour and medical management, although this permissive regime was not always suitable for all patients. The Unit was open several afternoons and one evening a week and patients were required to see Dr Owens once a week and have their urine tested. If drugs were prescribed, the prescriptions were posted to one or other of several pharmacies for collection on a daily basis. This procedure was intended to stop the addict from using more heroin than the daily dose prescribed, to stop forgeries of prescriptions and to keep addicts from congregating at one pharmacy. With the agreement of the police, the pharmacists and the local branch of the British Medical Association, Owens was able to restrict the prescribing of heroin to the Unit.

The Birmingham city fathers responded to the drug problem with far greater urgency than the national authorities. After considering a report on the local situation prepared by its Deputy Medical Officer of Health on 11 March 1966, the City Health Committee convened a meeting of the Education, Children's and Watch Committees, together with the Regional Hospital Board and general medical and pharmaceutical services, to discuss drug addiction and the action necessary to deal with it. It was agreed to ask the Regional Hospital Board to consider establishing special centres for inpatient treatment, to alter the health education programme to include lectures for school children and the general public on the dangers of drug taking and to consider the possibility of arranging for youths in remand centres to be tested for amphetamine use.[34]

The success of this approach in containing the problem of heroin addiction in the West Midlands, when the number of new addicts coming to notice in London was rising rapidly, is striking. By early 1967 the number of heroin addict patients at All Saints had peaked[35] and in 1972[36] Owens was able to say that since January 1967 the Unit had not had a new patient from the West Midlands who had become dependent on heroin in the area, although addicts from other parts of the UK had been accepted for treatment. Moreover, all reports indicated there was then virtually no illicit market in narcotics in the area, a view the police shared, as our Inspectors knew from close contact with the Birmingham Drug Squad.

Owens attended the September 1966 meeting of 'experts' to advise the Ministry of Health on the role of the hospital service in implementing the Brain Committee's recommendations on treatment, but only after the Inspectorate had brought his work to the Chief Medical Officer's attention. He was not invited to the follow-up meeting in December 1966. The wide gulf between his pragmatism, flexibility and tolerance, and the London medical establishment's traditionalism, was not bridgeable. With one exception, none of the London treatment centre doctors visited All Saints, despite the opinion of Dr Geoffrey Tooth, who was then very much involved at the Ministry of Health in setting up the centres, that Owens's approach was 'promising'.

Owens was promoting such heresies as allowing patients to participate in decision-making about their medical management. This was quite unacceptable and anathema to at least one senior consultant, who let it be known that under no circumstances would he entertain suggestions from his patients as to how they should be treated. This 'doctor (consultant psychiatrist) knows best' attitude persisted in London until the concept of patient–contracts was introduced. But even as late as 1987 the question of who should choose the appropriate treatment was being seen as one for either 'the drug taker or doctor', not, as it fell to another maverick, Dr John Marks, to suggest, a choice to be made by doctor and patient together.[37]

But there was another important factor. The All Saints Addiction Unit had received considerable coverage in the press and was an embarrassment, particularly as it had been described as 'the fore-runner of the drug dependency clinics' in *The Times* newspaper on 16 July 1967 by a future Secretary of State for Health, Norman Fowler, then home affairs correspondent of that paper. Furthermore, the Unit enjoyed a certain amount of political support. As Judson records, Roy Jenkins, who was Home Secretary at the time, told him in 1973 that he had been 'very encouraged' by the visit he had made to the Unit in the autumn of 1967.[38] William Deedes commended Owen's approach in the House of Commons on 6 May 1968.[39]

Historically, the importance of Owens's work in Birmingham lies less in the containment of heroin addiction in the area than in the introduction of treatment concepts which were not to be generally accepted for another two decades. Those who only then were discovering that more flexible attitudes were required, that 'individual patients needed individual treatments',[40] and that the community had a substantial part to play in the response to drug misuse, probably had little or no idea they were merely re-inventing yet another wheel. Even the later 'local difficulties' do not detract from the achievements of John Owens and his colleagues and they deserve their rightful place in any history of the early days of the British heroin problem.

## The appearance of Chinese heroin in London

But if the known heroin addict population had more than doubled between 1965 and 1967, and heroin addiction was no longer an exclusively London problem, the most serious consequence of the two-year delay in the implementation of the Brain recommendations was, without question, exactly that which those recommendations were intended to prevent. There has been a good deal of confusion about when illicitly imported heroin first appeared in London, with most commentators suggesting it was subsequent to the opening of the clinics. This is not correct. Well before 16 April 1968 there were rumours, soon to be confirmed, that non-pharmaceutical heroin was available in the West End. This was reported in the *Sunday Telegraph* newspaper on 10 September 1967 by Alan Bestic, a freelance writer, who understood and was well informed about the drug scene.

A sample of what was to become popularly known as 'Chinese heroin' was first obtained by the Metropolitan Police Drug Squad in September 1967, followed in October by the seizure of a small quantity of similar material from an elderly Chinese man in the East End of London. Laboratory analysis of this light brown granular powder confirmed it was a mixture of heroin and caffeine, commonly known in Hong Kong, where it was smoked, as No. 3 type. Shortly afterwards a young addict from Crawley was found in possession of a small quantity of this material. At around the same time, I obtained my own confirmation that Chinese heroin was now an established feature of the scene. This came in the course of a conversation with Lofty, a well-known denizen of Piccadilly Circus, who after failing to sell me a pair of trousers of dubious origin, told me that some addicts were using what they said was heroin, which they obtained from the Chinese. The initial contact had been made by an addict (whom he named) who lived in Wardour Street over a billiard hall frequented by Chinese. Lofty had doubts about the substance because 'the Chinese smoke it, can't be heroin can it?' This attitude contrasts with the enthusiasm with which 'chasing the dragon' was taken up in the late 1970s.[41]

That it was the Chinese community instead of the Mafia which was the source of this illicit heroin was quite unexpected. But it was not, as Griffith Edwards asserted in 1977[42] 'another illustration of supplies arriving to meet the demand'. 'Chasing the dragon' was a well-established method of taking heroin among younger addicts in Hong Kong[43] and it was inevitable that this would be reflected in the Chinese population in London and other cities, although hard evidence of the extent of its use was virtually impossible to obtain, given the close-knit nature of the Chinese communities. Don Aitken, another well-informed and experienced observer of the British drug scene, responded to Edwards by commenting:[44]

> What happened in 1968, when clinics were set up and doctors stopped prescribing (heroin), was predictable. There was a panic, street prices went up and Chinese heroin,

which had been widely used for smoking among the Chinese immigrant communities since the late forties, started being sold to white kids for the first time because it had become profitable, and so the illegal market was brought into existence. Before 1968, kilos of heroin used to pass through the country on the way to New York without being sold here because there was no demand.

Certainly as British addicts overcame their reluctance to use heroin of unknown strength and purity, and treatment centre prescribing policies began to have an effect, demand increased. This saw the 'rapid emergence of a compensating market supply in response to the prescribing controls of 1968'[45] as Norman Fowler warned in an article in *The Times* newspaper on 26 March 1969. The increase in demand, and consequently in supplies of Chinese heroin, was reflected in the number of samples submitted by the police for forensic examination. From two samples submitted in each of the years 1967 and 1968, the number increased dramatically to over 60 in 1969, most of which were from the Metropolitan Police, although a small number came from other forces in the Home Counties.

Information I obtained at the time from someone who knew the Chinese community well suggested that the distribution of this illicit heroin, although almost entirely in the hands of the Chinese, was not then organised and very much a cottage industry. Small quantities were brought into the country by Chinese crew members of the major shipping lines sailing between Hong Kong and the UK. In 1969 there was growing press and Parliamentary concern and the Metropolitan Police were asked for an assessment of the situation. As the heroin section of the central drug squad had been disbanded earlier in the year on the transfer of the senior of its two members, who had obtained the first sample of Chinese heroin in 1967, this assessment was prepared by an officer who I knew had only a nominal responsibility for drug work. He attributed the increase in availability of illicit heroin to the reduction in the quantity of heroin prescribed by the newly established treatment centres but did not consider it to be 'a widespread major problem in the London area', as suggested by the recent publicity, but the potential danger was not to be underestimated and a close watch was being kept on developments.

A further police report in April 1970 suggested there was no evidence of large-scale traffic, that use of Chinese heroin had decreased dramatically and was now 'virtually non-existent' because addicts had become very wary of the 'adulterated state in which it was sold'. This assessment appeared to have been based on the number of samples submitted for forensic examination (only one in the period January–April 1970), an indicator of police activity as much as of actual heroin use. This report concluded with the statement that there was 'no evidence whatsoever that the use of Chinese heroin could be an escalating problem amongst the drug addicts of this country'. There were other indications of a scarcity of supplies early in 1970, perhaps partly due to the unwelcome spotlight which the, by now, intense media attention was focusing on the Chinese community, but this proved to be an optimistic assessment.

The Drugs Inspectorate had other sources of information that cast doubt on the view that Chinese heroin was 'virtually non-existent', suggesting that the Metropolitan Police were not in touch with what was happening in the addict world. In the latter half of 1970 the Metropolitan Police Laboratory examined more samples than in the whole of the previous year. Not only was Chinese heroin becoming more acceptable to addicts, but the methods by which it was being distributed showed a degree of organisation not previously noticeable in the London heroin black market. A particularly sinister development was the appearance of so-called 'pushers', some of whom were not themselves addicted, who received their commission in the form of free supplies.

An obvious reason for the growing popularity of Chinese heroin was its competitive price, which at around £2.50 a grain (60mgms) compared very favourably to £5–6 for the now much more scarce pharmaceutical heroin. The purity of this illicit material was at this time reasonably consistent, with the samples analysed at the Home Office Central Research Establishment at Aldermaston averaging 38.5%, 42.6% and 31.6% in 1969, 1970 and 1971 respectively, although the highest during this period contained 50% heroin and the lowest 12%. Varying purity was apparently an acceptable hazard, as shown by the numbers of new addicts using Chinese heroin approaching the treatment centres.

If there were understandable practical difficulties for the Metropolitan Police in dealing successfully with the major traffickers, who were almost exclusively Chinese (there were no Chinese police officers at the time), there was nevertheless a growing impression, not confined to members of the Drugs Inspectorate, that the central drug squad was not prepared to devote much time and energy to this aspect of the drug problem. A number of people complained to me that they had passed information to the police, as indeed I had myself, but no action appeared to have been taken. It later became clear that at this time the central drug squad had other priorities, to be revealed by the later prosecution of some of its officers for perverting the course of justice and perjury.[46]

Operational police matters, of course, fell entirely within the responsibility of the Commissioner of Police for the Metropolis, and any representations by the Home Office would only have produced the stock assurance that the police were alive to the problem and keeping a close watch on it. In the event, it was felt at higher levels in the Home Office that there was insufficient evidence to disprove police denials that there was a serious threat and that the Inspectorate should continue to monitor the situation.

During 1971 expressions of concern about the increasing use of Chinese heroin were received from many quarters including the Department of Health, whose Ministers had been alerted during visits to London treatment centres. After submitting further reports on the situation, I was asked to obtain support for my various allegations from 'some independent and knowledgeable people'. As a result, the Home Secretary, then Reginald Maudling, received a number of letters confirming what I had been saying. Furthermore this 'independent' information supported our concern about the lack of police activity. One doctor commented that if he believed all he was being told about the police he would be 'very worried indeed', and a senior social worker in the Gerrard Street area (the centre of the Chinese population in the West End of London) reported that scores of users in possession of small quantities of Chinese heroin were being arrested but those in the chain between the importer and eventual seller remained 'relatively unmolested'.

These concerns was later borne out by a further Metropolitan Police report in September 1971 from West End Central police station which covered Gerrard Street. In addition to providing the latest arrest statistics, which showed that officers from this station had been active on the street, the reporting officer drew attention to 'the obvious physical difference between police officers and the majority of persons frequenting Gerrard Street making successful observation almost impossible'. That some special effort was necessary was obvious but this was not provided by the central drug squad until much later, when it came under the command of Detective Superintendent Fred Luff and a number of major Triad figures were successfully removed from the scene. But this effort was comparatively short-lived following the decision of a senior officer that Chinese heroin was not a problem in London. In fact, it remained a visible part of the London illicit market for several years, until it was superseded by purer heroin from South-East Asia and later the Middle East.[47]

## Medicinal preparations of cannabis

Most of the interest in drug misuse in the late 1960s and early 1970s has focused on the heroin problem and the responses to it. As a result, the prescribing of medicinal preparations of cannabis has passed almost entirely without notice. The justification for discussing it is that the episode provides a further illustration of the complete freedom which doctors have always enjoyed under the UK drug control legislation. Even though it was generally accepted by 1949 that there were no medical indications for the use of cannabis preparations, it was open to any British doctor to take a contrary view and until 1971 it was perfectly legal to prescribe them to those patients for whom they were thought to be beneficial.

In April 1968 the Drugs Inspectorate discovered that one London pharmacy had dispensed nearly 900 fluid ounces (approximately 22 litres) of Tincture of Cannabis BPC and 150 grams of Extract of Cannabis BPC to 151 different individuals. Most of the prescriptions were for four ounces (100mls) of tincture, with the majority receiving only one supply during the month, with 150 grams of extract supplied to one person. According to the pharmacist, the recipients were mainly young and his supply register, in addition to containing a number of well-known names, showed that the majority had addresses in London and the Home Counties. Almost all the prescriptions had been issued by Dr Ian Dunbar, then a general practitioner in an NHS practice in Fulham, who had been associated with St Anne's Soho and the treatment of addicts for some time.

In a talk at St Anne's on 31 August 1968 Dunbar told his audience that over the previous nine months he had prescribed the tincture 'quite freely to several hundred people', who could be divided into two groups. The first were patients under treatment with cannabis being used as 'a psychotherapeutic facilitator', and included a small number of former heroin addicts or individuals who seemed to him in danger of moving back to heroin. (A few other doctors were also prescribing cannabis preparations for this latter purpose but on a much more limited scale.) The second, and much larger, group was made up of people who had been smoking cannabis, to whom he prescribed tincture so that he could meet them in his consulting room, 'talk to them, find out what sort of people they are and learn of their aims, ambitions and outlook on life'.

However, some unwelcome publicity following a court case in Oxford in October 1968 led Dunbar to limit his prescribing to the small number of his patients who were either former heroin addicts or addicts he was trying to wean from heroin. Susan Ratcliffe had been prosecuted for permitting her house to be used for the smoking of cannabis resin, which was actually the smoking of ordinary cigarettes which had been impregnated with prescribed tincture of cannabis. (Most of those receiving prescriptions smoked ordinary cigarettes which had been soaked in the tincture and allowed to dry.) The prosecution's case was that the substance left after the evaporation of the alcohol in the tincture was cannabis resin, the possession of which was illegal. After hearing conflicting scientific evidence, the magistrates convicted Miss Ratcliffe and this was later upheld on appeal as reported in *The Daily Telegraph* newspaper on 18 October 1968 and 11 January 1969. In his appeal judgement the Recorder, Brian Gibbens QC, said he had no doubt that 'the substance used began as resin and remained so for all practical purposes' and suggested that there was a very wide gap in the law which could lead to unlimited use unless closed.

Whether or not this judgement was entirely responsible, prescriptions of cannabis tincture and extract decreased dramatically during 1969 and no other doctor appeared eager to exploit the legal loophole which the Recorder had identified. But in 1970 the late Dr Julian Reeves, who had previously been associated with various 'underground' organisations, announced that he would be taking over one or two of Dunbar's former patients. The West End pharmacy to which most of the prescriptions were taken again began to purchase regular quantities of

Extract of Cannabis BPC, increasing from 1,500 grams in 1970 to 4,500 grams in 1971, with a further 5,000 grams obtained in the first five months of 1972. Most of this had been dispensed on Dr Reeves' prescriptions and 34 different individuals received a total 1,500 grams of Extract and 450mls of Tincture in May 1972. The few prescriptions issued by three other doctors were for quite modest amounts. No doubt with the Oxford judgement very much in mind, Reeves was anxious for it to be known that he always instructed his patients they were not to smoke the extract.

Just as there had been no effective action which could be taken to curtail Lady Frankau's prescribing of heroin and cocaine, so there was nothing the Inspectorate could do in respect of this latest development. The prescribing restrictions which came into force on 16 April 1968 applied only to heroin and cocaine and their extension to include cannabis was not a realistic option. No one patient could be said to be receiving an excessive quantity of either preparation, and furthermore, it had been made clear by the General Medical Council's Disciplinary Committee, in a recent case involving a 'slimming clinic', that they were not prepared to condemn a practitioner simply because he was using a form of treatment not generally favoured by the majority of the profession.

There was an embarrassing aspect to the discovery that cannabis was being prescribed to regular cannabis smokers. At around the same time as this came to light, there was a request from the International Narcotics Control Board for information about 'the proposed therapeutic use of this drug and also the forms in which it will be utilized'. This was accompanied by a reminder that in the opinion of the World Health Organization 'the medical need for cannabis as such no longer exists'. The Board's enquiry was part of a general request addressed to all of the 133 countries which had submitted estimates for requirements of cannabis for medical and scientific purposes in 1968. The UK estimate, based on the actual consumption in preceding years of its various medicinal preparations and on the stocks of raw material held by the manufacturers, was for 15 kilograms, which was considerably less than that for some other European countries, for example, West Germany (40kgs), Netherlands (50kgs) and Switzerland (80kgs). When our estimate was submitted it was anticipated it would be sufficient to meet therapeutic needs for a number of years but at the current rate of consumption, stocks would have been exhausted by the end of 1968 and it was necessary to submit a supplementary estimate to enable the manufacturers of the tincture and extract to import additional raw material.

The solution to the 'problem' of cannabis prescribing, if such it was, was provided by Section 7(4) of the Misuse of Drugs Act 1971 which came into effect in 1973. This empowered the Secretary of State to prohibit the manufacture, supply and possession, 'except for research or other special purposes', of any controlled drug which in his opinion required such restriction. The drugs which were so designated, under the Misuse of Drugs (Designation) Order 1972, were those for which it was generally agreed there was no therapeutic need, and included LSD as well as cannabis preparations. Cannabis was included in the Designation Order after appropriate consultations with the interested professions confirmed that it was now regarded as having little therapeutic value, although it had previously been used for a variety of medical purposes, including, as I discovered on a visit to one of our licensees in the north of England many years ago, in the manufacture of corn plasters.

In recent years there has been a revival of interest in the use of cannabis preparations in the treatment of glaucoma, multiple sclerosis and as an anti-emetic. In 1994 the Annual Representative Meeting of the British Medical Association requested its Board of Science and Education to 'consider the benefits or otherwise of decriminalization or legalization of some or all controlled drugs'. The Board thought this should be considered only in terms of the therapeutic use of these drugs and reviewed 'the potential therapeutic benefits of cannabis and cannabinoids'.[48]

# 11

# The move to methadone: changes in the drug treatment centres' prescribing practice

The claim that 'both addicts and clinics had survived the transition period',[1] when addicts were transferred from general practitioner to treatment centre care, glosses over the fact that it was in the immediate post-16 April 1968 years that the multi-drug injecting scene became firmly established and that this was linked to how the centres and addicts responded to each other.

According to Glancy,[2] the quantity of heroin prescribed to addicts attending NHS outpatient clinics in England declined from 2,690 grams in July 1968 to 1,358 grams in December 1970, while the quantity of methadone rose from 918 grams in August 1969 to 1,331 grams in December 1970. The number of heroin addicts receiving outpatient treatment rose from 555 at the end of March 1968 to 1,131 at the end of December 1970. As the more cautious prescribing of heroin by the centres began to have an impact, there were now increasing numbers of addicts competing for a share of a decreasing pool of it. Not only did the black market in Chinese heroin expand and become more organised there was also a steady stream of pharmaceutical products on to the 'grey' market.

The increasing size of the grey market was not surprising as British addicts had, until very recently, been accustomed to using pharmaceutical heroin, obtained lawfully from doctors on prescriptions, or unlawfully from pharmacies by theft or forgery. Understandably, they first turned to these sources when they found their needs were not being satisfactorily met under the new arrangements. As a result, in the next few years a range of pharmaceutical drugs including injectable methadone (Physeptone), barbiturates, methylphenidate (Ritalin) and dipipanone (Diconal) replaced, or supplemented, what little heroin was prescribed by the treatment centres and converted what had hitherto been a relatively straightforward problem, involving only two pharmaceutical drugs, heroin and cocaine, into a multi-drug injecting one.

Power[3] argued that the continued existence of a grey market in diverted pharmaceutical drugs after April 1968 occurred 'despite legislation and controls'. This is misleading. The Misuse of Drugs Act 1971, which placed under more stringent control a number of drugs to become favoured by addicts and provided the much-needed control machinery for dealing with the 'irresponsible prescribing' which had been the major source of supply to the grey market, did not come into effect until July 1973. By then the treatment centres' prescribing practice had created a new problem which was to have an important effect on the dynamics of the grey market.

## Injectable methadone

One aspect of this grey market, the prescribing of injectable methadone, available under the proprietary name of Physeptone, featured prominently in the discussions at the consultants' meetings in 1969[4] when it was clear there was not the universal enthusiasm for methadone there is today. At the September meeting arranged by the Department of Health, Dr Philip Connell presented a memorandum which asked what treatment centre policy should be in relation to 'the increasing number of methadone addicts who have never taken heroin and who have received this drug from registered medical practitioners or from illegal sources'.

There were said to be a number of (unidentified) general practitioners who were prescribing methadone 'in considerable quantities'. There was some disagreement about when methadone should be prescribed, especially in injectable form,[5] and some concern about the belief, said to be encouraged by the press, that it was harmless. This belief was thought to be partly responsible for the alleged indiscriminate prescribing by some general practitioners. It was agreed that a letter to the medical journals, signed by the consultants at the meeting, might curtail the practice. The Home Office was also asked to consider extending the prescribing restrictions to include methadone. (It was at this meeting that Dr Dale Beckett provided details of the oral methadone mixture he was using and which was to become the basis of the Methadone D.T.F. oral preparation now in common use.)

A draft of the proposed letter was prepared for signature at the next meeting of the consultants in April 1970. I attended this meeting to present the results of a survey of sales of methadone ampoules between 1 January 1968 and 31 December 1969, which the Drugs Inspectorate had initiated on learning of the earlier discussions. The survey had confirmed what we already strongly suspected, that it was treatment centre prescribing which was the major source of the methadone ampoules now circulating in the grey market. Our enquiries showed that sales of methadone ampoules to retail pharmacies had increased since May 1968 and that about 70% were being made to five London pharmacies at which addicts' prescriptions from the treatment centres were usually dispensed. The survey showed there was a small amount of prescribing by general practitioners. However, whereas the number of ampoules dispensed by those five pharmacies had increased by 800% between January 1968 and December 1969, the relatively small number prescribed by general practitioners had decreased, and in December 1969 was only 20% of what it had been in May 1968. Apart from some use in hospitals, presumably for analgesic purposes, nearly 90% of the methadone ampoules being manufactured were being prescribed in the London area and the Home Counties.

The survey also raised doubts about the reliability of the statistics of quantities of methadone prescribed by the treatment centres which are quoted in accounts of this period.[6] According to the information supplied by the centres to the Department of Health, in the last quarter of 1969 a total of 309,300 ampoules of methadone had been prescribed, yet the five London pharmacies had in this same period dispensed 376,420 ampoules on treatment centre prescriptions. Included in this total were 6,000 ampoules prescribed in October by a centre which had sent a 'nil' return to the Department for that month.

Despite the results of this survey, the consultants' letter appeared in the *British Medical Journal* on 16 May 1970.[7] It expressed their anxiety at 'the increasing numbers of methadone addicts, a proportion of whom are receiving supplies from general practitioners'. (This letter also expressed concern about the prescribing of oral barbiturates and other sedatives which some addicts were using by injection.)

Although the treatment centre consultants had been left in no doubt in 1970 that they were the main suppliers of methadone ampoules to the grey market, their high level of prescribing continued unabated and ensured that injectable methadone remained an established feature of that market. The returns to the Department of Health showed the number of ampoules of methadone emanating from the centres reached a peak in 1974 when over 21 kilograms of methadone in injectable form (equivalent to more than two million ampoules) were supplied to addicts. If the centres were not prescribing with a Lady Frankau-like generosity, they were certainly providing enough methadone ampoules to sustain a significant grey market.

Independent confirmation of this came in January 1974 when the Chief Executive of the London Borough of Hillingdon wrote to the Home Office, on behalf of the Borough's Drug Advisory Panel, expressing alarm at the development of a local market in 'surplus' methadone ampoules which were initially obtained on prescriptions from treatment centres. This letter was passed to the Department of Health, which doubted if the consultants would respond to this 'sort of general information' and, in any event, doctors were fully aware of the dangers of over-prescribing drugs from advice given by the Department in recent years.

Like the change to oral methadone a few years later, the introduction of injectable methadone by the treatment centres was not based on any research or scientific study. As Dr John Strang, a consultant adviser on drug dependence to the Department of Health, commented in 1994 'regrettably there has been an extraordinary lack of properly conducted studies of injectable prescribing'.[8] The work of Dole and Nyswander in New York, using oral methadone to block the effects of the highly adulterated heroin being taken by addicts there, was, of course, well known but was hardly relevant to the United Kingdom (UK) situation, where addicts were injecting the pharmaceutically pure drug in much larger doses. In 1967 Bewley had discussed the possible benefits of an injectable methadone response but felt such prescribing was not 'desirable' and it was better if the drug was given orally under supervision.[9] A modified version of the Dole and Nyswander approach was being used by Chapple and Gray at their Chelsea clinic,[10] while at the Maudsley Hospital treatment centre 'oral methadone was reserved for those with a history of illegal opioid misuse especially if previously not known to the Home Office'.[11]

A number of reasons, some therapeutic, some ethical, have been advanced to explain the treatment centres' preference for injectable methadone over injectable heroin. These include its longer-lasting effects, which meant addicts would have to inject less frequently than with heroin, and methadone was therefore 'more conducive to social and occupational stability'.[12] Also, as methadone was prescribed in a form ready for injection, the risks of infection were considerably reduced and withdrawal from methadone was said by some doctors, if not by all addicts, to be easier than withdrawal from heroin.

Ethical considerations were probably more important, and according to Dr Martin Mitcheson,[13] methadone's 'respectable image' made it more acceptable to clinic staff. Strang et al.[14] also comment that methadone was seen as a medicinal drug, and its use therefore allayed 'the increased public and professional anxiety' about prescribing heroin. They go on to say that until there has been proper research or monitoring, 'no reliable conclusions' can be reached about the value of injectable methadone as a therapeutic option, leaving the issue 'open to hijack by those who wish to reinforce their pre-selected position within the prescribing debate'. They then provide an excellent example of hijacking the issue, by arguing that the greatest benefits are likely to be accrued from the prescribing of oral substitute drugs, on the sole evidence that 'this form of drug is prescribed to at least ten times as many heroin addicts in the UK and to at least one hundred times as many heroin addicts across the world'.

Injectable methadone's appeal and popularity with the addicts of the late 1960s raised conflicting opinions. On the one hand it was said that methadone does not 'produce the immediate exciting 'buzz' associated with heroin',[15] yet on the other that it had 'a hedonistic appeal and black market value which is similar to heroin when both drugs are compared in their injectable forms' with the 'committed injector' said to be 'amenable' to move from heroin to injectable methadone but unwilling to move from the injectable to the oral form.[16]

What is missing from such statements, that injectable methadone is acceptable to heroin injectors while the oral preparation may not be, is any assessment of the part played by the ritual of 'fixing' (injecting) in the pre-AIDS era. That 'fixing' can be important to addicts was confirmed by the subsequent changes in the drugs they misused by injection including barbiturates, methylphenidate and dipipanone, which they had little difficulty in persuading non-treatment centre doc-

tors to prescribe. The effects of these drugs are far removed, both pharmacologi-
cally and hedonistically, from the opioids but were nevertheless used in the same
way – inviting the interpretation that the fixing ritual was as, or more, significant
than the substance in the syringe.

The claim by Mitcheson[17] that ampoules of methadone were requested, im-
plying that consumer demand was a contributory factor in the clinical decision to
move away from heroin, must be challenged. On the same page as he makes this
claim, Mitcheson confirms what I know from many conversations with the older
addicts of the time, that their general opinion of Physeptone ampoules was 'they
were only good for rinsing out one's works'. If they were so highly valued un-
opened boxes of ampoules would surely not have been left in the toilets at Piccadilly Circus London Underground station to be returned to Boots chemist, from
whence they had recently originated. To anyone closely involved with the drug
scene in 1968 the suggestion that injectable methadone was prescribed because it
was requested by addicts can only be interpreted as a belated attempt to place
some of the responsibility for the creation of the primary methadone addiction
problem upon the addict population instead of wholly on the treatment centres'
prescribing practice, where it rightly belongs.

The reported benefits of methadone were certainly not appreciated by the established addicts of those days who promptly sold their ampoules to young people on the fringe of the heroin scene and bought illicit Chinese heroin with the
proceeds. One consultant recently recalled that while on 'jacks' (of heroin) his patients were 'as fit as fleas' but when switched to methadone they succumbed to one
infection after another. Even John Petro regarded it as 'a terrible drug'. And another consultant, not averse to prescribing heroin, could not remember ever being
asked for injectable methadone and suggested that if anyone did, it was probably
because they were due to appear in court the next day.

Few, if any, of the accounts of the prescribing of injectable methadone by the
centres have included any reference to the prevalence of methadone addiction in
the UK before the reconvened Brain Committee reported in 1965. Almost all the
known methadone addicts, who might also be receiving other opioids at the same
time, included in the statistics before 1965 were of therapeutic origin. The numbers, from 1960 to 1965, were 68, 59, 54, 55, 61 and 72 rising to 156 in 1966, as following the publicity given to the Committee's Report, some addicts previously
receiving heroin exclusively had also to be included as being addicted to
methadone, which they were now also being prescribed. In 1969, when the primary methadone addiction problem was first discussed by the treatment centre
consultants, the number of known methadone addicts had increased to 1,687. Although the statistics did not differentiate between primary methadone addicts,
those of therapeutic origin or former heroin addicts, the effect of the treatment
centres' prescribing is quite clear.

In the mid-1970s, following the centres' decision to reduce the prescribing of injectable drugs, the impact on the availability of injectable methadone on the grey market is also clear. Addicts turned increasingly to non-centre doctors, who did not require licences to prescribe methadone, and Piccadilly Circus once more became the major market place for diverted pharmaceutical opiates. Research into the 'Piccadilly Drug Scene', carried out by Angela Burr between December 1979 and February 1981, showed that 'most injectable Physeptone appeared to come from the overspill from Drug Dependency Unit scripts and private doctors, as did occasionally pharmaceutical heroin'.[18]

## The injectable versus oral prescribing debate of the 1970s

In 1987 the Royal College of Psychiatrists justified the departure from the original flexible treatment approach described in Hospital Memorandum H.M.(67)16, which allowed for the continuing 'supply (of heroin) in minimum quantities', on the grounds that 'experienced clinicians' had come to believe that for new patients 'a relatively short-term prescription of oral methadone ... is good (and better) practice'.[19] This 'doctor knows best' explanation begs the key question of why the change was effected without the benefit of the results of the scientific evaluation which Dr Philip Connell had deemed so essential even before the 16 April 1968.[20]

Discussion of the oral versus injectable methadone debate has centred on the reasons behind the shift in clinic treatment policy in the mid-1970s, rather than on how this actually came about. Most of the accounts which have so far appeared have been by individuals who were themselves not directly involved so that pride of place must be given to the reflections of someone who was. In his description of 'drug clinics in the 1970s' Dr Martin Mitcheson,[21] who was one of the influential voices during the discussions preceding the changes in prescribing policy, refers to the responses to the findings of the controlled trial conducted at his clinic between 1972 and 1975 comparing the consequences of prescribing injectable heroin with those of prescribing oral methadone.[22] Although there was 'not a clear indication that one treatment was superior to the other', the findings:

> ... formed the focus for a prolonged debate between colleagues working within the clinics and in street agencies ... Following this debate many clinics made a considered decision in 1976/1977 to move towards a more interventionist therapeutic approach with a refusal to prescribe injectable drugs to new patients.

Certainly there was much discussion at the London consultants meetings about the prescribing of injectable drugs but if there was 'a prolonged debate' with the street agencies it passed me by, as it did all those working in those agencies at the time, with whom I have checked my recollection. Moreover, the rebuff received by two of the agencies, ROMA and the Hungerford Centre, when they sought a meeting with the consultants in 1977 to discuss the effects of the changes in prescribing policy on the street, hardly subscribes to Mitcheson's picture of general agreement beyond the close-knit medical circle that 'the continued prescribing of injectable drugs was not achieving significant change or harm reduction' for the agencies' clients.

Nor is the impression Mitcheson gives, of a close relationship between the treatment centres and other agencies, entirely correct. At a meeting of the Drug Dependency Discussion Group at the King Edwards Fund Centre in November 1975, a senior Department of Health official commented on the 'isolation' of the London treatment centres from other community services and thought it was 'a pity', not only for the staff of the centres, but also for the other agencies who were thereby deprived of that resource and expertise.[23] That this 'isolation' was a self-imposed aloofness is evident from the London consultants' unwillingness to agree to their provincial colleagues' requests to attend some of their meetings and later, their refusal to share their expertise with the private practitioners, of whose involvement they were so highly critical. Their failure to pay sufficient attention to the social aspects of addiction, which was making the treatment centres increasingly irrelevant, was underlined by Release in 1976 in an important critique of centre policies,[24] which also called for greater contact with the voluntary agencies and 'more consultant/social worker dialogue'.

In his version of events, Mitcheson expressed his opinion that the replacement of injectable heroin maintenance with oral methadone prescribing:

> ... probably reflected the already formulated clinical opinion that the policy of prescribing injectable drugs was, either or both, unhelpful to the patient and/or insupportable to therapeutically inclined staff.

This is a reasonable interpretation, although he does not speculate on whether it might not also have been the re-emergence, in a more practicable form, of the 'reluctance' to prescribe injectable drugs by 'the doctors experienced in the treatment of addiction' with which Sir George Godber had had to contend at their meetings at the Ministry of Health in September and December 1966. But how did the 'already formulated clinical opinion' manifest itself? Before I attempt to answer that question, there is another account, by Dr J. S. Madden,[25] of how the prescribing policy change came about, against which my alternative version of what happened has to be set.

Dr Madden, who had attended the September 1966 meeting as one of the 'doctors experienced in the treatment of addiction', sought to divide responsibility for the change in treatment policy between the Advisory Council on the Misuse of Drugs and the Department of Health. He noted that in 1982, in its report

*Treatment and rehabilitation,* the Advisory Council said that 'the policy of treating opioid users by maintenance prescriptions is now less commonly accepted'.[26] This major shift in prescribing policy had, in fact, been implemented by the London consultants several years before the publication of the report, which was heavily representative of the views of this select group. Madden omits to mention that in the immediately succeeding paragraphs the Advisory Council also noted that 'a policy of not prescribing drugs has deterred opioid users from seeking treatment' at the drug treatment centres.[27]

He went on to say that 'the Department of Health expressed concern that treatment seemed to have become synonymous with issuing drugs and published guidelines which did not afford prominence to long-term prescribing'. In fact, it was the Advisory Council which recommended that 'guidelines should be prepared on good medical practice in the treatment of problem drug takers' by 'an *ad hoc* body of representatives of the medical profession' because 'of the wide differences in medical treatment offered to problem drug takers' and because 'dubious practices have escaped the censure they merit'.[28] Although *Guidelines of good clinical practice in the treatment of drug misuse*[29] was issued by the Department of Health in 1984, it was prepared by an independent Medical Working Group (on which Madden served). The group was chaired by Dr Philip Connell with the members nominated by the representative medical bodies and included treatment centre consultants, psychiatrists treating drug users in the private sector, and general practitioners.

The starting point for my alternative account of how prescribing policies came to be changed has to be the informal meetings of the London treatment centre consultants at which those policies were discussed and the change agreed. As I remember, it was at their meeting in September 1975 that a proposal for the cessation of all injectable prescribing first emerged and found general acceptance. An interesting footnote to this proposal is that it came from a consultant who, in 1981, was to seek the assistance of a colleague in dealing with a patient for whom, he now believed, the prescribing of injectable drugs was the only remaining option but which he could not do himself as this would be contrary to his own centre's policy. This absurd but not unique attitude was confirmed by Dr James Willis in 1983 when he recalled that while he was in charge of the centre at St Giles' Hospital in London, he would be asked by a colleague from another centre 'to prescribe heroin because he knew that I did, whereas he did not feel able to do so although he was licensed so to do'.[30]

The 1975 proposal to cease prescribing injectable drugs initiated a lengthy discussion among the consultants which revealed that some treatment centres were already giving new patients only oral methadone and were phasing out their use of injectables while others were considering moving in this direction. However, no firm decision was reached on this occasion as too few centres were represented and it was agreed to put the matter on the agenda of a future meeting. This did not take place until October 1976 when there was another inconclusive discussion which prompted me to note that the meeting 'was remarkable for the fact that there was, after eight years, no clear idea of what they were trying to achieve or how they should go about it'. There were, however, signs of a growing consensus in favour of prescribing only oral methadone, although there was some anxiety that a too rigid application of this approach might escalate the illicit drug problem.

Prescribing policy returned to the agenda of the June 1977 consultants' meeting, the first to be held at the Home Office (only as a matter of convenience because car parking spaces were available), and prompted an interesting and important exchange of views. It was suggested that policy could move either towards greater uniformity and rigidity and to the treatment of only 'amenable' patients, or it could turn back towards a more flexible approach which recognised patients' individuality. There was a danger that the fundamental purpose of the centres was being lost at the expense of the addict, a fear which drew from one consultant, very much in favour of the uniformity option, the admission that for various reasons, including his personal orientation and limited clinical facilities, he could not provide both rigid treatment and a flexible maintenance programme. On the other hand, this presented no difficulty to a colleague who was more concerned that if addicts became aware of a new rigid prescribing policy, they would cease to come to the centres.

Yet another consultant, the champion of 'uniformity', ignoring the possibility that the adequacy of the prescribed dosage might be relevant, asserted that whatever the prescribing policy, addicts would still obtain illicit supplementary supplies. It was patently easier for the centres to have a rigid treatment policy for all cases but the effect might be an increase in the crime statistics. I was asked if there was any sign of this and said there was. In Bristol, where a strict 'no prescribing' policy operated, there had been an increasing number of burglaries of pharmacies with opioids, mainly pethidine and Diconal, being stolen.[31] Such burglaries were being reported from other parts of the country where similar attitudes to prescribing prevailed. I also noted the evidence of a growing interest in Diconal, barbiturates and DF 118 (dihydrocodeine), which misusers appeared to have little difficulty in obtaining from general practitioners.

If the outcome of this discussion was inconclusive, by 1977 most of the London centres had adopted a policy of offering new patients oral methadone only. At the Lambeth centre, directed by Dr Thomas Bewley, then Consultant Adviser on Drug Dependence to the Ministry of Health, patients were informed of this policy by a notice posted in the centre. This announced that from 1 May 1977 all new or returning patients (except those briefly in prison on remand), would be prescribed only oral methadone after routine assessment, which as far as was known, was also the policy being followed at other London treatment centres.

## Effects of the change from hypodermic tablets of heroin to freeze-dried ampoules

Apart from the occasional obsessional repetition of the necessity of having a 'uniform' policy to prevent addicts from 'shopping around',[32] prescribing policies received little more detailed attention by the consultants until May 1979, by which time the centres were beginning to feel pressure from the growing number of new addicts, many of whom were sniffing heroin or inhaling the heated fumes ('chasing the dragon'). But there had been one important development, which if it played no part in the original decision to abandon the prescribing of injectable heroin, offered some reassurance to anyone inclined to question the correctness of that decision. This was the replacement of the popular, and cheaply produced, hypodermic tablets ('jacks') of heroin with the more expensive freeze-dried ampoules ('dry amps'), which within a short time saw the entry of 'treatment by accountant' into the drug dependency treatment field.

The change to freeze-dried ampoules was, I have always understood, precipitated partly by the imminent retirement of the person who made the tablets at Parke Davis & Co, and partly by their diminishing economic viability in the light of prevailing prescribing policies. For many years hypodermic tablets had also been made by British Drug Houses Ltd, and some addicts would insist they only received tablets from their preferred manufacturer. A proposal to replace the hypodermic tablets with ampoules was considered at one of the early treatment centre consultants' clinical conferences, in February 1969, but had been rejected, mainly on the grounds that they would not allow flexibility of dose and that dangerous errors of overdosage could occur if ampoules were exchanged or sold illicitly. The Department of Health accepted the consultants' views and promised to bring its influence to bear if the manufacturers planned to cease production of tablets.

In 1978 Parke Davis announced their intention to do so. The response of the London consultants was that it would be 'unfortunate' as the switch to freeze-dried ampoules would lead to considerably greater costs and create particular difficulty for those treatment centres with long-term patients. I well recall the surprise of one consultant when he calculated that the cost to the NHS of supplying just one of his veteran high-dose Canadian patients, and he had more than one, with freeze-dried ampoules was somewhere around £20,000 a year while the comparable cost of the 'jacks' would have been around £300. Another consultant recently told me that his centre would still be supplying heroin to those addicts for whom it was appropriate had it not been for the cost of ampoules.

Although the ampoules offered greater sterility it was unlikely there would be any reduction in the levels of sepsis, as addicts would still use their customary ways of preparing their injections. When the Department of Health Senior Medical Officer responsible for drug dependency matters, Dr Denis Cahal, announced

to the consultants that hypodermic tablets were to be withdrawn and it was unlikely a product licence under the Medicines Act would be granted to a new manufacturer, assuming one could be found, they placed on record their 'strong
concern' at the withdrawal of hypodermic tablets. The change-over took place at
the end of February 1979.

One of the first to be affected was Dr Sathananthan, at Rees House, Croydon,
a firm believer in the Rolleston philosophy, who had a number of long-term patients to whom he was prescribing heroin. In October 1980 he told his fellow consultants that his NHS Regional Health Authority had asked him to reduce his
prescribing costs, and to put no more patients on maintenance prescriptions, a
major factor being the cost of the freeze-dried ampoules. (He was later to apply
for, and receive, a licence to prescribe heroin privately.) Others confirmed they
were coming under similar pressure, with one anticipating being asked not to prescribe heroin to any new patients. Such decisions, they felt, ought to be based on
medical considerations rather than cost and they were unanimous that drug dependent patients should not be subject to any discrimination by comparison with
other patients. It was, of course, a pointless and hypocritical assertion of principle,
since the pressure to reduce costs assisted their long-term aim of eliminating entirely the limited prescribing of injectable heroin to a dwindling number of patients and did not apply to their favoured preparation, Methadone Mixture D.T.F.

## The reasons for the change in prescribing policy

An understanding of how the changes in the treatment centres' prescribing policy,
from injectable to oral drugs, came about does not throw much light on why they
were made, or on their timing. No particular aversion to the prescribing of injectable drugs had been noted during the special Department of Health review of
London and provincial clinics carried out between May 1970 and May 1971 and the
generous prescribing of methadone ampoules, rather than heroin, was clear evidence that it was the drug, and not the method of administration, at which the clinicians' objections were primarily directed.

Within a few years, and without any support from 'the literature', apart from
the inconclusive controlled trial comparing the effects of oral methadone and injectable heroin, the aim of H.M.(67)16 'of containing the spread of heroin addiction by continuing to supply the drug in minimum quantities where this is
necessary in the opinion of the doctor', had been set aside. The London consultants had for some time been receiving progress reports of the controlled trial but
the final results were not published until 1980, and then not in one of the mainstream UK journals. But, as Mitcheson[33] pointed out, 'the authors repeatedly
stated' the trial had produced little evidence for or against the prescribing changes
then under consideration. Yet, paradoxically, while critics of what the centres were

doing were required to produce data to support their criticisms, there was 'no scientific basis' for this major change, as Dr Philip Connell told visitors from the American University's Institute on Drugs, Crime and Justice, in July 1977.[34]

The prescribing of injectables for all new patients was abandoned, so that the fears *The Lancet* had expressed in 1967,[35] that it was 'unwise to rely on any single approach … [with] the hazard that orthodoxy will develop before even the superficial premises had been explored', were fulfilled.

The change to prescribing only oral methadone had been a gradual process and not the result of some formal agreement between the consultants. Similarly, the shift to what has been seen as a more confrontational therapeutic response did not occur overnight. In 1979, largely as a result of the worsening situation, but also I suspect, because some of the comments in the Interim Report by the Treatment and Rehabilitation working group of the Advisory Council[36] had not gone down too well with one or two of them, the consultants spent some time reviewing the role of the treatment centres, which was now unclear, and if the number of addicts increased significantly they would be unable to cope.

The consultants thought it could be argued that the centres had failed by not preventing or containing the 'grey' market in pharmaceutical drugs, although at the level of the individual they had provided a useful service. A purely medical response had its drawbacks but were they now to be seen as 'helpers of addicts' rather than 'agents of social control'? If they were also to move from merely prescribing to the wider role of supporting and advising non-medical services, as suggested by the Advisory Council, additional resources would be needed. But by now there were a number of other factors, such as the prescribing of injectable methadone by non-centre, often private, practitioners to be considered. No clear definition of a new role for the centres emerged from the discussions.

What then are the possible reasons for the abandonment of the H.M.(67)16 approach of containment? The two most frequently advanced are the failure of the treatment centres to prevent the spread of heroin addiction and the growth of a criminal black market, and the realisation that 'maintenance prescribing' did not change an addict's lifestyle or cure him or her of addiction. In 1987, after explaining that the 'tight-fisted prescribing policies' of the centres and the preference for short-term prescribing of oral methadone was a clinical decision, the Royal College of Psychiatrists invoked a number of 'background influences' to explain the increase in the number of heroin addicts. These included the 'large changes in the international heroin supply scene' and 'unemployment and urban deprivation'.[37] But important though these factors undoubtedly are in relation to today's drug problem, they were far less evident in this country during the early and mid-1970s, when the treatment centres prescribing policies were changing and, as I recall, were never a factor in discussions at the London consultants' meetings. Moreover, as was made abundantly clear at their meeting in July 1980, the consultants by then

no longer saw the centres as part of the drug control mechanism, or their prescribing policies as having any effect on the black market.

Although the Advisory Council commented in 1982 that the change in the nature and extent of the drug problem had been accompanied by changes in attitude
among some of those working in the hospital treatment services, and the policy of
treating opioid misusers by prescribing long-term maintenance was now less
commonly accepted, it offered no specific reasons for these changed attitudes. We
have to turn for assistance therefore to Dr Gerry Stimson, who has produced one
of the few accounts of the day-to-day workings of the London treatment centres
in the mid-1970s.[38] He argued that a contradiction between 'control' and 'treatment' was inherent in the policy formulations of the 1960s and it meant that for
treatment centre staff 'the task of controlling the drug problem came to over-
shadow the task of treatment'. In addition, dealing with the disruptive behaviour
of a minority of patients caused resentment among the staff at having to act 'like
policemen in white coats' and distracting them from their treatment tasks.

He noted that some doctors did, however, accept that for controlling the drug
problem a maintenance prescribing policy might be best, because it attracted patients to the clinics where they could be helped with their problems, and where
they could be provided with drugs of known purity and strength. On the other
hand, such prescribing conflicted with therapeutic ideals, patients who were
maintained showed little inclination to change their lifestyles and were not being
cured of their addiction. The latter is also the view of Dr John Strang who has
written that in the mid-1970s the London drug clinics appeared to have undergone
'a collective existentialist crisis', which gave rise to a 'more active and confrontational style of working'. These changes, he suggested, had come about partly because of contact with the new drug-free therapeutic communities, such as
Phoenix House, and partly 'out of a sense of stagnation resulting from an apparent lack of personal progress for many of the long-term maintenance patients'.[39]

## Therapeutic frustration

It is not altogether surprising to read of the growing 'frustration', 'stagnation' and
'battle-fatigue' of treatment centre staff by the mid-1970s. Probably for the first
time in their careers, doctors were dealing with patients who did not want to be
'cured', who did not see themselves as 'sick' or in need of psychiatric help and for
whom traditional therapeutic responses were unlikely to be effective. Add to this
the addict's capacity for lying, deviousness and dishonesty and the seeds of 'conflict' were sown. Although some were demanding and disruptive, for the most part
addicts were prepared, with varying degrees of reluctance, to jump through whatever therapeutic hoops were necessary if, at the end of the day, they were going to
receive a prescription for their favoured drug. Support for this view is provided by

Judson,[40] to whom one consultant he interviewed in 1972 declared, 'she is not going to get her prescription unless she goes through certain hoops for me'.

In the immediate post-1968 period treatment responses varied, from the inflexible, where consultants made no secret of the fact that they were not going to be told by any addict what drug they should prescribe, to a willingness to accept that addicts might conceivably have some thoughts on their own future, which could possibly form the basis of an ongoing rewarding therapeutic relationship. Of the few accounts of what it was like to work in a London treatment centre at the time, one of the best has been provided by Dr Margaret Tripp, then working at St Clement's Hospital.[41] Her analysis of her own feelings and initial anxieties (she was particularly concerned that she was giving her patients 'poison'), and of the relationship between the centre staff and the addicts, offers the personal perspective which is missing from so many of the accounts of this critical period. She described 'being bothered at first about over-prescribing (heroin), but wanted to be generous enough to net all the addicts at one go ... ' then 'we began to get the doses more nearly right; knowing the boys and their families'.

But even though it was always recognised that working with drug addicts was likely to be unrewarding, it was some time before 'frustration', 'stagnation' and 'battle-fatigue' began to appear. The 1970/1971 Department of Health review of the treatment centres had found that the staff agreed, in general, that they were performing a useful and positive function. What had happened in the meanwhile? Why, from the outset, was the balance tilted so heavily in favour of 'social control' and why was it nearly a decade before the staff began to devote a greater proportion of their time to the pursuit of their therapeutic ideals? Why had the problems besetting the London centres, particularly that of disruptive patient behaviour, not caused similar difficulties for John Owens at the All Saints Hospital in Birmingham or for Peter Chapple in Chelsea?

The answers to these questions are linked. In their papers in the *British Medical Journal* in 1967, Owens and Chapple[42] had shown an appreciation of the problem, the philosophy and intentions of the reconvened Brain Committee, and, in particular, the role of prescribing in relation to treatment, which were not shared by those who were to have an undue influence on the way the clinical response developed. Dr Max Glatt[43] in his review of the Committee's proposals, had been in no doubt that equating the prescribing of drugs with 'treatment' was a proposition with which 'many medical men would not agree' and that 'the main emphasis in such (treatment) centres should be in giving the addict the motivation and incentives to come off drugs and helping him to reach and maintain this objective'.

An important clue to why, for nearly a decade, most of the London treatment centres were little more than 'prescribing centres', offering minimal therapeutic help to their patients, came from Dr Hamid Ghodse in 1977.[44] He explained that the main problem for clinicians was that:

Unlike patients in general, addicts know their diagnosis, know what drug and dose they want and leave nothing for the doctor to do but sign the form. In this situation the doctor feels himself in an inferior role, perhaps angered by his therapeutic impotence.

To which one might add, 'therapeutic impotence' easily became therapeutic indolence.

Although these comments confirm that 'therapeutic endeavour' had a very low priority in the early years, they throw little light on why in 1968, the treatment centres had come to choose the non-therapeutic, non-interventionist road. Was this perhaps an aspect of the 'uniformity', which while paying lip-service to the notion of clinical freedom, had the real objective of imposing over the whole treatment field the moral and ethical values held by a few well-placed clinicians? This is an interpretation which cannot be dismissed out of hand. From close study of what was happening in the centres, Stimson and Oppenheimer[45] concluded that treatment 'was often a euphemism for other goals' and pointed to the need to look not only at what was being done to or for patients, but also 'at the clinicians' motivations in so acting'.

That these motivations included responding to 'discreet peer group pressure' to preserve a uniform clinical approach, has also been confirmed by Mitcheson writing in 1994,[46] although not as revealingly as in his interview with Judson some 20 years earlier.[47] Then he had explained that at the teaching hospitals the treatment centre consultants were 'much more subject to our colleagues' criticisms and unspoken controls' than if they had been working elsewhere. He also referred to the consultants' meetings at the Department of Health 'which we all have to go to, because we're terrified somebody else might get an extra ration of jam. Which is another control mechanism'.

The confusion over 'maintenance', and the accompanying obsession with not over-prescribing, certainly suggest that it was misunderstanding, coupled with the admitted inexperience of those who would now be responsible, which sent the London treatment centres on their frustrating journey. If so, their apologists cannot be allowed to shift responsibility for any failings, therapeutic or otherwise, on to the perceived contradictions in either the second Brain report or H.M.(67)16. It is on those who translated into practice the aims clearly expressed in these documents that the responsibility must be placed. It is they who failed to appreciate that the reconvened Brain Committee, in the much-quoted paragraph 15 of its report, was simply recognising and underscoring the difficulties inherent in its proposed solution, that such prescribing as might be necessary should, in future, be undertaken in an organised treatment setting. There was no expectation that heroin addiction would be totally eliminated, merely the hope that its spread would be contained.

That this was also the message in H.M.(67)16 was well understood by *The*

*Lancet*, which, in another important leading article, 'Drug-dependence clinics', published on 19 February 1977[48] (prompted by an article in *The Times* newspaper of 31 January 1977 'Drug clinics; What has gone wrong with the system other countries envied?') reminded its readers that:

> From the start these clinics were seen as having a dual function. They had firstly to offer care for the individual – and proper medical and psychiatric care rather than the mere dispensing of drugs … At the same time the clinics had a public-health function in controlling the epidemic: by bringing prescribing tightly under control they would curtail the risk of N.H.S. heroin spilling over to feed a black market; and, since they could legally supply maintenance drugs it was hoped that the potential black-market in illegal drugs would be forestalled.

*The Lancet* did not suggest, as so many of those seeking to explain the changes in treatment policy have done, that it was the task of the treatment centres, which were been set up 'primarily to deal with heroin users', to control 'the drug problem' in general. Nor had Lord Brain and his colleagues been asked to consider whether control of the drug problem could be exercised through control of the treatment. The Committee had been asked for advice on how the gap through which the existing 'grey' market was being medically supplied with unlimited quantities of heroin could be plugged, and their proposals were an answer to that question alone. It is an important point which bears repetition as the notion that 'competitive prescribing', as 'maintenance prescribing' came to be known, was 'official' policy is one of the more deeply-embedded myths of the treatment centre era.

But if the first of the two main justifications for the move away from injectables – that is, the failure to prevent the creation of a criminal black market – is untenable; what of the second, the growing therapeutic frustration of clinic staff? From the start, it was accepted that there was no guaranteed cure of addiction and that the prospect of relapse was high. Nevertheless, as the 1970/1971 Department of Health review found, not only was there general support for the outpatient approach but the majority of treatment centres felt that, within their limited resources, they were able to help patients achieve 'a more settled and less unhappy way of life', even if that improvement was sometimes only marginal. Why then within a few years should there be such dissatisfaction, low morale and frustration?

One important factor, addressed by the Advisory Council in 1982,[49] was undoubtedly the inadequacy of the resources available to meet growing demands, which, because of the widely held belief that the heroin problem had been contained, were still largely unrecognised. In some instances, the primitive resources reluctantly provided in 1968 had not been improved, in others there had been a reduction in staff numbers and the accuracy of the prediction that, following the reorganisation of the NHS, addiction services would lose out in the competition for scarce resources, was only too apparent. This was a factor over which, as long as the general complacency persisted, the centres could have little influence.

Some of the therapeutic frustration of the centres' staff could have been avoided if there had been a little more pragmatism and a little less moralising. By April 1968 heroin addiction had been a growing problem for well over a decade and many of the patients who were transferred from the care of general practitioners to the newly opened treatment centres had been addicted and receiving prescriptions for heroin for much of that time, having obstinately resisted all attempts to convert them to a drug-free lifestyle. Although they were not all middle class and their addiction was not iatrogenic in origin, they were in many instances the 1968 counterparts of the Rolleston Committee's stable addicts and unless the clinics had some innovative approaches to offer, it was unlikely their addiction would be 'cured'. But few clinicians were prepared to accept the continued use of drugs by their patients and considered abstinence to be the only satisfactory outcome of treatment. This was consistent with psychiatry's thinking at the time, as expressed by Dr Griffith Edwards in 1970:[50]

> ... the common core of treatment is to advise the patient to abstain totally from drink or narcotics; invite him to review the present pattern of his social existence; explain to him the advantages of abstinence and the disadvantages of continued chemical abuse; and to suggest various strategies which will help him to get through life without his favoured chemical, hoping that he will have a good opinion of us and take our advice.

## The long-term addict

The long-term addicts, the dinosaurs of the 1950s and early 1960s, were the main source of frustration to treatment centre staff committed to the objective of total abstinence for all patients. That they were unprepared for such patient resistance to their therapeutic endeavours is further evidence of the lack of training of those entering the addiction treatment field for the first time in 1968, a situation which still obtained over a decade later and attracted strong criticism from the Advisory Council.[51] In the circumstances it was perhaps not surprising that as Mitcheson[52] said:

> The 1970s saw the erosion of the capacity of therapists to tolerate a numerically stable, but disorganised and distressing long-term clinic clientele who were persistent in their continued misuse of drugs ...

He goes on to say that the London treatment centre staff collectively responded to these patients by discontinuing maintenance prescribing and moving towards 'confrontation' and 'active intervention and emphasis on facilitating change'.

However, the impression that all the long-term addicts were 'disorganized and distressing' is misleading and unfair. It is unfair to those treatment centres, which, as the 1970/71 Department of Health review showed, had been able to improve the social functioning of a number of their patients. It is also unfair to the not insignificant number of addicts who, while still using injectable drugs, were nevertheless leading reasonably normal lives which were, in many instances, seriously disrupted by the new policy of confrontation and oral methadone.

There was a simple solution to the problem which these long-term patients presented. General practitioners could have been asked to undertake their 'maintenance' in close collaboration with the centre consultants. The need to retain and take full advantage of the experience of the responsible general practitioners who had carried the burden of treating addicts up until 16 April 1968 had been argued in the Parliamentary debates on the Dangerous Drugs Act 1967. The idea of returning the chronic, and realistically untreatable, addicts to general practice care was first put forward by Dale Beckett in 1967 at one of the London consultants' meetings, where it was raised again in 1979.

Yet as far as I am aware, the transfer of these long-term addicts back to general practitioners was never seriously considered, possibly because such a move would have undermined the 'understanding' on which the psychiatric establishment had agreed to co-operate in implementing the Brain recommendations. If it had been accepted it would have allowed the treatment centres' limited resources and frustrated therapeutic energies to be directed to those patients offering the best prospects for successful intervention. It would also have avoided the analogy drawn by The Lancet[53] in 1982 between a clinic with patients on long-term methadone maintenance as 'a geriatric ward with its beds blocked' when discussing the inadequacy of the facilities currently available to meet the new wave of heroin addiction.

Perhaps the most pertinent comment on long-term addicts and the therapeutic goal of total abstinence has come from the pioneer of oral methadone therapy, Professor Vincent Dole[54] when he commented:

> ... a medication is prescribed to enable the patient with a chronic disease to be as functional as possible, to live as effectively as he can, for as long as he can, with whatever pharmacological support optimizes his functional state.

He expressed his hope that 'some day it will be possible to bring to addiction the same perspective that applies to the medical problems of chronic heart disease, diabetes, gout and the like' rather than assuming that addiction was a behaviour disorder and that the 'only acceptable goal of treatment is total abstinence'.

But the chronic addicts who obstinately refused to change their lifestyle were not the only declared reason for the frustration of the treatment centre staff. One of the most frequent justifications for the abandonment of maintenance heroin prescribing is the claim that even if addicts are receiving a regular prescription they would continue to supplement their supplies from illicit sources. This, of course, begs the answer that if they were not receiving regular prescriptions they would have to rely even more on the illicit market. In 1977 Mitcheson, discussing the findings of the controlled trial later reported by Hartnoll et al.,[55] posed as a dilemma:

> ... the implication of maintaining addicts with heroin includes the prospect of a steadily accumulating clinic population of chronic addicts who are rather less criminally involved and who buy illicit drugs in smaller quantities.

The frustration in the treatment centres puts into perspective the burden carried before April 1968 by those few responsible general practitioners whose tolerance of addicts' behaviour and lack of progress towards a drug-free existence has been so grossly misrepresented. By the time the Brain Committee was reconvened in 1964, this small band of dedicated practitioners were well versed in addict chicanery but more importantly, understood the need for 'inexhaustible patience and goodwill'. They appreciated that, in many cases 'sooner or later, some insight breaks through', offering possibilities for progress towards a drug-free lifestyle and that until then their function was essentially a holding operation, or 'harm minimisation', as it is now called. The staff in the new treatment centres had none of this experience and for the most part were quite unprepared for what was ahead of them. They had received no training and little guidance from those who were fashioning the post-Brain response and who had themselves very limited practical experience upon which to draw.

But why the London clinicians agreed to abandon injectable prescribing for all except a few of the very long-term addicts cannot be explained solely on the basis of the frustrating lack of therapeutic success, inadequate resources or the problems presented by difficult, devious and disruptive patients. Addiction had long been recognised as a chronic, relapsing condition, and the addicts' unsavoury reputation was well known. Furthermore, the challenge had been clearly set out in 1968[56] and had been accepted, albeit with 'reluctance'.

Why, then, were the goal posts moved, just when it was becoming increasingly apparent that the successful containment of the heroin problem was a myth? The Department of Health had reported to the Advisory Council that the London treatment centres were beginning to come under pressure from addicts from other parts of the Home Counties where, as the Council's 1982 report *Treatment and rehabilitation* was to note,[57] there was 'little enthusiasm for providing services for such an unpopular group of patients'. Could it be, as Strang[58] suggested, that:

> After the initial excitement of the introduction of the new drug services and the considerable success with which addicts had been attracted into the clinics, there came about a gradual realization of the cumulative enormity of the problem being tackled.

Or is a more likely explanation to be found in Trebach's[59] suggestion that it was the doubts British doctors had always entertained about 'the basic "rightness" of legal heroin for young healthy addicts' which were to re-emerge in the 1970s? Furthermore, as he also pointed out, the Rolleston Committee's requirement that for the indefinitely prolonged administration of morphine or heroin an addict had to be capable of leading 'a fairly normal and useful life', was now being more narrowly interpreted as a requirement for a satisfactory work record, which effectively disqualified all but a few of the new generation of heroin addicts.

Despite the numerous attempts to rationalise the changes to a rigid, inflexible prescribing policy of oral methadone and a more 'confrontational' and 'contract-oriented' treatment response, there will always remain the strong suspicion that this approach, which met the personal, moral and ethical views, and prejudices, of a few senior consultants, was the 'already formulated clinical opinion' upon which the changes were based. What has not been conceded is that the changes were in effect, a tacit admission of the failure, not of the fundamental ethos of the Brain proposals, but of the manner in which those proposals were interpreted and implemented.

The enthusiastic replacement of injectable heroin with injectable methadone and the setting, in some centres, of a maximum daily dosage of oral methadone for all patients, are examples of the assumption that all addicts have identical needs and problems which can be met by a standard clinical response. Why addicts alone, of all patients, should be singled out for such treatment has never been satisfactorily explained. In 1994 uniformity of treatment was being pursued with even more vigour by some psychiatrists,[60] the intellectual descendants of those who, in the mid-1970s, were intent on denying the exercise of the clinical freedom inherent in the 'British system'.

# 12

# Grey and black markets: barbiturates, Diconal, Ritalin and heroin

In 1965 I predicted that a reduction in the prescribing of pharmaceutical heroin to addicts might lead to the development of American-style illicit traffic unless a synthetic drug capable of producing the same degree of euphoria as heroin found favour. The first such drug was Methedrine, introduced by Dr Petro, which, with the assistance of the manufacturers, had disappeared from the grey market by the end of 1968 but not before it had introduced the hypodermic needle to a new population of drug misusers who had not existed in 1967 when the plans to provide outpatient treatment facilities for heroin and cocaine addicts were being drawn up.

In late 1968, around the same time as the appearance of primary methadone addicts, as a result of the generous prescribing of the treatment centres, the intravenous use of barbiturates by established heroin addicts emerged, particularly in London. In 1969 and 1970 dipipanone (Diconal) and methylphenidate (Ritalin) were discovered by addicts, and the ease with which they could be obtained from gullible doctors created considerable control problems.

## Intravenous barbiturate use

A proposal to include barbiturates under the Drugs (Prevention of Misuse) Act 1964 was considered but dropped in view of their extensive medical use and the opposition of the pharmaceutical industry, because the police did not regard barbiturate misuse as a serious problem, and because of Home Office concern about the difficulty of knowing where to draw the line with regard to other sedatives.

Hewetson and Ollendorff had reported extensive oral use of Nembutal (pentobarbitone) by the London addicts they saw in the early 1960s,[1] and by 1969, with the decreasing prescribing of heroin and the unpopularity of methadone, addicts' attention began to turn to the injection of Nembutal and Tuinal (quinalbarbitone). Of 65 London heroin addicts interviewed by Mitcheson and colleagues in a three-month period in 1969, 80% admitted injecting barbiturates at some time.[2] The drugs were easily obtained from general practitioners and by thefts from the manufacturers and pharmacies.

In addition to the normal hazards attendant on the all-too-often non-sterile use of hypodermic syringes, the intravenous injection of barbiturates in preparations intended for oral administration brought a much greater incidence of abscesses and infections, frequently resulting in gangrene, amputations and death. The voluntary agencies and the casualty departments of the central London hospitals were hard-pressed to cope with the increasing numbers of barbiturate injectors requiring help which could not be provided by the newly established drug treatment centres. Mitcheson[3] noted that this 'eventually resulted in the Department of Health funding a short-stay residential crisis intervention centre in London – known as City Roads'. However, what he did not make clear was that 'eventually' meant almost a decade later, in 1978.

By early 1970 there was mounting pressure for more effective controls over the availability of barbiturates, then subject only to the limited 'prescription only' restrictions of the Poisons Rules. The Poisons Board had been consulted about the problem but after taking soundings from a number of police forces about the scale of the misuse, concluded it was a matter which fell more appropriately within the ambit of the Advisory Committee on Drug Dependence.

A possible solution seemed at hand – the inclusion of barbiturates under the provisions of the Misuse of Drugs Bill, which was about to start its passage through Parliament – but when it was discussed on 25 February 1970 the Home Secretary explained that he did not at this stage propose to add them to the list of drugs to be controlled under the Bill.[4] He said the (still) wide medical use of barbiturates made the effective prevention of intravenous use very difficult to achieve and he therefore proposed to seek the advice of the Advisory Committee on Drug Dependence.

The London treatment centre consultants added their voices to the demands for strengthening the control of barbiturates. They wrote to the Home Secretary and also to the *British Medical Journal*[5] where they expressed their opinion that the intravenous injection of barbiturates now presented 'a problem as serious as any in the field of drug abuse among young people'. They urged that the medical profession be alerted to the dangers of prescribing habit-forming sedatives and stimulants of any kind to young people. Another letter to the Home Secretary, and to the *British Medical Journal* on 4 April 1970, asking for greater control over the availability of barbiturates came from Dr Elizabeth Tylden and Dr Christine Saville[6] working at the treatment centre at University College Hospital. Over 40 patients were co-signatories to their letter, a number of whom had 'lost friends as a result of the intravenous injection of Nembutal or Tuinal'.

In June 1970, following the request from the Home Secretary for advice on the new development, the Advisory Committee on Drug Dependence appointed a sub-committee to consider what action might be taken, although there was a general feeling that barbiturate misuse was not capable of a quick solution. In December 1970 the Advisory Committee accepted the recommendations of the sub-committee that barbiturates should be subject to a measure of control under the proposed new legislation and that the profession should take urgent steps to educate doctors in the use of psychotropic drugs and the treatment of drug dependence. But this firm recommendation was not implemented, even though there was support within the medical profession when in July 1971 the British Medical Association's Annual Representative Meeting carried a motion proposing that barbiturates should be added to the drugs covered by the new legislation.[7] Instead, the argument which had first surfaced during the discussions in 1964 about amphetamine misuse, that because these drugs were so widely used in medical practice the dangerous drug controls would place an intolerable burden on doctors and pharmacists, won the day.

The fact that barbiturates were being prescribed 'widely' does not mean that they were always being prescribed wisely. Over the years two good, if non-scientific, indicators of the therapeutic indispensability of a drug have been, first, the reaction of the manufacturers when control under the Dangerous Drugs Act was proposed, and, second, and not entirely unconnected, the noticeable decline in its prescribing which often followed its rescheduling as a dangerous drug. Rescheduling imposes no limitation on a doctor's clinical freedom to prescribe a drug nor does it have any effect on its therapeutic value; the only consequence is to impose some clerical obligations, such as requiring the prescription to take a particular form. But rescheduling also brings to the doctor's attention the fact that he or she is proposing to provide a dangerous drug ('controlled drug' under the Misuse of Drugs Act 1971), allowing the possibility of then prescribing an alternative.

The more stringent requirements of the Misuse of Drugs Act Regulations, under which, unless they had a special exemption, doctors had to complete every controlled drug prescription in their own handwriting, could have an even greater effect, as was seen after methaqualone (Mandrax) became a controlled drug in 1971. As the number of prescriptions for Mandrax diminished so did its misuse, which had been a limited problem in some areas since 1967. It is therefore not entirely fanciful to suggest that if the nettle had been firmly grasped in 1970, and barbiturates brought within the scope of the new legislation, much of the damage which their misuse caused in the 15 years before this eventually had to be done, in 1985, would have been averted. Not only would much of the therapeutically doubtful prescribing have ceased, with the consequent effect of reducing the stocks pharmacies needed to hold and thereby reducing the risk of thefts, but it would have been possible, under the new provisions of the 1971 Act, to deal swiftly with any doctor prescribing them 'in an irresponsible manner'.

But other counsels prevailed, barbiturate misuse continued and there were soon indications that it was spreading around the country. In June 1973 Lady Wootton told the newly appointed Advisory Council on the Misuse of Drugs that police officers from Manchester, South Wales and Thames Valley had expressed concern about the misuse of these drugs to her working group on the social and personal aspects of drug misuse. This trend was reflected in the assessments of the national drug misuse situation in 1973 and 1974 presented to the Council by the Drugs Inspectorate. In 1973 most police forces reported an increase in the oral use of barbiturates (often taken with alcohol) with intravenous use coming to notice in a few areas, mainly in the north of England, but by 1974 about a fifth of police forces were reporting some degree of intravenous use.

## The Campaign on the Use and Restriction of Barbiturates

The Advisory Council's response was to initiate, in September 1975, a two-year Campaign on the Use and Restriction of Barbiturates (CURB). This had two main aims: to persuade doctors to curtail their prescribing of these preparations and to warn the public of their dangers, particularly when they were used regularly for the relief of insomnia. As an effective response to the barbiturate-injecting problem, CURB was a singularly futile exercise, which merely postponed the day when realistic controls would have to be imposed. It was most effective where it was least needed, with conscientious doctors having one or two middle-aged insomniacs who had been long-term recipients of barbiturate prescriptions now being transferred to one of the benzodiazepine group of drugs. But CURB had little success with those doctors, often elderly and working single-handed and therefore particularly vulnerable, who did not attend medical meetings, read the medical journals or pay much heed to official circulars, or whose prescribing was motivated by financial, rather than therapeutic considerations. As was only too clear, from past experience, it did not require many such doctors to ensure there were sufficient supplies to meet any likely demand.

The predictable result of the CURB campaign was that while there was some reduction in the general level of barbiturate prescribing, the availability of these drugs to the drug-misusing population was hardly affected. Nembutal and Tuinal continued to be prescribed virtually on demand by some doctors, and in one or two instances on a Petro-like scale, with additional quantities coming from burglaries of pharmacies, where, as had previously been the case with amphetamines, no special security precautions were required.

By 1978 the Advisory Council was satisfied that, as a result of the CURB campaign, there was now a more favourable climate of opinion within the medical profession for the acceptance of control of barbiturate preparations under the Misuse of Drugs Act, and consultations began with the various professional and other interests about the appropriate regime of control to be imposed. There was by now another important consideration. Since 1966 the United Nations (UN) Commission on Narcotic Drugs had been examining the possibility of extending international control to substances such as amphetamines and LSD, and international pressure was mounting for a new convention to deal with the wide range of psychotropic drugs developed since controls over the narcotics were first introduced. It was therefore probable that, if only in the interests of international co-operation against drug misuse, the United Kingdom (UK) would be forced to introduce a measure of control over a number of drugs for which it had hitherto been felt unnecessary.

The UN Convention on Psychotropic Substances 1971 was ratified by the UK and came into force in 1984. On 1 January 1985, almost 15 years after the firm recommendation of the Advisory Committee on Drug Dependence, 'any 5,5 disubstituted barbituric acid' and their various salts and preparations became controlled under the Misuse of Drugs Act (an exemption from the handwriting requirements for prescriptions for phenobarbitone, used in the treatment of epilepsy, was provided). The delay in taking the step of bringing barbiturates under control made nonsense of the claims made when the Misuse of Drugs Bill was under Parliamentary scrutiny, that its main virtue would be that it would allow a swift response to rapidly changing fashions in drug misuse. It also demonstrates the pointlessness of having flexible legislative machinery if the will to use it is lacking.

## Diconal

Diconal (dipipanone), a synthetic analgesic developed by Burroughs Wellcome & Co., was first brought under the control of the Dangerous Drugs Act in November 1954. Dipipanone had originally been marketed as a 25mgm injection but one of its side effects was found to be an unacceptably high level of vomiting. An oral preparation, Pipadone Co, containing 25mgm dipipanone and 50mgm cyclizine (an anti-nausea drug commonly used in travel sickness preparations) was developed and introduced in 1961. This was soon found to be too potent and was replaced with another formulation, Diconal, an oral tablet containing 10mgm of dipipanone in combination with 30mgm cyclizine. The British National Formulary describes moderate to severe pain as the indication for prescribing it.

It is ironic that the pharmacologist responsible for this new preparation was Dr Denis Cahal, who in the 1970s was the Senior Principal Medical Officer at the Department of Health with responsibility for drug dependency matters. In 1977 Cahal, who had investigated dipipanone's analgesic activity some years earlier, sent the Inspectorate unpublished extracts from his MD thesis, which he said contained probably 'the most complete account of the development of Diconal in existence', and at the same time confirmed that 'this confounded preparation' had been his brain-child.

However, unlike some of the post-war analgesics such as pethidine, which for a short period both before and following its control on 1 January 1947 was popular with the small group of older heroin addicts in the West End of London, and been the most favoured drug of addicts in the medical and para-medical professions, Diconal showed no immediate signs of being attractive to the addict population. The few addicts who did come to Home Office notice had invariably become addicted through receiving the drug for the relief of pain from some organic condition, with the first appearing in 1959. For the decade from 1963 to 1973, the average annual number of known Diconal addicts, who often also received other drugs such as methadone or pethidine, was just under 40. But this was soon to change.

The first hint of Diconal misuse came from a report in the *Portsmouth Evening News* on 17 February 1968 that it had been mentioned at an inquest in Portsmouth into the death of a 21-year-old man who had also been taking Romilar (dextromethorphan) tablets, which the police told the coroner were then popular with local teenagers. Romilar had been prescribed to the deceased by a local general practitioner who felt it was better he should take it than heroin, and had also prescribed him Diconal because he claimed to have toothache.

It was not long before Diconal had become an established feature of the drug scene in Portsmouth, where the drug squad had a well-deserved reputation for being quick to detect new drug misuse trends. Using the pretext that they were suffering from backache or dysmenorrhoea, the local addicts found little difficulty in obtaining prescriptions from Dr Brennan, an elderly Irish practitioner, who would have been an ideal candidate for the tribunal procedures for dealing with 'irresponsible prescribing' included in the 1971 Act. But as these did not come into operation until July 1973 there was little the Drugs Inspectorate could do except try to persuade him to be more circumspect in his prescribing. After I 'had a word' with Brennan he decided to have nothing further to do with addicts.

But this did not solve the problem. Addicts, now often claiming to be temporary residents, quickly found other willing prescribers in Portsmouth and in other parts of Hampshire. In April 1973 the local Medical Committee drew the attention of all doctors in the area to the popularity of Diconal as a drug of misuse and prescriptions for it decreased significantly. This was not the end of the problem as addicts simply travelled farther afield, to Luton and London, where they had little difficulty in finding other gullible prescribers. In 1974 the Portsmouth illicit market received a welcome boost when, because of lax security in the dispensary, a young female assistant in a large pharmacy in the area was able over a short period to steal some 2,000 tablets which she passed on to her boy friend for sale at £3 a tablet.

Further along the coast, another elderly doctor, Dr North, was also contributing to the growing popularity of Diconal. North had already come to notice in 1968 in respect of his prescribing of methadone to addicts who were also attending the local treatment centre and to others who came down from London to see him. By 1971 he was prescribing Diconal to patients again including some who were also attending the treatment centre, as well as others from farther afield.

Moreover, it was not unknown for addicts to visit him twice on the same day and receive a prescription on each occasion. When he was seen by a member of the Drugs Inspectorate he maintained none of his patients were addicts and there was always a valid medical reason, more often than not backache, when he prescribed Diconal. Fortunately the police were able to prosecute some of his patients, which led to his conduct being criticised by both the court and defending lawyers. As a result he successfully applied to the General Medical Council for the voluntary removal of his name from the Medical Register.

In the meantime, a small number of people addicted to Diconal were notified in 1970 by the treatment centre in Doncaster. Enquiries revealed that although there had been some misuse of this drug in the area, the patients concerned had been prescribed it as a means of weaning them off opiates. The consultant had tried a number of other oral preparations before deciding that Diconal was the most effective alternative, although he had found it necessary to increase dosages as tolerance developed. Information from the local drug squad showed that the addicts shared the consultant's view that Diconal was an effective substitute for heroin, especially when the tablets were crushed and injected, and within a short time it became fairly freely available on the local illicit market. Some of these supplies had undoubtedly come from prescriptions issued by one general practitioner but, following the death of one of his patients, and the unwelcome publicity this received, he withdrew from the scene.

The misuse of Diconal was also becoming a problem in the Republic of Ireland. In January 1972 Detective Sergeant Dennis Mullins of the Garda Siochana, on a visit to London, told me there had been a recent dramatic four-to-fivefold increase in the number of regular Diconal users. This he attributed partly to the activities of a few 'rogue' doctors and partly to 'a lot of movement between England and the Republic' (whether Dr Brennan was one of the common factors, as had been alleged, was never established). The situation had become so serious that the manufacturers agreed to a temporary freeze on general sales of Diconal to the Republic, one consequence of which was the increased movement of addicts across the border in the hope they would be able to have their prescriptions dispensed in Northern Ireland. (An account of the Irish Diconal epidemic by Dr Michael Kelly, the consultant in charge of the Jervis Street Drug Addiction and Treatment Centre, appeared in the *Journal of the Irish Medical Association* on 19 August 1972.)

The methods used in both countries to obtain supplies of Diconal were very similar. Addicts showed an uncanny instinct in identifying susceptible, usually elderly, doctors who were not familiar with the dependence-producing potential of the drug and who could be persuaded to prescribe it on the pretext of some obscure backache or other orthopaedic problem or dysmenorrhoea. Occasionally these claims would be supported by bogus letters purporting to be from their previous doctors, whom the new prescribers made no attempt to contact. The most enterprising of these were undoubtedly the dozen or so letters from a non-existent 'David Mirton, S.M.O., Home Department', written on the genuine notepaper of the Secretary of State. These appeared in 1981 and requested that Diconal be pre-scribed for a man who had recently been medically discharged from the army as a consequence of the severe injuries he sustained when the armoured car in which he was travelling was blown up by a landmine in Northern Ireland. Unfortunately for the addict, one of the doctors approached was a neighbour of the then Home Secretary, William Whitelaw, and he passed the letter proffered to him to Mrs Whitelaw. In due course two men were arrested but the police were never able to disprove their claim that they had found the notepaper in a squat.

Forged prescriptions and thefts from pharmacies also contributed signifi-cantly to the increasing general availability of Diconal. This was soon to be re-flected in the Home Office addict statistics, which showed the number of newly notified Diconal addicts steadily increasing, from 52 in 1973 to 627 in 1982, then dropping to 539 in 1983. As many of the prescribers did not realise they were deal-ing with addicts, and/or were unfamiliar with the Notification Regulations, these numbers were an even less reliable indicator of the extent of Diconal addiction than the addict statistics were of addiction to other notifiable drugs. The increased use of Diconal was also shown in the drug offender statistics, with the number of offenders dealt with increasing from 198 in 1973, peaking at 566 in 1982 and falling to 370 in 1983.

The Advisory Council on the Misuse of Drugs was first alerted to growing in-terest in Diconal at its meeting in June 1974, when Charles Jeffery presented the In-spectorate's drug misuse situation report. This provoked little response, apart from an enquiry from one member whether there was any link with the Diconal problem in the Republic of Ireland, and an incorrect comment from another, a general practitioner, that as the controls on Diconal had only been in force since 1 July 1973, doctors were gradually 'becoming educated'.

By 1974 there were clear signs that Diconal misuse was becoming a very serious problem. Not only was the injection of crushed tablets attended by similar physi-cal damage to that which had attracted such concern at the time of the barbiturate injecting epidemic in 1969, but the press had not been slow to tell those (few) ad-dicts who did not already know, that Diconal was a satisfactory heroin substitute. In December 1975 I submitted an internal report reviewing the current situation: black market prices ranged from 5p a tablet, indicating an abundant local supply, to £3, and many of those involved were drug misusers already well known to their local drug squads, if not to the Home Office as notified addicts. There were also many addicts who were attending treatment centres and using Diconal to supple-ment their prescribed supplies of methadone.

The Advisory Council's Technical sub-committee considered Diconal at their meeting in January 1976. Apart from showing a preference for some sort of publicity campaign to alert doctors to the popularity of the preparation with drug misusers and recognising the need to keep the full Council informed of the current state of affairs, the sub-committee decided to keep the matter 'under review'. At their next meeting, in May 1976, Jeffery reported that the Inspectorate was still receiving reports of increasing Diconal misuse. He was supported by Dr Ian Pierce James, who, in a comment on the Bristol drug scene, which he amplified at the full Council meeting the following month, said that Diconal was now probably the drug of first choice for street addicts. He referred the Council to a study shortly to be published showing that Diconal was the main target of pharmacy thefts in the Bristol area, averaging about one a week in 1975, although he was careful not to draw any link between this and the non-prescribing policy being following by the local treatment centre.[8]

The general feeling of the Advisory Council was that the best way of tackling this problem was by ensuring prescribers knew of the appeal of Diconal to drug misusers, although this would not be possible within the CURB remit. Nor, as Cahal explained on behalf of the Department of Health, would it be possible to send a letter to every doctor as there was insufficient prescribing of Diconal to justify such a course. The Council agreed to continue to keep the situation 'under review'.

The Technical sub-committee did not meet again until July 1977 when I told them that the Inspectorate's intelligence left no doubt Diconal misuse was increasing rapidly, although it was difficult to assess the full scale of the problem. Their reaction on this occasion was that while a complete ban was out of the question because the preparation had a valuable therapeutic role, it might be possible to alert practitioners to its abuse potential by means of an appropriate entry in the next edition of the *British National Formulary*. (In due course the Secretary contacted the Joint Formulary Committee, but the initiative came to nothing because of the uncertainty then existing over the future of the *Formulary*.) At the next meeting of the Advisory Council, in October 1977, the Inspectorate once more stressed both our concern and that of the police at the relentless increase in the misuse of this drug. The Technical sub-committee was formally asked to examine the problem and to consider whether education or more stringent controls could provide a solution.

In January 1978 the Technical sub-committee agreed with advice from the Ministry of Health that the medical profession would not take kindly to any further restrictions unless 'a strong case' was presented, and made the suggestion that the manufacturer's sales representatives might be used to alert practitioners to the misuse potential of Diconal. This, in due course, received the full and willing co-operation of the manufacturers. Accordingly, at their next meeting in April 1978, the Advisory Council was told that in the Technical sub-committee's opinion the choice appeared to lie between educating the medical profession about the dangers of Diconal or imposing additional controls. However, it was felt that both would be premature, and a firm recommendation from the sub-committee was promised for the Council's autumn meeting. Unfortunately this promise could not be fulfilled as other more urgent work on the general review of the classification of drugs included in Schedule 2 to the Misuse of Drugs Act intervened.

At its October 1978 meeting, the Council still had no firm proposals before them for tackling the Diconal problem. I told the Council that misuse of Diconal was continuing to spread and was now to be found in all areas where there were injecting drug misusers, many of whom were said to prefer it to heroin. (When he told me in 1972 about the Diconal problem in Ireland, Detective Sergeant Mullins had said 'after a few fixes the addicts go crazy for this drug'. More recently a former addict recalled to me that when swallowed Diconal was 'no great shakes' but when injected gave the user a 'rush' which many regarded as possibly the greatest physical experience available to humans.) The problem was particularly severe in London and the Home Counties, on the south coast, and in a number of provincial cities.

An indication of the popularity of Diconal was provided by surveys of the contents of syringes submitted by the police to forensic science laboratories. These consistently showed that nearly 40% of syringes had contained dipipanone, either alone or in combination with other drugs, the corresponding figures for barbiturates and heroin being 20% and 10% respectively, although by 1979 the latter had almost doubled. The major source continued to be legitimate prescriptions, but forged prescriptions and thefts from pharmacies were also important sources and in 1981 over 60,000 tablets were stolen in a series of successful raids on wholesalers premises, mainly in south-east England. But Diconal prescribed, or otherwise acquired, in one area was not necessarily used there and addicts from many parts of the country where treatment facilities were inadequate, or unattractive, travelled to London to obtain it.

Following my 1978 updating of the situation, the Council decided that some action was needed to reduce the 'foolish and irresponsible' prescribing which was clearly to blame for the ready availability of Diconal to addicts, without at the same time interfering with its legitimate use. The Technical sub-committee was therefore again asked to consider the matter before the Council's next meeting in April 1979.

In January 1979 the sub-committee concluded there should be a government-backed education campaign directed at doctors and pharmacists and that there was an 'a priori' case for asking the Council's Legal and Administrative working group to look into the possibility of adding dipipanone to the Schedule to the Misuse of Drugs (Notification of and Supply to Addicts) Regulations 1973. However, there was no consensus for this latter proposal, with one medical member expressing his opinion that any tightening of control was likely to be 'a waste of time' as there was no evidence that Diconal was being prescribed to addicts. In fact, by 1978 the 'temporary resident with backache' approach had been largely abandoned and addicts were frankly admitting their addiction and asking doctors for Diconal as the drug which suited them best and which, they claimed, they were unable to obtain from the treatment centres.

The failure to reach a consensus was reported to the Council in April 1979 and the Technical sub-committee were yet again asked to take the matter away for further study. In the meantime the Council invited the Department of Health to discuss with the British Medical Association the possibility of mounting an education campaign to bring the dangers of Diconal to wider attention. This further reference back to the Technical sub-committee resulted in a firm recommendation to the October 1979 Council meeting that the matter should be referred to its Legal and Administrative working group to consider bringing dipipanone under the same prescribing restrictions as currently applied to heroin and cocaine. But the working group declined to accept the invitation and the saga was to continue for another five years.

A proposal that dipipanone should be more tightly controlled finally emerged in the Council's report on treatment and rehabilitation published in 1982.[9] As they knew their proposal would now have to be considered by the working group, they added a recommendation, made perhaps with a collective tongue in cheek, that this should be done 'as a matter of urgency'. Dipipanone was eventually added to the Schedule to the Misuse of Drugs (Notification of and Supply to Addicts) Regulations 1973 with effect from 1 April 1984 – fourteen years after the Inspectorate and the police had expressed concern about its misuse.

What was happening on the street while the Advisory Council was shilly-shallying? The addicts' claim that Diconal was not available to them from the treatment centres was largely true, especially in the London area, where the consultants were first alerted to the problem in November 1977. They were told by one of their number that prices currently ranged from £1 a tablet in Piccadilly, to five tablets for £1 in Battersea. This disclosure prompted them to draw attention to the dangers of Diconal in a letter to the *British Medical Journal* on 6 May 1978.[10] Strangely though, there was no mention whatsoever of the particular problems caused by Diconal in the guidelines they had commended and which were published by Dr Thomas Bewley in the Journal in August 1980.[11]

A few provincial treatment centre consultants, however, were prepared to prescribe Diconal to addicts, with one taking the view that it was best initially to prescribe the drug the addict was taking at their first attendance. Some of this prescribing was unduly generous and for a time one consultant was viewed by our Northern Region Inspectorate as a potential 'irresponsible prescriber', who might have to be referred to a tribunal. In Cheltenham, Dr Jeffrey Marks introduced a special preparation of Diconal, similar to the widely used oral methadone mixture, which proved to have 'considerable advantages over any other opiate preparation currently being prescribed to maintain addicts' and was a major factor in containing the Diconal problem in the area, as the local drug squad confirmed. Yet, although he described his results in a letter to the *British Medical Journal* on 1 May 1982,[12] this encouraging development aroused little interest elsewhere.

Towards the end of 1982 there were the first signs that the Diconal problem had peaked and the number of new notifications dropped in 1983, no doubt in part due to the impending tightening of the controls and to the publicity given to action taken by the Inspectorate and the General Medical Council against a number of 'irresponsible' and 'non *bona fide*' prescribers. But much more importantly, as a Drugs Inspector reported from our northern region, there was 'so much illicit heroin available that users can satisfy their addiction without breaking into pharmacies or stealing and forging prescriptions', or by pestering doctors now much more alert to the abuse potential of Diconal. The implementation of the Advisory Council's recommendation on 1 April 1984 virtually removed Diconal from the illicit market, although inevitably there were a few doctors who continued to prescribe it to addicts after that date, professing they were unaware of the new restrictions.

The abysmal failure of the Advisory Council to deal more speedily with the Diconal problem despite being kept fully aware of the seriousness of the situation had a considerable cost, resulting in increases in the addict population, and in the deaths and physical complications so reminiscent of the barbiturate injecting epidemic of the late 1960s. As a former Merseyside addict recently recalled, 'the scene was littered with injectors with limbs missing'.

The Council's failure also placed an unwelcome and unnecessary strain on the Inspectorate's already over-stretched resources, as we were forced to spend much time and effort 'chasing' those doctors who had been persuaded, duped, occasionally frightened and physically assaulted, and in a few instances financially attracted, into prescribing Diconal. Fortunately, many of the more doubtful prescribers were quickly brought to our notice, by the police, pharmacists, street agencies or sometimes, surprisingly, by addicts concerned about the willingness of some doctors to prescribe for anyone approaching them.

These doubtful prescribers would have been far fewer in number, and much easier to deal with, had the restrictions been imposed years earlier. Yet paradoxically, it could be argued that the delay may have been beneficial. It has always been my view that one of the reasons why the increasing use of illicit heroin, apparent in many Western European countries in the early 1970s, was not immediately mirrored to the same extent in the UK was the ready availability and acceptability of Diconal to our addict population. It could be obtained without too much difficulty from legitimate sources by addicts who knew their way around the medical/pharmaceutical world and who therefore had much less need to become customers of an entirely illicit market.

If Diconal was no longer a serious problem by 1986, it did not disappear entirely with the discovery that it apparently still had an appeal to drug misusers in 1988.[13]

## Ritalin

Another drug to find favour as a substitute for the diminishing supply of prescribed pharmaceutical heroin was methylphenidate, in the proprietary form of Ritalin. The Drugs Inspectorate knew from the March 1968 issue of *Microgram*, a technical publication of the then United States Bureau of Narcotics and Dangerous Drugs, that Ritalin had been popular for some time with heroin addicts in the United States, as it appeared both to reduce the amount of heroin they needed to produce the desired effect and to extend its duration. It was reported to give a 'flash' similar to that of amphetamines when injected and was a useful drug for minimising withdrawal distress in times of heroin shortage.

In 1968, when the Methedrine epidemic was at its peak, it had largely escaped notice that Ritalin was also available in injectable form. However, anticipating this product might receive similar unwelcome attention, the manufacturers, Ciba, immediately decided that supplies of Ritalin injections should similarly be restricted to hospital pharmacies. Ciba's responsible action ensured that Ritalin injections did not replace Methedrine in the addicts' affections.

A less academic description of the effect of the informal controls on Methedrine appeared a year later, in the 5–17 December 1969 issue of *International Times*, an invaluable if not always reliable and unbiased, 'underground' publication of the day. According to the *International Times*, one of the results of Methedrine being 'taken off the market' was to force 'speed freaks':

> … to use junk or to take speed in the diluted form of ritalin, dex, blues and other tablets which must be reduced to a fixable solution by grinding to powder and adding water. Among the available 'speed' pills, ritalin is probably the most innocuous (and thus only used as a last resort) but things are desperate indeed for the speedos nowadays, and ritalin has been used in great quantities, which is why the medical big-wigs are freaking out.

The *International Times* reference to Ritalin is important as the oral version, a tablet containing 10mgm methylphenidate, was to cause us considerable problems for several years. In July 1970 one of the central London hospitals began to see increasing numbers of Ritalin users in their casualty department for the treatment of infections resulting from the injection of the crushed tablets. Thereafter there were other indications that Ritalin was becoming an established feature of the London injecting drug scene, although there was less evidence of its misuse being a problem elsewhere. As with Diconal, it could be obtained with very little difficulty from doctors whose awareness of, or concern about, its potential for misuse were minimal and whose prescribing could not be dealt with under the, as yet, non-operative tribunal provisions of the Misuse of Drugs Act 1971. Once more the Drugs Inspectorate was forced to rely, with varying degrees of success, on our ability to persuade a doctor to exercise more caution, and common sense, before prescribing Ritalin to a 'casual' patient.

Fortunately by this time the General Medical Council was showing a greater willingness to deal with doctors' prescribing 'other than in the course of *bona fide* treatment' and was now prepared to consider cases referred by the Home Office. As a result, enquiries by the Inspectorate in 1972 led to two of the most prolific prescribers of Ritalin appearing before the Council's Disciplinary Committee.

The removal of these two sources of Ritalin tablets in London did have a temporary effect on its availability but there remained a considerable demand until later in the decade when illicitly manufactured amphetamine appeared on the scene. The existence of a continuing market for Ritalin was well illustrated by the case of Toby Ann Cathro, who was arrested by the Metropolitan Police in June 1977. Cathro, an American, was the 'master-mind' of a small group, who, over a fairly short period, obtained Ritalin prescriptions, some for as many as 250 tablets, from around 200 doctors, nearly half of whom practised in the Harley Street/West End areas. The gang, using over 20 different aliases and giving a variety of reasons for needing Ritalin, would often visit seven or eight doctors a day and then sell the tablets prescribed for them for £1 each around the Piccadilly area, as reported in *Sunday Telegraph* newspaper on 7 August 1977. Cathro was sentenced to seven years' imprisonment but this was reduced on appeal to four years, with Lord Justice Shaw expressing his considerable disquiet that 'reputable doctors of experience' could so easily be imposed upon, and deceived time and again into giving her prescriptions for Ritalin.[14]

## Illicitly imported amphetamine, cocaine and heroin

At the meeting of the Advisory Council in June 1974 the Drugs Inspectorate presented for the first time their assessment of the drug misuse situation for the previous year. This, and subsequent annual assessments, placed greater emphasis on the subjective impressions of those working close to the drug problem with whom we liaised, including police drug squad officers, treatment centre staff, social workers, street agencies and the occasional misuser, than on the Home Office statistics of notifications of addicts, drug seizures and drug offenders. These statistics were already a year out of date when published, and until the 1980s were not accompanied by much interpretation.

We noted that in 1973 there had been a reappearance of cocaine, which by then was prescribed only exceptionally by the treatment centres. Because of its high cost, cocaine was being used by 'snorting' and by a different clientele from the injecting addicts of the 1960s, gaining popularity especially in social circles where there was 'champagne, style and money'.[15]

In 1975 the most significant development, reported to the Council at their June 1976 meeting, was the appearance of illicitly manufactured amphetamine powder which was being both injected intravenously and sniffed. It was to become popular as 'the poor man's cocaine' and was possibly a reason why the frequently predicted explosion in cocaine use was so long delayed.[16] Since the reduction in the prescribing of amphetamine tablets, following the British Medical Association's earlier initiative,[17] there had been a growing market in illicitly made tablets imported from the continent, but in 1974 the Metropolitan Police discovered a 16-punch rotary tablet machine operating in south London. The advent of illicit drug manufacture in this country added a new dimension to enforcement problems.

There were also worrying signs on the international front of increased production of opium and hence of heroin. At a meeting of the heads of European drug enforcement agencies, held in Thailand in July 1976, there was concern about the excess quantities of illicit opium available in South-East Asia, and the possibility that, as the US heroin market was being supplied from other sources, Europe might now become the target for illicit traffickers. Seizures of heroin in Europe were already running at several times their 1975 level and there had been an accompanying increase in the number of addicts. These developments were reported to the Advisory Council at their October 1976 meeting, in an addendum to the 1975 Inspectorate's report, together with the assessment that while there was no immediate crisis it would no longer be safe to assume that heroin seized by HM Customs was in transit, or to place as much reliance as hitherto on the notification statistics. The substance of this addendum was promptly reported in *The Times* newspaper on 19 October 1976, as a prediction from experts that 'heroin use may get out of control'.

By October 1977 there were distinct signs that the UK was providing a growing market for illicitly imported heroin. However, there was a considerable credibility gap between addicts' stories of its ready availability and the picture emerging from the seizure and prosecution statistics. Diconal remained the most popular substitute for heroin and for the injectable methadone no longer so readily available from the treatment centres. Amphetamine use had certainly increased during the past year, to an extent that in some police areas it was now said to rival cannabis both in popularity and availability.

When the Drugs Inspectorate took stock of the illicit heroin scene at the specially convened conference with the police in December 1977, there was little evidence of any significant heroin misuse outside south-east England but in 1978 there were persistent rumours of the availability of illicit heroin in other parts of the country. Few of these rumours could be confirmed, although in Edinburgh several samples of illicit heroin were submitted by the police to their forensic science laboratory for examination.

By 1978 there was also evidence of substantial heroin use among a growing Iranian community in London and some parts of the south-east. In 1979 just over 100 Iranian opium or heroin addicts were notified to the Home Office. Although this Iranian 'epidemic' was comparatively short-lived, and was linked to the political upheavals in their home country, it was an important development which probably laid the foundations of a fresh upsurge of heroin use soon to become a serious problem in a number of our inner-city areas. Most of the Iranian addicts smoked heroin, as, of course, did some of the more closely knit and well-established Chinese community, but the discovery by our heroin addicts of 'Chinese' heroin a decade or so earlier had not then resulted in 'chasing the dragon' becoming a popular practice.[18] For a time Iranian heroin made a significant contribution to our domestic illicit market[19] and British addicts were said to prefer it to Chinese variety, no doubt because it was usually of higher purity. It did, however, have the disadvantage that as it was the base drug it was necessary to dissolve it in lemon juice or vinegar before it could be injected.

At around the same time heroin sniffing was becoming popular at trendy parties held in some of the more affluent parts of West London.[20] A fair proportion of the party-goers were the children of the 'great and the good' and several were later notified to the Chief Medical Officer as heroin addicts.

As Roger Lewis commented,[21] the years 1978 to 1980 had a profound effect on heroin use in Britain and Western Europe when:

> Increased availability and falling prices filled existing demand, encouraged experimentation and generated new demand. There was a decline in subcultural taboos against heroin and a concurrent spread in consumption to provincial towns and cities.

The addict statistics clearly reflected the worsening situation. The number of new notified heroin addicts more than doubled from 511 in 1975 to 1,181 in 1980; and there was a dramatic increase in the number being notified by general practitioners and police surgeons, from 118 in 1975 (23% of new addicts) to 791 (48% of new addicts) in 1981. However, because of the known limitations of the statistics, it was more convenient in some quarters to interpret the increases as the result of greater awareness and observance by doctors of the requirements of the Notification Regulations.[22] If the number of new addicts was still not large, these increases, and the indication that more addicts than ever before were being notified from outside London and the Home Counties, were significant. Yet these warning signs of serious trouble ahead could not penetrate the cloud of complacency which had once more settled over the Home Office, the Department of Health, the Advisory Council on the Misuse of Drugs and the medical profession.

The release of the addict statistics for 1978, when 1,347 new addicts were notified – a 21% increase over 1977 – saw some recognition that there was an increased demand for opiates and a wide range of other psychotropic substances. In August 1979, commenting on the increases in the addict statistics, a leading article in *The Lancet*[23] shared the fear, which some had already expressed, that we might be 'on the brink of another drugs explosion' and went on to say:

> The experience of the past decade must be evaluated critically and used to plan purposely for the next ... The treatment of drug dependence has little emotional appeal or political muscle and that probably accounts for the fact that the service offered to currently notified addicts is worse now than it was in 1968.

*The Lancet*'s worries were echoed in two debates, in the House of Lords on 30 October 1979 and in the House of Commons on 21 December 1979. The first of these was initiated by the Earl of Denbigh, then Chairman of the Standing Conference on Drug Abuse (SCODA), who drew attention to 'an underestimated and growing problem', and to the inadequacy of the existing treatment and rehabilitation facilities, which were now threatened by the government's cuts in public expenditure.[24]

In an adjournment debate in the House of Commons[25] on 21 December 1979 Bernard Braine also referred to the increasing numbers of drug misusers, now drawn from all sections of the population, including 'well-known families', and to a recent prediction by David Turner, then director of SCODA, that the UK could now be on the brink of another heroin epidemic. Braine commented that the current large-scale illicit importation of drugs had not been foreseen and treatment centres were dealing with a small section of the addict population, with the rest dependent on the street market, which had an effect on crime and the quality of life in the inner cities.

While acknowledging that there were signs of a growing problem, government spokesmen (Lord Belstead in the House of Lords[26] and Timothy Raison in the House of Commons[27]) were careful to point out that a partial explanation for the increase in the number of known addicts lay in improved notification, following a special effort to remind doctors of their obligation to notify, and that it was estimated that 90% of the heroin seized in 1978 was destined for re-export. Both Houses could be assured the UK was playing a very active part in the work of the United Nations Commission on Narcotic Drugs, was contributing to the United Nations Fund for Drug Abuse Control, that the government was 'far from complacent', was 'watching the problem closely' and would 'consider most carefully the recommendations received from the Advisory Council on the Misuse of Drugs'. These anodyne comments could have come from the guide for ministerial speechwriters, which had been so well used by Kenneth Robinson's officials between 1965 and 1968. One positive response was announced, the decision, eventually implemented on 1 January 1985, to bring barbiturates within the controls of the Misuse of Drugs Act 1971 when certain practical problems involving the Forensic Science Service had been resolved.

To anyone familiar with the workings of an Advisory Council seemingly content to note or receive, rather than respond to, warnings of a rapidly deteriorating situation, the clear indication that the government was quite content to rely on the Council to fulfil its statutory duty to advise on measures needed to prevent drug misuse, or to deal with the social problems connected with such misuse, was depressing. Not only was the heroin addict population much greater that in the 1960s, there were now a number of sinister features which had not then been present. All of the fears entertained by those closely involved with the scene were to be confirmed over the next few years, yet Lord Belstead's hopes of receiving recommendations, or even a warning, from the Advisory Council, remained unfulfilled.

For the most part the annual situation reports by the Drugs Inspectorate to the Council were consigned to the black hole into which so much of the paper provided by the Council's hard-working secretariat also disappeared and prompted no warnings, or advice, to Ministers about the worsening situation. One or two members with first-hand experience of what was actually happening did endorse the picture the Inspectorate presented to the Council, and at the meeting in April 1979, at which the 1978 report was considered, David Turner suggested that the current situation, with the alarming increase in heroin misuse outside London, called for an urgent reappraisal of the national response to the problem.

## The increase in heroin misuse in the early 1980s

It was the marked deterioration in the overall situation in 1981 which prompted me to revive the practice of preparing a Drugs Inspectorate Annual Report and to warn that if present trends continued the problem would 'undoubtedly increasingly occupy the attention of Ministers'. The 44% rise in new notifications of heroin addicts in 1981 compared with 1980, from 1,151 to 1,660, could not now only be attributed to improved compliance by doctors with their statutory obligations. Subsequently the picture presented to the Advisory Council, and in the Inspectorate's internal reports, was one of increased availability of heroin and of increased extent of the misuse problem. Wagstaff and Maynard[28] estimated that illicit shipments to the UK in 1981 were between 760 and 1,770kgs of heroin, with a Customs interception rate of between 4.8% and 11.3%, while 1984 shipments were estimated at between 1,610 and 3,560kgs with interception rates of between 8.8% and 19.4%.

In some areas of the country there had been an almost explosive increase in heroin misuse since 1980, with Scotland and Merseyside particularly badly affected.[29] Although heroin was not unknown in some of these places, its use had hitherto been mainly associated with older injecting addicts who had returned home after experience of the London drug scene. Now there were abundant supplies of heroin which could be smoked and perhaps understandably, and not surprisingly, the practice of 'chasing the dragon' spread rapidly and, as Gilman and Pearson[30] commented:

> ... settled as just one more problem among the residents of 'multi-problem' estates – housing decay; unemployment; generalised poverty; multi-racial tension and conflict; crime and the fear of crime; lack of access to transport facilities and private cars; and lack of play facilities and other amenities.

But illicit heroin was not the only problem. From the Inspectorate's point of view there were two other unwelcome developments which confirmed that, in addition to the traditional spillage from prescriptions, both from the treatment centres and independent doctors, legitimate pharmaceutical outlets remained, and would always be, an important supplementary source of drugs to the black market. The first development was that, despite improved security measures introduced under the 1971 Act, thefts from retail pharmacies continued to cause problems, often in areas where treatment services were non-existent, inadequate or inflexible. The second development was the increase seen in 1981 in armed attacks on retail pharmacies together, with a number of attempted thefts from wholesale premises, mainly in the south of England. Six of these attempts, including an armed attack during working hours, were successful and in all some 63,000 tablets of Diconal, 20,000 ampoules of Physeptone (methadone), 16,000 ampoules of heroin, 800gms of heroin powder, 275gms of cocaine and 18,000 tablets of Ritalin were stolen. What was particularly worrying about this development was that these wholesaler attacks were clearly the work of professional criminals, providing further confirmation that drug trafficking, offering high profits for very low risk, was no longer a 'no go' area for our domestic criminals.

In January 1982 an editorial in *The Lancet* castigated the Advisory Council on the Misuse of Drugs for its failure to suggest a response to the worsening situation, suggesting that 'overwhelmed by the complexity of the matter, has itself succumbed to the hypnotic influence of Papaver somniferum'.[31] It was not until 1984 that the political profile of drug misuse was raised significantly when the government established an interdepartmental Ministerial Group on the Misuse of Drugs under the chairmanship of David Mellor, then the Parliamentary Under-Secretary of State at the Home Office with special responsibility for drugs. The departments represented on the Group, or which received papers, included the Home Office, the Department of Health and Social Security, HM Customs and Excise, the Department of Education and Science, the Foreign and Commonwealth Office, the Overseas Development Administration, the Department of the Environment, and the Welsh, Scottish and Northern Ireland Offices.

Its terms of reference required the Group 'to develop the government's strategy for combating the misuse of drugs of addiction and to oversee its implementation' with regard to 'the development of proposals for the more effective implementation of that strategy', 'priorities for the allocation and deployment of resources' and 'the arrangements within and outside government for the co-ordination, development and enforcement of the policy on drug misuse'.

With the twin objectives of reducing the supply and the demand for drugs, the Group 'developed a coherent strategy which attacks drug misuse by simultaneous action on five main fronts: reducing supplies from abroad, tightening controls on drugs produced and prescribed here, making policing even more effective, strengthening deterrence, and improving treatment and rehabilitation.' The details of the implementation of the strategy, with examples of 'successful initiatives' at home and abroad, and the amount of their funding, were published by the Home Office in *Tackling Drug Misuse: a summary of the government's strategy* in 1985, 1986 and 1988.

# 13

# Treatment guidelines and other prescribing safeguards

In 1975 the Advisory Council on the Misuse of Drugs set up a working group 'to undertake a comprehensive review of the treatment and rehabilitation services for drug misusers and to make recommendations for dealing both with immediate problems and the situation generally'.[1] The working group published its final report, *Treatment and rehabilitation,* in 1982. The recommendations of this report were to herald the end of the treatment centre era and the dominance of hospital-based treatment services by emphasising 'the need for a co-ordinated multidisciplinary approach' to treatment, which was no longer to be simply a matter of 'opioid prescribing versus non-opioid prescribing or injectable medication versus oral medication'.[2]

The report was a damning indictment of the consequences for drug misuse treatment services of the reorganisation of the National Health Service (NHS) in 1975 and the placing of responsibility for service provision with regional health authorities. It noted that the services were 'now less able than ever to cope with the problems of drug misuse'[3] because of the increasing number of people misusing drugs and inadequate funding both from regional authorities and central government. The treatment of drug misusers had rated a very low priority and the clear evidence of a worsening situation had failed to prompt any sense of urgency.

The report also noted that 'an increasing proportion of drug misusers is being treated ... by doctors in general practice (both NHS and private) and in other forms of private practice'. It was recognised that this was partly due to some misusers living at 'a considerable' distance from a hospital-based clinic but also because of 'profound differences in professional opinion on the prescribing of opioids'.[4]

Although primarily concerned with the provision of services, the report touched on a number of matters in which the Home Office had a direct interest. These were discussed in Chapter 7, under the heading 'Prescribing Safeguards', and included proposals for the more effective use of the tribunal machinery, the control of dipipanone (Diconal), the preparation of guidelines on good medical practice in the treatment of those who had been redefined as 'problem drug takers',[5] and the extension of the current prescribing restrictions to all opioid drugs.

These interrelated issues had already surfaced at meetings of the London treatment centre consultants who, by 1979, were expressing their grave disquiet about their loss of control over treatment practice, as shown by the increased prescribing of injectable methadone and other opioids such as Diconal by doctors working outside the centres both in and beyond the London area. This posed a serious threat to their oral methadone-only prescribing policy and to their hitherto unchallenged primacy in the treatment of heroin addiction. It is not over-fanciful to suggest that the more politically motivated and forceful members of the consultants' group saw in the Advisory Council's review of treatment services an opportunity to regain the influence they feared they were in danger of losing.

The elimination of both the independent doctor and the NHS general practitioner from the field became their primary objective, as it had been in the negotiations before 16 April 1968. Their success in persuading the Advisory Council that this was both a desirable and viable objective is shown by the inclusion of their proposals as firm recommendations in the final report and in the justification for these recommendations, which were little more than an elaboration of the consultants' views.[6]

The efforts of the London consultants to preserve their monopoly position took various forms. They not only put forward their suggestions to the Advisory Council's working group, but also trawled them in a number of contributions to the medical press, both before and after the Council's report was published. As I recall, when the proposal for formal prescribing guidelines was sent to the working group it was accompanied by a copy of Dr Thomas Bewley's paper, 'Prescribing psychoactive drugs to addicts', which appeared in the British Medical Journal in August 1980.[7] A draft of this paper, which had been discussed and agreed at earlier meetings of the consultants, offered elementary rather than detailed clinical advice to doctors unfamiliar with the ways and wiles of drug misusers, and was the first overt attack on the private prescribers.

In March 1983 The Lancet published a paper by Dr Hamid Ghodse entitled 'Treatment of drug addiction in London'.[8] Although he discussed frankly the inadequacies of the hospital treatment services, his message was quite clear: the 'frugal prescription of oral methadone' would keep the overspill of prescribed drugs to the illicit market to a minimum. Dr Ghodse justified this by the questionable statement that, although the oral methadone policy had been criticised on the grounds it forced addicts to seek other sources of the injectable drugs they preferred, there was 'no evidence to support this hypothesis'. He went on to say that some addicts 'are opting out of the clinic system in consulting private, independent doctors who ... will prescribe injectable opiates (usually methadone)'.

Yet a further distillation of the London treatment centres' experience appeared in a paper by Dr Philip Connell and Dr Martin Mitcheson in the British Medical Journal in March 1984.[9] They too referred to 'the liberality of prescribing by independent doctors' while acknowledging there had been criticism of 'the reluctance to prescribe by special clinics'. The publication of this paper coincided with the establishment by the Department of Health of the Medical Working Group on Drug Dependence (of which Connell was the Chairman) to prepare the guidelines recommended by the Advisory Council. The Group was also to consider the proposal to extend the licensing restrictions to all opioid drugs.

## The guidelines of good clinical practice

After six meetings of the Medical Working Group, between February and July 1984, the *Guidelines of good clinical practice in the treatment of drug misuse*[10] duly appeared. In October 1984 a copy was sent to every hospital doctor and general practitioner in England by the Department of Health with a covering letter from the Chief Medical Officer who endorsed:

> ... the hope that the guidelines will provide a useful background against which treatment plans for an individual patient can be drawn up, and a flexible framework within which doctors can continue to develop a constructive response to the problem of drug misuse.

There was little criticism of the guidelines in the medical press. The representatives of the NHS general practitioners who had attended the Conference which preceded the appointment of the Medical Working Group were more than content for psychiatry to take the lead. In my (last) annual report, for 1985, I commented:

> The hopes expressed in the *Guidelines of good clinical practice in the treatment of drug misuse,* that more general practitioners would become involved, have not been fulfilled and reports of unfeeling, unsympathetic responses to approaches by the worried families of addicts are still quite common. I know of one addict who visited 18 general practitioners seeking help; 16 were distinctly hostile whilst the other two would not offer any help. Such responses make a mockery of the guidelines.

This lack of interest by the non-specialist section of the medical profession, which should have been in the front line of the new response, was disappointing – especially in view of the impression given by the guidelines that all that was required for a successful 'treatment' outcome was a little counselling, support from an appropriate social agency and, if unavoidable, a short course of oral methadone. The relapsing nature of heroin dependence was not discussed in the guidelines, with the word 'relapse' appearing only once. No helpful advice was offered on the management of those long-term users who could not be persuaded to reduce their drug consumption and who were determined to continue to obtain drugs for intravenous use from legal or illegal sources or both. It was these 'treatment resistant' patients who were responsible for the therapeutic frustration in the treatment centres and for much of the pressure on elderly, gullible and naive general practitioners.

The issue of the official guidelines had important implications for the Home Office because their main purpose, as seen by the consultant who suggested their production in 1979, was twofold. First, to provide some corporate statement about prescribing that might be adopted by one of the medical bodies such as the Royal College of Psychiatrists. Second, to be used as a benchmark by Misuse of drugs Act tribunals or the General Medical Council when cases of irresponsible or non-*bona fide* prescribing.

It is ironic that some 50 years after Sir Malcolm Delevingne had unsuccessfully sought a clear statement from the medical profession of what constituted acceptable prescribing practice in the treatment of addiction, a similar proposal should now emerge from the profession itself. But the motives were different. Whereas Delevingne was anxious to have some guidance on whether or not a doctor's prescribing breached the spirit, if not the precise letter of the law, the objective in 1979, with total disregard to the long-established traditions of clinical freedom, was to impose uniform (London consultant-approved) prescribing practices.

As I saw it, and noted in my 1984 annual report, there was now a danger that a doctor who did not follow the guidelines, for example, by preferring to prescribe an injectable drug rather than oral methadone, would be regarded as being automatically guilty of 'irresponsible' prescribing. The Advisory Council had virtually said as much, suggesting that guidelines would 'help identify those cases where prescribing practice might be regarded as *prima facie* irresponsible and will do much to bring the tribunal procedure into line with the original intention'.[11] That statement was a gross distortion of the 'original intention', which had been set out in 1970 by the Advisory Committee on Drug Dependence in its report on the amphetamines and LSD; it recommended that 'flexible machinery is needed to deal immediately with reckless and grossly negligent prescribing'.[12]

The publication of the guidelines, in conjunction with the fully justified criticism of the Home Office in the Advisory Council's report[13] for using a narrow legalistic approach to the problem of 'irresponsible prescribing', increased the pressure on the Drugs Inspectorate to make better use of the tribunal machinery, particularly against those independent doctors whose prescribing of injectables was anathema to the London consultants. No doubt our failure to respond by immediately taking every current private prescriber before a tribunal, interpreted by some as tacit approval if not encouragement of the 'opposition', was a considerable disappointment.

The tribunal procedure had been established to deal with 'irresponsible' prescribing and it had never been envisaged that the members of the tribunal would be adjudicators of differences in clinical opinion. Any doctor in the United Kingdom was perfectly entitled to prescribe for an addict any controlled drug (except one for which a special licence was required) provided it was done responsibly. The fact that a doctor's clinical judgement did not conform to the current consensus or that prescribing was done privately, would not, *per se*, be sufficient reason to refer details of their prescribing to a tribunal. 'Nonconformity' and 'irresponsibility' are not synonymous.

In any case, the guidelines had no more statutory force than the Memorandum for Doctors and Dentists (DD 101) and were, as their 1991 revision explained, merely 'suggestions offered to doctors by a group of medical colleagues for interpretation in the light of the doctors' own situations'.[14] Furthermore, Connell[15] had admitted in March 1984, before the guidelines were published, that at regular meetings of staff at a London treatment centres (my emphasis):

> It has never been possible to obtain agreement that might result in the imposition of a uniform clinical approach with formal agreed procedures for the management of all patients; nor, indeed, in the view of the majority of members, is this even desirable.

But if lip service was being paid to the concept of clinical freedom to prescribe any controlled drug (provided it was oral methadone), conformity and psychiatric domination of the drug misuse field remained the ultimate goals. And by 1984 these had been partially achieved, as the London treatment centres' experience and treatment policies had been a major influence on the drawing up of the guidelines.

The Medical Working Group was now to turn its attention to the suggestion that the current licensing arrangements should be extended to cover more drugs. This, too, had been the brainchild of the consultant who first proposed there should be prescribing guidelines, and at the November 1979 meeting of the London consultants it was agreed to forward the proposal to the Advisory Council working group. Much earlier, in 1965, when commenting on the second Brain Committee's report, *The Lancet* had prophesied that 'the prescription of any dangerous drug besides heroin and cocaine to an addict by any doctor not on the staff of a treatment centre might be prohibited'.[16]

## Proposals to extend the restrictions on prescribing to addicts

In order that the London consultants and the voluntary drug agencies might discuss and agree on recommendations to send to the Advisory Council's treatment and rehabilitation working group, a private meeting had been arranged by the Institute for the Study of Drug Dependence (ISDD) in 1979. This meeting had been unproductive due largely, as reported back to the consultants, to the failure of the voluntary agencies to take the opportunity for a frank exchange of views. In October 1980, the ISDD organised a conference to 'bring together' the consultants and the leaders of the voluntary agencies 'to see if sufficient common ground existed for agreed recommendations to be forwarded to the Advisory Council'.[17] The conference was chaired by Sir Robert Bradlaw, then Chairman of the Advisory Council. The main conclusions were reported to the Council and more widely in a letter to *The Times* on 23 January 1981 signed by several of the London consultants and representatives of some voluntary agencies.

The letter set out three recommendations on which there had been 'clear agreement':

(a) Central government should accept the financial responsibility for provision of the core costs of specialist drug services.

(b) All drugs used to maintain drug addicts should only be prescribable by specially licensed doctors. As a corollary, the possibility of extending licensing to doctors outside hospitals, who are engaged in maintenance prescribing, should be urgently examined, a possible condition of the licence being that the doctor should work in close consultation with, or under the supervision of the nearest appropriate specialist facility.

(c) Detoxification facilities should be more readily and promptly available for those drug users wishing to withdraw.

It soon became apparent, however, that the 'clear agreement' applied only to the recommendations on funding and detoxification facilities. Several voluntary agencies had considerable reservations about the proposed extension of the licensing arrangements.[18] Release considered that the introduction of this further control would give 'encouragement of illicit manufacture and a consequent increase in the size of an already flourishing black market ... without doubt substitute drugs will be found by those who need or want to obtain them'. The Blenheim Project considered that the licensing arrangements should be 'an enabling rather than a restrictive measure', encouraging general practitioners to 'undertake the treatment of addicts in the community by providing a guarantee of access to consultation and to appropriate social work support'. This view was supported by the Hungerford Centre, which argued that an extension of the licensing restrictions 'would certainly not encourage GPs to treat addicts if they were answerable to a consultant psychiatrist'.

The Hungerford Centre made a further suggestion that it was time to rethink the role of the medical profession in relation to drug misuse. The Lifeline Project was critical of a system which encouraged people to see themselves as 'sick' and where the siting of treatment centres in psychiatric hospitals added 'overtones of insanity and uncontrollability'. These views echoed those expressed by Dr Raj Rathod of Crawley in a letter to *The Lancet* on 29 September 1979.[19]

Dr Rathod's letter was a response to an editorial, 'Drug addiction: a time for reappraisal', which appeared in *The Lancet* on 11 August 1979.[20] Dr Rathod's letter raised for his peers a number of fundamental, and in some respects highly inconvenient, questions. Suggesting that a debate on substance abuse in the United Kingdom was overdue, as the availability and use of illicit drugs showed no sign of decline, he wondered whether this trend was a portent of 'a socially unacceptable endemic' in a few years. He asked whether the statutory notification system had obscured the fact, which had been clear for some years, that most drug misusers used a variety of substances and not only by injection. In practice, 'treatment' amounted to little more than substitute or competitive prescribing, which 'increased the availability of potentially harmful substances only to enable others to initiate novices and even to sell the prescribed drugs illegally'. Dr Rathod doubted whether the substance abuser should continue to be viewed as a 'sick person', because 'substance abuse starts not as a disease or illness (in the medical sense)' rather than as someone with 'socially and legally unacceptable behaviour', with the medical and psychosocial consequences of secondary importance. He asked 'Why, and how, did the medical profession come to connive with society and accept every substance user as a sick person and thus inadvertently make a rod for their own back?'

Rathod's letter failed to initiate any debate in the correspondence columns of the medical journals at the time. Nor were the similar reservations of the voluntary agencies mentioned in the Advisory Council's report *Treatment and rehabilitation*. This was not altogether surprising, since these were heresies which struck at the very foundations of the post-Brain response and which the Council's working group had shown no inclination to review, far less challenge. The medical model of drug dependence was sacrosanct, although the report acknowledged the emergence of the multiple drug misuser who was 'not necessarily physically dependent on any one drug, but psychologically dependent on drug misuse'[21] and for whom the hospital-based treatment centre response was no longer appropriate.

But if the response was to be repackaged, the delivery system was to be unchanged. The multi-disciplinary regional health authority drug problem teams were now charged with monitoring and assessing the extent of problem drug taking and the services needed to deal with it and the development of regional policy. They were to be headed by consultant psychiatrists, assisted by full-time junior psychiatric medical staff.[22] This unqualified endorsement by the Advisory Council's working group, over half of whose medical members were psychiatrists, that psychiatry should continue to take the lead in determining the response to a 'problem drug taker', whose problems were mainly social and legal and minimally medical,[23] did not escape the attention of the report's critics. Their objections to the proposed extension of the licensing restrictions were set out by Mike Ashton in a comprehensive review of the responses to the report.[24]

The most serious objection was that this proposal would result in the handing of yet more power to treatment centre consultants. They would be in a position to control all other doctors engaged in the treatment of addiction, and through them to exert control over drug takers who had previously been able to avoid becoming subject to the centres' ministrations. Whether this was always, or became, the underlying objective of the proposal must remain an unanswered question. What there is much less doubt about is that additional statutory restrictions on prescribing were seen from the outset by the London consultants who had proposed them, as a means of dealing with what they saw as 'deviant' or 'injudicious' prescribing and of eliminating the private, and the few NHS, general practitioners who were undermining their agreed non-injectable prescribing policy.

Even if, as the Advisory Council proposed,[25] there was to be some relaxation of the 1968 policy of not licensing general practitioners, regional drug problem teams headed by consultant psychiatrists would be closely involved in the vetting of licence applicants. Furthermore, if the 'strict safeguards' imposed on non-hospital doctors included the suggested condition that they should work 'in consultation with or under the supervision' of the nearest treatment centre, there should be no threat to the conformity which the London consultants were seeking to impose over the contentious area of prescribing policy.

But there was little likelihood that non-hospital doctors would rush to apply for licences. The General Medical Services Committee of the British Medical Association had supported the proposal but, as Ashton noted, not a single general practitioner appeared publicly 'to have come out unreservedly against the proposed legislation to further limit their freedom to prescribe to addicts'. The only serious medical criticism came from the Association of Independent Doctors in Addiction (represented by Dr Ann Dally on the Medical Working Group, which drew up the 1984 guidelines), whose members believed that the proper people to treat addicts were their general practitioners or doctors to whom they had been referred by their general practitioners, and they 'rejected the suggestion that independent doctors should treat drug addicts only under the supervision of hospital consultants'.[26]

It is not difficult to understand why there was such widespread support for a proposal which would impose additional limitations on clinical freedom. For the vast majority of doctors, drug misusers were no more acceptable as patients in 1982 than they had been in 1962. There was, as the 1984 Guidelines recognised, and endeavoured to dispel, a 'pre-conceived idea that these patients are difficult and unrewarding'.[27] If a prescribing licence was to be required for all opioids, a doctor who did not hold such a licence would be protected from the importunings of drug misusers seeking prescriptions.

Not surprisingly, the Medical Working Group later recommended that licensing restrictions should be extended to all opioids, except oral liquid forms of methadone, and a similar recommendation emerged in the Fourth Report of the House of Commons Social Services Committee.[28] However, the government decided not to implement the recommendation, considering that any advantage to be gained from an extension of the licensing restrictions would be slight, and would be outweighed by the risk that some general practitioners might be deterred from treating drug misusers.[29] The Group's proposal that, if licensing restrictions were extended, licences should be available to general practitioners was similarly rejected and the existing practice of licensing only consultants, or doctors working under their direct supervision, would continue.

## The attack on private prescribing

The Advisory Council had strongly criticised the role of private medical practice in the treatment of drug misusers on the grounds that it raised 'moral and ethical aspects' giving 'grave cause for concern'. The most important concerns were the possible inhibiting effect the payment of fees might have on the establishment of an effective therapeutic relationship between doctor and patient, and the patient's ability to pay those fees.[30]

But while these were important issues, they obscured the real reason for the Council's criticisms. The intrusion of the independent practitioner into the drug addiction treatment field was seen as a direct challenge to the pre-eminence and prestige of a few influential clinicians, whose personal views and prejudices had dominated treatment policy in London. Those views and prejudices were soon to be felt by clinicians in other parts of the country, despite the fact that, although much canvassed, there had been no comprehensive evaluation of the effects of treatment policy and practices to support them.

The entry of the independent doctor into the treatment centres' domain provided addicts, for the first time, with a choice besides the criminal black market or the inflexible approach of most treatment centres and, not surprisingly, led to the rapid expansion of the private sector. This raised the interesting, and unresearched, question of why addicts who were not prepared to seek help from the 'official' treatment centres, would be willing to seek that help from private practitioners. Of course, the treatment centres had a simple answer. Addicts were not seeking treatment or help, they were merely looking for liberal supplies of injectable drugs, partly for their personal use but primarily for resale. What were seen by the independent doctor as patients' 'needs' became 'demands' in the treatment centre setting.

Given the timing and provenance of most of the public criticism of the private practitioners, described in 1983 as 'paranoia' by Dr Dale Beckett, then an independent doctor who had been providing outpatient treatment under the NHS both before and after April 1968,[31] it is difficult to avoid the conclusion that the campaign against them was well orchestrated. Bewley's 1980 paper, 'Prescribing psychoactive drugs to addicts',[32] set the tone of much of what was to follow, with the essence of the case against private prescribing set out in its first paragraph (using terms which neither I nor a number of old-time addicts with whom I have checked, have ever heard):

> Professional disrepute may occur if a doctor, under the guise of treating patients, provides addicts with large amounts of addictive drugs in return for a fee. Addicts label this type of practitioner as 'easy writer' or 'Doctor Scripts'.

There followed an estimate that a doctor who decided to prescribe for 20 addicts a week could earn over £25,000 a year, an estimate which was later revised to £100,000 a year,[33] on the basis of writing 20 prescriptions daily. Bewley's paper asked two questions: whether it was ever wise to prescribe psychoactive drugs privately to an addict in return for a fee; and what further safeguards were necessary to control 'improper' prescribing. He suggested the medical profession should now consider whether there was any place for private treatment of addicts 'where a fee is contingent on a prescription'. However, on the evidence of the correspondence columns of the *British Medical Journal*, the profession showed no inclination to regard this as a matter requiring urgent attention.

In January 1982 *The Lancet* added its weight to the campaign in a leading article, 'Drug addiction: British system failing'.[34] This argued, perfectly validly, that the uniformity of treatment offered by the treatment centres together with long waiting lists and the unlikelihood that addicts would be prescribed their drug of choice, had encouraged many addicts to stay outside the system and approach doctors working outside the centres. The writer then proceeded to say that most NHS general practitioners would be unwilling to comply with addicts' requests, but there would be some private independent doctors who, under the guise of saving the addict from the black market, would be prepared to prescribe, 'knowingly or (with a stretch of the imagination) unknowingly' doing so with the awareness that most addicts could only finance their private consultations by selling part of the their prescriptions. It was suggested that there were far more 'liberally prescribing doctors' in 1980 than there had been in the 1960s and 'today ... there is a potential clientele of many thousands'.

The writer acknowledged the opposition to the proposal to extend the licensing restrictions to all drugs that may be prescribed to maintain addicts, and suggested:

> Alternatively, the private treatment of drug-dependent patients could be prohibited on the grounds that any treatment involving the prescription of a dependence-producing

drug in return for a fee smacks so strongly of legalised drug-dealing with potentially enormous financial rewards that the medical profession should reject it outright.

The article stated, quite inaccurately, that there was 'clear evidence' that Diconal and Ritalin were prescribed 'almost exclusively' by private doctors. The Drugs Inspectorate had found that much of the Diconal was being prescribed by elderly, gullible and vulnerable NHS doctors to patients on a 'temporary resident' basis, or less often, on private prescriptions for which they rarely received more than a nominal fee, if at all. There were a very few private Diconal and Ritalin prescribers who fitted the popular Petro-inspired profile and who were dealt with either under the cumbersome Misuse of Drugs Act tribunal procedure or the General Medical Council's disciplinary machinery (sometimes both). An observational study of the Piccadilly Circus 'grey' market in pharmaceutical drugs, conducted between 1979 and 1981 by Angela Burr, confirmed that most of the non-opiate drugs, such as Ritalin, came from NHS doctors and only 'occasionally' from private prescribers, but these findings were not published until March 1983.[35]

Presumably not to be outdone, the *British Medical Journal* entered the debate in March 1982 with a contribution from Dr John Strang to the 'Personal View' column.[36] He endeavoured to reinforce the case against the private practitioner but succeeded only in revealing its fundamental weaknesses and the hypocrisy upon which it was largely based. He noted there was 'a fundamental incompatibility between the private practice of medicine and the treatment of the drug addict'. This is ambiguous, since it was the relationship between fee and prescription, and not the private treatment of drug addiction which was at issue. As the Advisory Council was shortly to conclude,[37] the payment of a fee by a person in receipt of state welfare benefits 'may also inhibit the establishment of an effective therapeutic relationship between doctor and patient'.

The implication that the private sector had no part to play would not have been accepted in 1966 by the British Medical Association's working party on the reconvened Brain Committee's proposals, which had considered it to be important that 'addicts should remain at liberty to obtain treatment privately and to travel freely if they wished to do so'.[38] Strang's statement on 'the fundamental incompatibility' was also unfortunate because the private treatment of drug addicts, which might involve the prescribing of drugs, was not unknown among the London consultants, as Dr Philip Connell was to tell the House of Commons Social Services Committee on 6 March 1985.[39]

Nor were treatment centre doctors averse to referring addicts to the private sector. During the influx of Iranian addicts it was common practice for them to be referred to Bowden House, a private nursing home at Harrow, where at least one of the doctors held a heroin-prescribing licence. Dr Ann Dally, one of the private prescribers, disclosed in September 1981[40] that she had been sent patients by doctors working in the treatment centres who said they could not prescribe 'what they believe the patient needs because they think they must not step out of line and arouse the hostility of colleagues'. Dr James Willis reported similar experiences in 1983.[41]

Strang went on to criticise private practitioners because they had 'virtually no system of monitoring, supports, or national (or even regional) policy making'. Why the private sector should be criticised on these grounds is puzzling. On the NHS front the periodic meetings of treatment centre consultants convened by the Department of Health had not been continued by the regional health authorities after 1974, as had been intended. The London consultants did hold regular informal meetings but they were disinclined to share their thoughts and greater experience with provincial colleagues. In any case, the independent doctors had banded together to form the Association of Independent Doctors in Addiction (AIDA) 'dedicated to achieving and maintaining high standards in the field of medical practice', and had produced a code of practice concerned more with setting those standards than with the imposition of uniformity of treatment.[42]

What is equally puzzling is why Strang should argue that independent doctors should be required to 'take into account the wider perspective of not only the problem but also the effect of treatment'. Over the years the London consultants had shown little concern for the consequences of their treatment policies on the wider problem and the black market in particular. If the second wave of heroin addiction and the criminal black market which began in the late 1970s and early 1980s were not their creation, much of the responsibility for the appearance of 'Chinese' heroin, and the later developments in the pharmaceutical 'grey' market, can be laid at their door. The multi-drug injecting problem, which saw the use of barbiturates, Diconal, Ritalin and a variety of other psychotropic preparations undoubtedly had its origins in treatment centre prescribing policies. Yet the consultants remained myopically aloof from the 'wider problem' and unmoved by any criticism that their unevaluated, uniform, inflexible treatment policies were responsible for the majority of addicts not seeking their help.

Apart from the central issue of 'the transfer of money' for treatment, much of the criticism of the private practitioners was quite clearly based on supposition and highly questionable hearsay evidence provided by treatment centres' addict patients. It was certainly not based on direct contact between the two differing clinical camps, because if the London consultants were reluctant to meet their provincial colleagues or the London voluntary agencies, they were even more determined to have nothing to do with the private sector. As early as April 1980, when the consultants gave some thought to arranging a meeting with their provincial colleagues, it was agreed that no doctor prescribing privately would be invited. This attitude persisted. Not only was a formal request from AIDA for a meeting rejected, it was quite obvious the London consultants did not take too kindly to the contact the Drugs Inspectorate had with AIDA and with individual private practitioners. That contact was perfectly consistent with our long-established policy of keeping in contact with anyone working in the drug dependence field. It did not imply approval, or disapproval, of the clinical judgements of those concerned. I remember, after attending an AIDA meeting at which a very doubtful prescriber was present, noting that we should be careful in our dealings with the Association because it was by no means unlikely that some of those who applied for membership might in due course be regarded as candidates for tribunal action.

Strang suggested that, as the policy of most private doctors was at variance with that of the centres, there were two treatment 'systems'. This is misleading because the majority of private prescribers subscribed to the aims of treatment he set out, including 'Helping him (the addict) to establish order to a chaotic life, to stabilise his pattern of use of drugs, and eventually to reduce and stop his dependence on drugs'. What was at issue was how those aims were to be achieved.

In June 1983, under the title, 'Unacceptable face of private practice: prescription of controlled drugs to addicts', the *British Medical Journal* published the results of a survey conducted by Drs Bewley and Ghodse of 100 addict patients attending the outpatient clinics at St Thomas's and St George's Hospitals.[43] The addicts, of whom 69 returned fully or partially completed questionnaires, were asked for their views on the private prescribing of drugs. As the senior author had recently held the post of Consultant Adviser on Drug Dependence to the Chief Medical Officer, and was of considerable standing in the drug dependence field, this paper can be seen as an authoritative establishment attack on the private sector.

The conclusions Bewley and Ghodse drew from the survey were that there were some private general practitioners who were easily persuaded to prescribe methadone, Diconal and Ritalin. This could lead to a severe spread of addiction, as in the 1960s, and, if the General Medical Council or the Misuse of Drugs Act tribunal machinery could not 'stop the practice', the present licensing system should be extended to include all controlled drugs. They suggested the reasons for such large numbers of addicts attending private practitioners could be that 'these doctors prescribe larger doses of drugs'.

Bewley and Ghodse noted that hospital doctors did not work single-handed or in isolation but had the backing of a multidisciplinary team and access to other NHS facilities such as toxicological analysis, and could therefore prescribe 'more objectively'. Inevitably, they raised the linked questions of fees and the need for addicts to sell some of their prescribed drugs, 'from the Harley Street and Piccadilly Circus Golden Triangle'. The possibility that the treatment centres were not providing a service attractive to prospective patients, as conceded by Strang[44] and

*The Lancet*,[45] was not mentioned while the alleged differences in prescribing practices between the NHS centres and private doctors presented a wholly false picture of the conditions prevailing in the generality of centres.

It is not unfair to say that as a justification for additional controls on prescribing, the Bewley and Ghodse paper was an abject failure. Nor is it an exaggeration to say that its conclusions were totally demolished in the *British Medical Journal*'s correspondence columns where it was described by Dale Beckett as 'propaganda disguised as a scientific paper'.[46] The critics included three consultant psychiatrists who had been involved in the early days of the treatment centres, when, as Dr Peter Dally recalled, the general psychiatrists who were responsible for starting them in 1968 were 'enthusiastic and interested in their new patients' before 'the clinics came to be run by specialist staff who took a narrow, restricted view of their addicts ... that smacked of Victorian paternalism'.[47] Others highly critical of the paper were Richard Hartnoll and Roger Lewis,[48] two respected researchers from the Drug Indicators Project, and an addict who provided a graphic and damning account of his own experiences at one of the NHS centres.[49]

Between them the critics laid bare the true purpose of the paper, which Dr Peter Dally, after drawing attention to the highly questionable methodology of the survey, described as 'unworthy of the normally high standards of the BMJ'. Hartnoll and Lewis raised the key question, which the authors had not addressed, of what the NHS had to offer to those addicts who 'perceive their needs in terms of an amenable legitimate supply of drugs or who decide ... that existing services, NHS or private, are irrelevant to their needs'. They argued that the treatment centres:

> ... have yet to find a positive role and a set of creative alternatives to offer that were both relevant and acceptable to a larger proportion of the addict population than currently make use of their services.

Some support for the Bewley and Ghodse attack was to come a few months later from Angela Burr who had returned to Piccadilly Circus in the autumn of 1982. Then she found that although 'not all doctors from Harley Street and the surrounding area or doctors outside drug dependency units in general are injudiciously over-prescribing to addicts ... a considerable proportion of the opiates' they prescribed found its way to the black market in Piccadilly.[50]

Burr's report drew fire from two of the independent doctors, Ann Dally[51] and Dale Beckett,[52] who both pointed out that the main black market was in smuggled heroin, with Dally remarking that this market was to be found in every town. Dally raised the fundamental question which Strang, Bewley and Ghodse had chosen not to address in their attacks on the private prescriber. She argued that if the treatment centres broadened their approach to the treatment and management of addicts and increased the numbers they treat 'and keep them away from the black market ... then, and only then, will the need for private doctors disappear'.

Strang had, in fact, already made this point in another 'Personal View' contribution to the *British Medical Journal*[53] in August 1981, only seven months before his criticisms of the private sector. Then he had said that it was virtually impossible for some new patients 'to obtain service of any valuable nature from the drug clinics'. Because of the 'ever-tightening restrictions' on those seeking treatment for the first time, the result of the bitterness felt by clinics at being exploited by those they had set out to help, addicts who wished to instil some order in their chaotic lives could expect little immediate help, or an interim prescription for heroin or methadone, from any clinic they approached. The clinics were 'unable or unwilling' to offer such a service. In these circumstances, Strang asked, could he really blame his patients for turning to private doctors for prescriptions?

But such frankness from within the system was rare and the deficiencies of NHS treatment services were conveniently ignored as pressure on the private sector continued to mount. In September 1981 the London consultants had considered making a formal complaint to the General Medical Council (GMC) but were persuaded by one of their members that an informal approach might be a better tactic. The result, reported to the March 1982 meeting, was that the private prescribing of opioid drugs to addicts was not considered to be unethical but it was undesirable, principally because all the problems of drug misusers could not be catered for on a one-to-one basis. The approach to the GMC led to the matter being taken up by the Professional Standards Committee for consideration.

When the GMC's representatives gave evidence to the House of Commons Social Services Committee on 20 February 1985 they welcomed the recent publication of the guidelines which would be of great benefit to the Professional Conduct Committee in dealing with the difficult cases of alleged improper prescribing. At their May 1985 meeting, the GMC approved the guidelines and commended them to all practising members of the profession. The Professional Standards Committee also suggested, in this context, that the attention of the profession should be drawn to three other related matters: the danger of disregarding warnings from the Home Office (Drugs Branch) and advice from the police about the effect of prescribing in certain areas; the inadvisability of prescribing to patients who travel considerable distances from other centres where adequate medical care is readily available; the serious view taken by the Committee of evidence that a doctor has prescribed opioid drugs to addicts in private practice where the financial circumstances of a patient were such that he or she would have needed to sell part of the drugs prescribed in order to cover the expenses of obtaining them, or where the fees charged have varied according to the amounts of drugs prescribed.[54]

Despite the GMC's ready acceptance of the guidelines as 'the corporate view of what constitutes proper practice in this field'[55] and the identification of some of the key elements of 'non-*bona fide* prescribing', there remained the issue at the centre of the NHS treatment versus private doctor debate. The guidelines had not offered advice on how to deal with long-term addicts who were determined against all advice to continue injecting, many of whom had become patients of private doctors and were receiving injectable prescriptions.

# 14

# What happened to the British system in 1968?

By mid-1973, with the treatment centres up and running since 1968, new comprehensive and flexible legislation in the Misuse of Drugs Act 1971, an Advisory Council to monitor, warn and advise on new trends in drug misuse (and provide a useful siding into which any awkward questions could be shunted) and the restoration of tribunals, 'the heroin problem' might be thought to be resolved. Complacency and apathy were once more the order of the day. Heroin addicts were now in safe expert hands and while there remained the considerable, and growing, use of cannabis, LSD and other 'mind-expanding' substances, this could be dealt with by the police. Research was catered for with the creation, in 1967, of the Addiction Research Unit and the Clinical Research and Treatment Unit by the Institute of Psychiatry, University of London.

As heroin misuse did not impinge on the lives of ordinary citizens in the 1970s as it does today, it is not altogether surprising that press, public and political interest in it diminished. In his 1979 review of the 'revised response' Griffith Edwards[1] described the current situation as giving 'the comforting appearance' of 'an epidemic seemingly brought under control' but cautioned against allowing the development of a complacency based on a feeling that 'not much else need now be done'. He noted that there were factors, such as youth unemployment, not present in the 1960s, which could lead to 'a rapidly developing instability in drug ecology'.

This prophetic, and already belated warning, like many before, was to receive little attention and it was not until the early 1980s that the public, media and Parliament awoke to the new flood of heroin misusers appearing on Merseyside[2] and in Edinburgh.[3] For some this was the final proof that the 'British system', both in its original Rolleston and post-1968 forms, was flawed and could never have prevented the development of a major heroin problem in the United Kingdom (UK) once there was an endemic demand fed by illicitly imported supplies. Therefore, as the treatment centres were clearly irrelevant to the needs of the contemporary drug world, a new strategy was necessary. The new way forward was a community-based approach (adopted by John Owens in Birmingham 20 years earlier), in which community drug teams, as proposed in 1982 by the Advisory Council on the Misuse of Drugs, would have a key role.[4] This, according to Strang and Clement, heralded 'the end of an era with the death of the exclusive and excluding specialist'.[5] But there remain a number of questions about what actually happened before and during the treatment centre years, about the centres' impact upon the course of drug misuse and, above all, why the hopes, aspirations and visions of the immediate post-second Brain Report years were apparently not fulfilled.

## The British system and the prevalence of opiate addiction

Any attempt to answer some of these questions must start by challenging the widely held belief that the British system, by accepting the prescribing of morphine and heroin to addicts as legitimate medical practice, was designed to reduce the prevalence of addiction to these drugs by preventing the development of a black market and, until the 1960s, was successful in doing so. This notion was largely fostered by American academics such as Alfred Lindesmith[6] and Edwin Schur[7] who, as the Royal College of Psychiatrists pointed out, 'wrongly presumed that the British approach caused the UK's low prevalence of opiate problems and the absence of an organised black-market'.[8] Some British commentators, such as Gillespie and his co-authors,[9] appreciated that 'the system was not developed to prevent the growth of drug dependence, or a drug oriented underworld', but the majority appear to have paid little heed to the reasons for the appointment of the Rolleston Committee, or the reconvening of the Brain Committee in 1964. For example, Griffith Edwards[10] had no doubt that:

> The British response to drugs as founded in the 1920s, was founded to deal with a small problem – no one could claim that it was initially set up to bring a large problem under control, for the historical evidence is quite in the other direction.

This is misleading. In laying the foundations of the 1920s response, as their terms of reference make clear, the Rolleston Committee was dealing with a narrow question of interpretation: whether a doctor who prescribed morphine or heroin to an addict was properly exercising the authority given him under the recently introduced Dangerous Drugs Act 1920. The Committee was not concerned with the wider non-medical aspects of drug addiction and there is no evidence that they wished to extend their enquiry beyond their terms of reference. The only comment in their report about the extent of addiction referred not to the possible consequences of their recommendations but to the effect of the controls introduced under the 1920 Dangerous Drugs Act.[11]

It must be remembered that the British system after 1953, when the provisions for tribunals were dropped from the dangerous drugs legislation, was not that which had emerged in 1926 from the Rolleston Committee's deliberations. Griffith Edwards[12] made much the same point in 1977, but from a different perspective, when he argued that the prisons, probation service, and even the black market, were also part of the British system and as important as its more widely recognised features.

An essential part of the British system, the tribunal safeguard proposed by Rolleston to deal with doctors in cases 'which involved the question whether the drugs had been supplied, administered or prescribed for other than legitimate medical purposes',[13] was not available when it was most needed to deal with the prescribing of heroin by Maguire, Rourke and Lady Frankau. This is not to suggest that if there had not been this gap in our defences, there would have been no heroin problem in the 1960s, and far less so in the 1980s. The case-to-case spread of heroin addiction would have continued, slowly at first but gathering momentum as the numbers increased, creating a demand which would have had to be met, either from a 'grey' market of over-prescribed or under-consumed pharmaceutical heroin, or, as it is today, from illicitly imported supplies.

Admittedly, all the use of tribunals could have done was to reduce the amount of surplus prescribed pharmaceutical heroin, an important step nevertheless because it would have been much more difficult for those on the fringes of the addict community to obtain it. Then there would have been no need to reconvene the Brain Committee in 1964 to deal with 'lunatic' prescribing, and therefore, no 'treatment centre era'. Furthermore, the damage caused by the delay in implementing the reconvened Committee's recommendations would have been averted and heroin misuse would probably have remained a non-issue until the heroin epidemic of the early 1980s fuelled by illicitly imported supplies and linked with 'high levels of unemployment, housing decay, and other forms of social deprivation',[14] forced it back on to the political agenda.

## The 'failed experiment'

Much of the confusion about the British system is the result of focusing on what is seen as the unique feature of the system, the prescribing of heroin to addicts, which has been described by some commentators in the United States (US) as 'the failed experiment in the legalisation of heroin'.[15] Unfortunately, this interpretation has been given some credence by Griffith Edwards[16] when he asserted that:

> It is crucial to realise that the period before 1968 was in effect an 'experiment' in liberal prescribing which was coincidental with growth in the general illicit drug traffic and with a burgeoning increase in the incidence of drug addiction.

He argued the result was 'an explosive growth in narcotic usage' and cited as examples of 'liberal' prescribing, the much-quoted six kilograms of heroin prescribed by one doctor (Lady Frankau) in 1962, referred to in paragraph 11 of the second Brain Report, and to the estimate that by 1965 one female addict had obtained on NHS prescriptions some 40,000 grains (2.4 kilograms) of heroin and 30,000 grains (1.8 kilograms) of cocaine during her 16-year addiction career.[17] The interpretation of what happened before 1968 as an 'experiment' is simply not tenable. As anyone directly involved at the time knows only too well, the prescribing of heroin by a few doctors during the early and mid-1960s was uncontrolled and uncontrollable and by no stretch of the imagination could it be called an 'experiment'.

The reason the increase in heroin addiction in the 1960s would have continued inexorably was that the breakdown in what Edwards called the 'drug ecology' had already begun to occur. Blackwell,[18] reviewing the very few descriptive studies of the late 1950s and early 1960s addicts that were not conducted from a medical or psychopathological perspective, concluded that the 1950s saw the appearance of 'a new deviant drug user, American-style "junkie" in the UK' who had begun to appear long before American and Canadian addicts began to emigrate to London. She noted that finding a 'script doctor' was 'an integral part of the lore of American "junkies"'.

One of these studies[19] described as 'jazz junkies' the heroin users who, in the late 1950s and early 1960s, identified with the US addict subculture, using its drug argot, and admiring American jazz musicians, many of whom were known to be heroin users. A considerable proportion of the addicts at the time were jazz musicians. Hewetson and Ollendorf[20] had 12 among the 100 addict patients they treated in 1963/64 and 12 of the 26 of 'Mark's' clients who came to notice as heroin addicts in the 1950s were musicians.[21]

Young[22] also emphasised the importance of subcultural factors, but described the 'new brand of addict' of the early 1960s as being 'part of a subculture which was more unashamedly hedonistic' who 'often recommended and actively spread heroin use to others' and who:

> ... wheedled, cheated and extorted excessive supplies of heroin from their physicians. The motive behind their sale of surplus was to supplement unemployment benefits and maintain a style of life without work consistent with the values of the subculture.

The important point Blackwell and Young made is that it was the demand, not the prescribing, or even the over-prescribing, of heroin which was the primary cause of the problem presented to the reconvened Brain Committee. In today's parlance the increase in heroin use the 1960s was demand, rather than supply, led.

## Treatment centre practice

There can be no objective account of what happened, and what was achieved, during the treatment centre years without some reference to the thinking of those who were to influence the way in which the centres responded to the new challenge. The translation of the reconvened Brain Committee's intended therapeutic approach was set out in Hospital Memorandum H.M.(67)16. The rationale of this approach, provided by Dr Philip Connell in April 1968[23] and in September 1969,[24] centred on the reduction of the prescribing of heroin and cocaine and the need to prevent addicts from 'shopping around' the treatment centres by ensuring uniformity of prescribing both in terms of dose and drug.

What is evident from these early indications of the intended clinical response is the very considerable impact on thinking, and on the planning process, of paragraph 15 of the second Brain Committee's Report. Here the Committee had drawn attention to the inherent dangers both of insufficient and of unduly stringent control over the provision of lawful supplies of heroin to addicts. As a result, fear of over-prescribing was the dominant theme of the early treatment centre years, although in due course this was to be replaced by a callous indifference on the part of a few consultants to the possibility there could be any interaction between what was happening in the centres and what was happening on the street.

Most of the 'practical arrangements' set out by Connell in his September 1969 memorandum are so elementary it is difficult to see why they needed to be detailed. For example, it would seem to be obvious that 'no new case shall be prescribed heroin and/or cocaine until the physician is satisfied that he is in fact taking such drugs regularly' and 'each patient will be assessed weekly or fortnightly as to the appropriate dose of drugs to be prescribed'.

But why was it felt necessary to go beyond setting down general principles for the guidance of those who would now be entering a field in which they had little or no previous experience? Was it simply the fear that in the early days inexperienced staff would be easily outwitted and outmanoeuvred by devious and manipulative patients? Or was the desire for 'uniformity' an early, and unrecognised, indication of a hidden agenda – which later events were to suggest to some observers[25] was aimed at making the consultant psychiatrist in charge of a treatment centre 'the uncrowned king of the drug abuse industry', who would eventually be 'in a position to control all other doctors engaged in the treatment of drug addiction'? There was no doubting the determination of the 'new treaters' not to make the same mistakes as the general practitioners they were replacing, but why did this require agreements between them on prescribing practice? Although voluntary, these agreements imposed limitations on the clinical freedom the profession had always fought so hard to preserve.

In 1968 Connell appeared to have had no doubts that the new challenge 'might mean agreement to give up the complete right to do exactly what the physician wishes in some circumstances'.[26] But by 1975, coincidentally at the same time as the important, and controversial, move to prescribing only oral methadone in treatment centres, Connell was asserting that 'each physician in charge of a special drug dependence clinic is a law unto himself as to how he treats and manages patients'.[27]

Why, apparently, only in the field of drug dependence, should the need for 'uniformity' of treatment override the traditional clinical freedom of the medical profession to which the British Medical Association drew attention during the furore over the proposed heroin ban in 1955?[28] This question is central to any debate about the success or failure of the treatment centres and therefore, by implication, of the basic philosophy of the British system. Much has been written about the difficulties faced by the centres in balancing their dual therapeutic and social control roles and in defence of the changes in prescribing policies and practices made in the mid-1970s, but the inherent inflexibility of the proposed uniform approach, the confusion over maintenance prescribing of heroin, the considerable reluctance of the profession to accept the concept of the 'stabilised addict', and pervasive influences from across the Atlantic, have all received far less attention.

So, too, have the changing positions, and occasional contradictory statements of some of those involved. What has also yet to be determined is whether there was from the outset the 'really resolute determination to make a success of the new approach', which Griffith Edwards argued it demanded,[29] or as Max Glatt asked, whether that approach would 'be sufficiently elastic and adaptive to enable them to deal with any emergent problems?'[30] The first public indication that uniformity of treatment would be the chosen route appeared in papers by Bewley and Connell in May 1967,[31] although shortly afterwards, on 25 July 1967, the Minister of Health told the House of Commons it was unlikely that 'a standard pattern of treatment' would emerge in the immediate future.[32]

## The stable addict and maintenance prescribing of heroin

It was Connell who seems to have been the first publicly to link prescribing heroin with maintenance, thereby laying the foundations both for the inflexibility of the new approach and much of the confusion about the role of prescribing in the treatment of opiate addiction. Accepting that the prescribing of heroin to an addict was anathema to many doctors, in 1967 he nevertheless agreed that the case for doing so had been 'well made'.[33] It was therefore:

> ... essential that a uniform scheme of maintenance should be used in all maintenance centres, and that the scheme is rigid enough to debar prescription of heroin to an addict because he has lost his drug or sold it or given it away. If an addict comes with such a story and his wishes are met gross over-prescribing will continue ...

This he followed in 1968[34] with:

> Physicians, chiefly for medico-social reasons, have agreed to take part in a treatment setting which includes maintaining a heroin addict on heroin, which is a very bad drug for maintenance purposes because of its short-lived action.

296

'Maintenance' was now to take on a new meaning and to become, as *The Lancet*[35] and Owens[36] had feared, a euphemism for prescribing heroin. It is not a semantic quibble to suggest that the continuation of the supply of heroin to an addict as envisaged by H.M.(67)16, was not the same as 'maintenance', as the 'indefinitely prolonged administration of morphine or heroin' of the Rolleston Committee came to be known. H.M.(67)16 merely proposed that heroin should be supplied, in minimum quantities, where this was considered necessary by the doctor, alongside continued attempts 'to persuade addicts to accept withdrawal treatment'.

The Rolleston Committee's conclusions, set out in paragraph 47 of their report, are well known but the qualifications in paragraph 49 are less often mentioned. Here the Committee made it quite clear that prolonged administration of morphine or heroin was to be considered *only* after every effort possible in the circumstances has been made, *and* made unsuccessfully, to bring patients to a condition in which they are independent of the drug and even then:

> It should not, however, be too lightly assumed in any case, however unpromising it may appear to be at first sight, that an irreducible minimum of the drug had been reached which cannot be withdrawn and which, therefore, must be continued indefinitely.

Rolleston-style 'maintenance' was inextricably linked with the concept of the 'stabilised addict', a term introduced by the first Brain Committee.[37] However, as the Committee had failed to detect the existence of the new generation of heroin addicts, the endorsement of the concept was based on the same type of addict, often middle aged and therapeutic in origin, familiar to the Rolleston Committee. By 1966, as Connell[38] later revealed, there was a reluctance to accept the notion of the 'stabilised addict'. That the increasing nonconformity and 'alternative' lifestyles of the 1960s may have been a factor is reflected in Bewley's statement that the patients he had seen by 1965[39] 'fell outside this (stabilised addict) category in that most had unsatisfactory work records, which were not improved by taking drugs'. Yet by 1967[40] he seems to have accepted that stable addicts might exist among the new wave and argued that co-operation between the treatment centres should lead to:

> … a standard practice in deciding which patients are otherwise incurable or untreatable, but thought to be capable of leading a more normal life with long-term drug taking.

For a variety of reasons, not least the widespread apathy and unwillingness of the medical profession to become involved with these unpopular and unrewarding patients, and the perfunctory nature of such treatment as was available, the majority of the new generation of heroin addicts had not been exposed to the therapeutic pressure implicit in paragraph 49 of the Rolleston report. While this offers some support for the reluctance to accept the concept of the 'stabilised addict', it has also to be remembered that by 1966 the number of young non-therapeutic heroin addicts had been increasing for well over a decade and among them were several who had been receiving prescriptions for heroin continuously for most of that time.

These addicts presented a problem for those who would now have responsibility for their treatment and management. This was discussed in 1969 by Max Glatt,[41] one of the few clinicians with practical experience of the new problem but who had not attended either of the meetings of the 'doctors experienced in the treatment of addiction' convened by the government's Chief Medical Officer in 1966 to advise on the role of the NHS hospital service in treating addicts. Glatt suggested that for the addicts 'who have been able to function fairly well without increasing the dosage and without selling drugs' it might be difficult for the doctor to decide whether or not it was advisable to 'leave well alone'. He sent on to say:

> In this country the problem how to discover those for whom total abstinence, at least for the time being, must remain an unrealistic goal, is at present often left to the intuition or kind heart (or 'state of battle fatigue') of the Treatment Centre practitioner whom the claimant for drugs happens to meet at his first attendance.

Stimson and Ogborne, from their study of addicts who were being prescribed heroin by the London treatment centres in 1969,[42] recognised the existence of a group of stable addicts, comprising around a third of their sample, and described them as:

> ... although addicted led reasonably ordinary lives; they were inconspicuous in dress and manner, kept themselves apart from other addicts and suffered few problems.

It is therefore surprising to read in Gardner and Connell's[43] description of the first year of operation of the treatment centre at the Maudsley Hospital that, apart from an elderly Indian opium addict, there were apparently no stable addicts strictly within the first Brain Committee's definition among their patients, although 'a few cases were functioning reasonably well socially – but the minimum daily dosage of this group was 480mgm of heroin'. This interpretation of stability, which seems to attach a higher priority to size of dose than to social functioning, provides a further indication of the obsession with prescribing which dominated the early treatment centre years.

The implication that addicts taking more than 480mgms heroin daily could not be 'stable', is not supported by the two Canadian addicts whose cases are quoted in the paper. They were referred to the treatment centre with daily pre-scriptions of 1,500mgms and 1,200mgms of powdered heroin. Both Arnold and Joe, whom I knew quite well, had a lengthy addiction history in Canada before coming to England in 1960. During the whole of this time, until they became pa-tients at the Maudsley Hospital in 1968, they had been prescribed large quantities of heroin, and in Joe's case cocaine also, by Lady Frankau. Perhaps as croupiers their lifestyles were not 'ordinary' but on the Stimson criteria of dress and de-meanour they undoubtedly qualified as 'stable' addicts. (They had no difficulty in being admitted to the Home Office when they came to see me to complain that whenever a new registrar was appointed they were required to demonstrate that they had high tolerances.)

## What did the treatment centres offer?

Gardner and Connell's paper is important not only because it is one of the few pub-lished reports on how the proposals in H.M.(67)16 were being implemented in 1968/69 but also because the Maudsley Hospital treatment centre was seen as the flagship of the new arrangements, being reasonably well staffed, with access to good laboratory services, and under the direction of the Chief Medical Officer's Consul-tant Adviser on Drug Dependence. As the authors commented, the experience of the clinic was 'likely to be minimal in terms of errors and untoward events' yet they admitted that ten patients received a regular prescription of opiates 'despite a nega-tive urine, and some of these became addicted during their attendance at the clinic'.

Gardner and Connell's main conclusions were that the diagnosis of addiction and decisions on the amount of maintenance doses were especially difficult prob-lems, that heroin maintenance therapy should be re-evaluated, and with young persons it should be used with great caution, if at all, because of the risk of turn-ing a sporadic or occasional user into an addict. They had found that regular urine analysis played a vital role in diagnosis and in 'the continued supervision and treatment of addicts'.

On the basis of a very limited experience of applying their own highly individ-ual interpretation of the aims set out in the second Brain Committee report and HM(67)16, Gardner and Connell suggested there now seemed to be:

> ... a need to re-evaluate the principles and practice of heroin maintenance therapy for new cases, nearly all of whom will be young persons who have used opioids for less than a year and some of whom may be sporadic users.

But where did the concept of 'maintenance for all' originate? Certainly not from the reconvened Brain Committee or H.M.(67)16, both of which made it abundantly clear that the prescribing of heroin to an addict was to be entirely at the doctor's discretion. What then is to be made of the complaint that 'a procedure which still allows of prescribing opioids to the occasional user is inadequate and harmful'? Even allowing that 'maintenance' had now acquired a new, and less-qualified meaning, where had it been proposed that 'sporadic users' should be given a regular supply of heroin?

Max Glatt had a different understanding of the role of prescribing in relation to newly or barely addicted young persons when in 1966[44] and again in 1969[45] he urged that heroin maintenance should be used with caution in young people. There were a few other psychiatrists who did not regard treatment, maintenance and prescribing as synonymous and who did not see themselves as mere providers of heroin to all and sundry.

In 1968 Dr Julius Merry,[46] who had been treating young heroin addicts on an outpatient basis well before the second Brain report, had no doubt about the function of the treatment centres, saying 'The outpatient centre is not just a place where drugs are prescribed – it should also provide the very important preparatory stage of a very formidable treatment programme.'

In 1973 Dr Gisela Oppenheim, the consultant at the Charing Cross Hospital centre, described prescribing as taking a subordinate role to a 'community orientated approach' which included counselling to 'present to the patient a clearly perceivable pleasurable alternative way of life to that of being a drug addict' with regular follow-up visits at home.[47]

## Prescribing heroin and the elimination of the black market

From the outset, and for several years to come, the major anxiety of the 'new treaters' was to ensure their prescriptions of heroin did not fuel the black market. Griffith Edwards, writing in 1969, was categoric in stating 'The aim of the British system is to deprive a criminally organised black market (in heroin) of its potential customers' and at 'pre-empting the Mafia'.[48] He noted there would have to be accuracy both in diagnosis and in determining the minimum dosage appropriate to the addicts' needs. Unfortunately, the fear of making the same mistakes as the pre-1968 prescribers tended to take precedence over pragmatism and the realities of the drug misuse world beyond the centre's doors.

There was never any prospect, or any expectation, at least by the Drugs Inspectorate, of the treatment centres eliminating the black market in pharmaceutical heroin. By 1968 a demand for heroin had been firmly established and the most that could be hoped for was that it could be contained, the aim expressed in paragraph 8 of H.M.(67)16. If those addicts who successfully persuaded a doctor they needed heroin were given a prescription to be dispensed at a retail pharmacy, they could then dispose of that heroin in any way they chose, by using it themselves or by selling or lending some to others. Some consideration had been given by the 'doctors experienced in the treatment of addiction' to the suggestion that every administration of the drug should be under the personal supervision of treatment centre staff, but this had been rejected.

Nor was it desirable that the 'grey' market in pharmaceutical heroin should cease to exist. This, of course, is heresy. But it is pragmatic heresy because if, as was generally accepted in 1968, drug addiction was a chronic relapsing condition, it was surely far better that anyone determined to return to drugs should be able to do so by using heroin of known strength and purity. The issue in 1964, when Lord Brain was asked to take another look at the problem, was not the existence of a grey market in pharmaceutical heroin but the size of that market, which apathy, complacency and inadequate controls had allowed to expand to a quite unacceptable extent. If there had then been a smaller surplus of heroin, the increase in the addict population would have been less dramatic as it is more than likely any surplus would have remained within the existing addict circles. This, in fact, happened in the immediate post-1968 period when the more conservative prescribing by the treatment centres began to take effect, resulting in far less pharmaceutical heroin in circulation than there had been during the heydays of Lady Frankau and John Petro.

The difficulty of relating a dosage to an addict's actual needs has been, and still is, a cornerstone in the debate about the success, failure or even the validity, of the British system of maintenance prescribing and ambulatory treatment. In 1965 Chapple and Marks[49] had drawn attention to the absence of any accurate quantitative method for assessing an addict's dosage. In 1968 Connell[50] had identified the development of such a method as one of the urgent research priorities but, as far as I am aware, this has yet to materialise.

Given the difficulties in determining the dosage to be prescribed, why was inpatient assessment not more commonly used? It was made clear in H.M.(67)16 it was expected that 'where possible the dosage will be determined by assessment during inpatient observation and that this will usually be offered, though continued treatment cannot be made conditional on acceptance'. In 1969 Griffith Edwards[51] noted that because of pressure of work and limited facilities inpatient assessment was not usually offered. Gardner and Connell reported that the majority of patients to whom they refused to prescribe opioids at the first attendance did not return, so that inpatient assessment was not an option. In any case, they rejected it as a reliable means of observing signs of withdrawal on the grounds that 'some patients seem well able to mimic these ... whatever method is used to assess the dose, the opioid user may still reduce this after the test and sell the surplus unless the drug is administered daily in the clinic'.

The fear of over-prescribing was undoubtedly the driving force behind the relentless pursuit of 'uniformity', exemplified by Connell's proposal in 1968 that once the treatment centres were 'working smoothly', on an appointed day they would all reduce by half, over a period of a month, the amount of heroin pre-scribed to their patients, and by the agreements governing the transfer of addicts between clinics.[52] This was an early example of the thinking which, a few years later, was to lead to the collective decision by the London treatment centres to dis-continue the prescribing of injectables to all new patients. It was also the first in-dication that addicts were no longer to be treated as individuals, as they had been by their much-maligned general practitioners. Now they were members of a sin-gle homogenous group whose differing needs and problems could be met by a uniform inflexible response, which would not recognise that from time to time, al-though certainly not as frequently as they claimed, addicts did lose their tablets or wasted a 'fix', that some of the crises to which addicts seem to be particularly prone might conceivably have been genuine, justifying a temporary increase in dose, or that not all requests for extra supplies were based on commercial considerations.

In Connell's[53] 1969 memorandum to treatment centre consultants on 'Practi-cal matters relating to the treatment of drug-dependent patients', he pointed out that 'a patient already attending a treatment centre should not be taken on at an-other centre unless by agreement with the other centre'. This is further evidence that addicts were not to be regarded as ordinary patients. They were to be tied to the treatment centre to which, in many instances, they had been allocated and were to be denied the right to seek a second opinion if dissatisfied with the treat-ment they were receiving. Admittedly such dissatisfaction would usually stem from what they saw as an inadequate supply of heroin but it was possible that in some instances the wish to transfer to another clinic was prompted by other con-siderations. For instance, the addict might have found it impossible to form the vi-tally necessary therapeutic relationship with the clinic staff or was seeking the 'tolerance, kindness and understanding' which in 1967 the *British Medical Journal*'s leader writer had identified as the first requirement in the planning of treatment for drug addiction.[54] But whatever reason an addict might have for seeking a change of treatment centre, there is little doubt that this particular 'practical mat-ter' was a further deliberate incursion into the clinical freedom of any British doc-tor to treat a patient in accordance with his or her own professional judgement.

This is supported by the concern which Connell showed in his memorandum that one treatment centre had recently 'shown a very rapid increase of new cases of heroin dependence'. He offered a number of possible explanations for this in-crease, including a epidemic due to a local source of illegal heroin, the taking over of cases from other clinics outside the 'agreement', additional medical staff and 'a liberal prescribing policy ... leading to an 'epidemic' of drug taking created by overprescribing'. Action should be taken 'to explore the reasons for the phenome-non and to prevent the spread of addiction' and the collective responsibilities of physicians in special centres, as well as those of the Department of Health and the Home Office, for such a situation, should then be considered.

This 'concern' was, in reality, little more than a thinly disguised attack on Dr James Willis, the consultant at St Giles Hospital in Camberwell, which in 1969 was unquestionably at the top of the addicts' league table of treatment centres. Not only did Willis understand and believe in the Rolleston principles, he applied them in practice, and as some of his patients had been addicted for several years, their dosages were often appreciably higher than those provided by other centres. At a time of increasing parsimony elsewhere, it was inevitable that he should be seen as a 'liberal prescriber', attracting addicts from all over London, and therefore a threat to any 'uniformity of practice'. Recalling that his policy had been 'subjected to a moderate amount of criticism', Willis[55] referred to these events in a letter to the *British Medical Journal* in 1983:

> I was a consultant in charge of one of these clinics when it first opened in 1967 and felt no misgivings about the maintenance prescription of injectable heroin. Unhappily, these feelings were not shared by many of my colleagues, and the clinic experience changed into a race between colleagues to see who could prescribe the least heroin. I think that this race was engendered by a mixture of good and bad motives, the good motives having to do with a genuine wish to replace injectable drugs with oral drugs such as methadone, and the bad motives having to do with the innate tendency of many doctors to moralise to and about their fellow creatures.[56]

The suggestion by Willis that there had been a 'race to see who could prescribe the least heroin' is not as ridiculous as might at first appear. From the time of the establishment of the treatment centres, information about the number of patients attending each centre, and the quantities of addictive drugs prescribed was collected by the Department of Health.[56] This was presented to the Advisory Committee on Drug Dependence, sometimes accompanied by a comment from an official that an 'encouraging feature' was the decrease in the amount of heroin being prescribed. The information was also presented to treatment centre consultants at their regular meetings where, as Mitcheson[57] has noted, 'discreet peer group pressure' to moderate the prescribing of heroin tended to be applied. Information which allowed the calculation of 'a mean dose of opioids per patient for each clinic' was therefore particularly helpful to those seeking to apply such pressure, and the technique was to be used again in the mid-1970s when there was a further move away from injectable prescribing.

But if there was satisfaction with the steady decrease in the quantity of heroin prescribed by the treatment centres after 16 April 1968, this was not primarily because there would now be less leaking into the black market. From the outset, when senior clinicians, to whom the prescribing of heroin to an addict was anathema, agreed with 'considerable reluctance' to co-operate in a scheme in which this was to be a treatment option, the writing had been on the wall for heroin. The main clinical objections to heroin were that it was 'a very bad drug for mainte-nance purposes because of its short-lived action'[58] and also that its intravenous use could lead to serious medical complications, which presumably did not arise with injectable methadone which, by the end of 1968, the centres were prescribing in increasing quantities. Suspicion that peer group pressure to reduce the amount of heroin being prescribed, was, however, largely motivated by other than phar-macological considerations was soon to emerge – although this was not to be tac-itly admitted for several years.

By 1972 Chinese heroin had become an established feature of the illicit market, a development which prompted an interesting discussion at the November 1972 meeting of the London consultants on the relative merits of heroin and methadone. One consultant commented that virtually all his new patients had been using 'Chinese' heroin and that it was all too often the practice for patients receiving methadone ampoules to sell these in order to buy it. (When this was brought to the notice of the Advisory Committee on Drug Dependence, the reac-tion of the late Arthur Blenkinsop MP was to suggest that if prescribed methadone was being traded for illicit heroin it might be better if more heroin were pre-scribed.) The consultant went on to say that the patients he referred to other treat-ment centres, and who for various reasons were not accepted, immediately returned to the black market where they had little difficulty in obtaining heroin, leading him to the conclusion that by prescribing heroin he would at least be doing something to keep some of them away from the black market. But there was no slowing down in the 'rush to methadone' and in 1973, for the first time, the quantity of methadone prescribed in injectable form (19 kilograms) exceeded the quantity of heroin prescribed (14 kilograms) with a further 9 kilograms of methadone being prescribed in the form of linctus or tablets.[59]

As the unacceptable public and political image of heroin had been acquired mainly in the US, it was perhaps natural that those most exposed to transatlantic thinking, and who were doing their best to 'transfer American treatment trends to the UK'[60] should be anxious to ensure there was international, as well as domestic 'uniformity of practice'. Heroin was also the drug which had recently caused an unwelcome spotlight to be focused on the UK medical profession. However, it was not until 1985 that there was confirmation of these early suspicions, that the unique feature of the 'British system', the use of heroin in the treatment of addic-tion at a doctor's discretion, was being abandoned for ethical and political, rather than clinical, reasons.

Philip Connell's 1985 Dent Memorial Lecture,[61] included in the title the phrase 'I need heroin', a common statement made by those who use heroin and by their parents, friends, politicians and others. Connell, then enjoying a second spell as Consultant Adviser on Drug Dependence to the Department of Health, offered the following:

But those who have used it [heroin] may claim to need it because they want it either for direct hedonistic pleasure, or for the removal of or diminution of dysphoria; or to prevent the withdrawal symptoms (whether imaginary, feigned or real) which can occur when a regular user of heroin ceases to take the drug, and in order to obtain or justify the use of the drug. 'I need heroin' is a phrase which has produced and will continue to produce complex personal emotive and societal responses as we all know. Indeed a doctor (I hope speaking as a private individual) has recently raised again the question of the legal and commercial availability of heroin.

There is a revealing and sinister implication in this last sentence, which refers to a suggestion made by Dr David Marjot, an experienced treatment centre consultant, at a meeting of medical journalists in September 1985, that as *de facto* prohibition had failed to control the use of heroin by addicts, there was a need to consider other ways of dealing with the problem. Marjot's reported remarks attracted the attention of his Regional Medical Officer and the Chairman of his health authority, and provoked an outburst from David Mellor, then a Minister of State at the Home Office, in which he described the remarks as 'grotesque and fatheaded'. Marjot commented that 'such remarks were clearly meant to intimidate and at the same time to discredit me because my views did not follow the party line'.[62]

But as Connell's[63] brief reply to Marjot's letter of protest confirmed, it was precisely because Marjot was speaking about matters of which he had expert knowledge that he was being criticised. Connell was concerned that 'the lay public is often confused when doctors speak on social issues, as to which hat they are using (doctor or private individual) and which part of the argument derives from which hat'. Whether a 'lay' person would have failed to appreciate that someone as experienced as Marjot was making a serious point and had a perfectly legitimate right to do so, is debatable. His remarks represented a challenge to the 'discreet peer group' pressure of the psychiatric establishment to impose standard treatment responses and the relevance of those responses to the new epidemic of heroin misuse of the 1980s. Moreover, there was in Marjot's remarks a recognition of the unpalatable fact that heroin occupied a special place in the perception of addiction and its treatment by the media and politicians worldwide, and this might conceivably have a bearing on how addicts responded to the 'uniformity of practice' which, since 1968, Connell and most of his fellow treatment consultants had perversely failed to take into account.

## Was there 'really resolute determination' to implement the British system by the treatment centres?

There are two other aspects of these early years which should be borne in mind by anyone embarking on a critical appreciation of the achievements and failures of the treatment centres. The first was the level of experience available both among, and to, those who would be influential in developing the new approach. The second was identified by Edwards[64] in 1969 in his critical examination of the central hypotheses underpinning the new system. He acknowledged that the new legislative provisions restricting the prescribing of heroin and cocaine to addicts represented 'no abrupt departure from the fundamental ethic' of the 'British system', and expressed the view that it would be 'tragic' if the 'British system' failed, 'not because of any fundamental flaw in its conception but simply because of lack of really resolute determination to implement it'. Both these issues were touched on in 1982 by the Advisory Council on the Misuse of Drugs, noting in *Treatment and rehabilitation*[65] that:

> ... there was little enthusiasm for providing services for such an unpopular group of patients ... the problem had developed so rapidly that very few doctors or other professional staff had the training, experience or interest to respond in other than an ad hoc manner.

Despite the pleas of William Deedes MP, the Reverend Kenneth Leech and the British Medical Association, who understood the contribution which could still be made by those responsible general practitioners who had previously carried the burden, their invaluable experience had been jettisoned. It would, of course, have been *infra dig* for those who had been vociferous in the condemnation of the part general practitioners were perceived to have played in the creation and development of the heroin problem, then to be seen to be drawing on that experience. Yet, as Connell remarked in 1967, despite the recognition that the setting up of outpatient services 'staffed by people who have little basic knowledge or little basic interest in the problems of addiction may well be disastrous',[66] there was no organised effort, either before or after 16 April 1968, to improve that basic knowledge, or to stimulate the interest of those who would now shoulder the main burden of working with heroin addicts.

It was a deficiency which had still not been repaired by 1982 when the Advisory Council were highly critical of the 'lack of training available to those working with the problem drug takers, whether in the generic services or in more specialised agencies'.[67] It was not until 1990 that the Advisory Council published a report 'to establish a framework from which drugs education and training might appropriately be developed' for the 'main disciplines and all the specialist services' that 'deal with problem drug users and their problems'.[68]

If there were no real disasters, the lack of experience and training did mean there would be errors of judgement – such as the unjustifiable prescribing of opiates to patients who did not require them – while treatment centre staff were gaining experience. The official dawning of the treatment centre era on 16 April 1968 was to be followed by a period of uncertainty and aimlessness which had still not been dispelled by 1982, as shown by the comments of one doctor whose major problem was knowing 'just what we are supposed to be doing as a clinic; and the lack of guidance from anywhere on this subject'.[69]

How much greater was that uncertainty in 1968? An early indication of the extent of the 'really resolute determination' of some of those who would be involved in the new approach had surfaced in the correspondence pages of *The Lancet*. In a letter of 7 December 1968, Dr Ian Pierce James (a psychiatrist, later to be appointed to the Advisory Council on the Misuse of Drugs) estimated that the cost of treating addicts in 1968 would be between £2–3,000,000, and he wondered whether the economy could 'really afford to treat addicts in the way to which they have become accustomed'.[70] This drew support from Dr L. H. Field,[71] who agreed there were no grounds, economic or logical, for treating addicts on the NHS and suggested they should all be treated by the Prison Medical Service in units attached to prisons. Field further commented that:

> The alleged treatment of drug addicts by psychiatrists is merely another example of the lack of humility on the part of psychiatrists and their refusal to face what must be painful to them, namely that there are conditions which are not amenable to their treatment.

This upset Dr F. P. Haldane, then consultant in charge of the treatment centre at the West Middlesex Hospital. In his reply,[72] he explained that:

> ... far from 'undertaking the burden of addiction units' out of 'lack of humility', we agreed to do this with the utmost reluctance and largely because we were told that failure to do so would be socially irresponsible, since there was an imminent danger of a Chicago gangster-style black market developing if we did not. Many of us protested this was a police responsibility. Many psychiatrists who feel obliged to take part in the scheme appreciate perfectly that the idea of successfully 'treating' our present addict population is wildly unrealistic, especially with the resources available.

Haldane was not alone in regarding the 'challenge to the practice of medicine' of treating addicts with some degree of scepticism and rather less than whole-hearted enthusiasm, or in taking such a pessimistic view of the likely outcome of treatment. Some years later, at one of the London consultants' meetings, it was said by one of those who had been involved from the beginning, that when the treatment centres were set up it was anticipated 'they were going to cure very few'. And there are innumerable references in the literature to narcotic addiction being 'a chronic relapsing disorder' with a very poor prognosis.

The Rolleston Committee had accepted that 'relapse, sooner or later, appears to be the rule, and permanent cure the exception',[73] a situation which had not markedly improved by the time the first Brain Committee came to study the problem 30 years later. They found[74] that 'information about the ultimate prognosis for drug addicts is extremely scanty and ... the long-term results have hitherto been disappointing' and suggested this might be due to 'the intractability of the condition and the inadequacy of the treatment'. Moreover, at the first meeting of the Chief Medical Officer's 'experts', in September 1966, it was recognised that there would be addicts who could not be induced to accept inpatient withdrawal treatment or who, having been treated, would still be addicted.

## The effectiveness of treatment

In January 1982 an editorial in *The Lancet* pointed out that because the London treatment centres had co-operated in treatment policies 'specifically to prevent addicts from shopping around for a better deal ... the resultant uniformity of treatment seems to have stultified research into different treatment options'.[75]

In a review in 1981 of the findings of longitudinal studies of drug dependence Dr Anthony Thorley noted, 'Regrettably, and somewhat surprisingly, there are no specific longitudinal studies, controlled or otherwise, which attempt to evaluate the effectiveness or work of the Clinics' (treatment centres).[76] From the study of a random sample of addicts being prescribed heroin by London treatment centres in 1969, all he could conclude was that after seven years, 'something over a third of dependent subjects will cease opiate use and a very small number will have moved to intermittent use'. When these subjects were followed up for ten years it was found that 38% had stopped using heroin and another 38% were still attending a treatment centre, a majority of whom had continuously received prescriptions for opiates throughout the period. The remaining 24% were dead or could not be traced.[77]

In 1982 the Advisory Council drew attention to the dearth of research at the time into 'the questions which might fairly be deemed crucial to any improvement in service organisation or the actual techniques and processes for the treatment and rehabilitation of problem drugs takers'. The Council doubted that it would be possible to demonstrate that 'one type of intervention is in absolute terms "better" than another: the challenge is rather to determine the best match between intervention type and type of patient and client'. Examples of the issues that it thought might be studied included 'maintenance treatment versus no offer of maintenance; maintenance with and without "contract" expectations related to aspects of personal or social change'.[78]

By 1986 the Council's challenge had still to be taken up when Philip Connell argued:[79]

... that in the absence of clear-cut treatments, all efforts to help drug misusers should be supported whatever their philosophical framework since they clearly meet the needs of some drug misusers.

## Government involvement in treatment policy and practice

The attribution, both directly or by implication, to the reconvened Brain Committee and the government, of responsibility for the clinical practices followed in the treatment centres is a common feature of many of the accounts of what happened in the centres after April 1968. The clinical response is often mistakenly interpreted by policy analysts as being the government's 'policy' to deal with the heroin misuse problem instead of what it was, the result of 'discreet peer group pressure', largely reflecting the prejudices and attitudes of a small number of influential medical figures. What then is to be made of the assertion by Stimson and Oppenheimer's anonymous consultant that he and his colleagues had been told, 'In the early days ... you will prescribe [heroin]'[80] and by Gardner[81] in 1970 that it 'remains official policy to prescribe heroin at Treatment Centres' to individuals misusing it?

Paragraph 15 of the second Brain report set neither 'policy' nor 'practice' but merely underlined the dangers inherent in any therapeutic response which involved the supply of 'dangerous drugs' to an addict. As Sir George Godber, the Chief Medical Officer, told the Advisory Committee on Drug Dependence, a few days before Hospital Memorandum H.M.(67)16 was issued in March 1968, the new regime was aimed at 'reducing the size of the black market by eliminating overprescribing'. The consistency of the 'official' position on prescribing was confirmed a few years later in a situation report presented by the Department of Health to the Advisory Council on the Misuse of Drugs which made the point that the provision of a licit supply of drugs to addicts, as a means of 'restricting' the extent of the illicit market, was subordinate to the main objective of regarding addicts as having a medical problem which should be dealt with clinically. By qualifying the reference to the supply of drugs with the words 'whose doctors consider they need them', this report reaffirmed, as had the reconvened Brain Committee and H.M.(67)16, that the decision whether or not to supply an addict with drugs was one for each individual clinician.

Nowadays the heroin addict is most likely to be prescribed oral methadone, as recommended by official, but not legally binding, treatment guidelines issued by the Department of Health in 1984 and 1991,[82] in the drafting of which the treatment centre consultant psychiatrists had considerable influence. But this policy did not result from properly conducted evaluations of the effectiveness in the short and long term of the treatment centre prescribing practices. It was not until March 1995, almost 30 years after the treatment centres were opened, that the National Treatment Outcome Research Study was initiated by the Department of Health.[83]

With the benefit of hindsight there is no doubt that the treatment centre era was an unmitigated disaster, not because the basic idea was wrong but because of the way in which that idea was developed and implemented. What happened was that the moral high ground was seized by a small group within the medical establishment, and by psychiatrists in particular, who, over the years succeeded in imposing their own ethical and judgemental values on treatment policy. As a consequence there is now very little prescribing of heroin, or any injectable drug, to addicts. But this does not mean the British system has failed or been abandoned. The basic principle, that a person addicted to drugs should voluntarily be able to seek medical help which, at the discretion of the doctor, may or may not include the regular prescribing of drugs including heroin, remains intact.

# Notes and references

## Chapter 1

1. The Departmental Committee on Morphine and Heroin Addiction was appointed by John Wheatley, Minister of Health, on 30 September 1924. The Chairman, Sir Humphrey Rolleston, was the President of the Royal College of Physicians and all nine members of the Committee were physicians. The terms of reference of the Committee were:

   > To consider and advise as to the circumstances, if any, in which the supply of heroin and morphine (including preparations including heroin and morphine) to persons suffering from addiction to those drugs may be regarded as medically advisable, and as to the precautions which it is desirable that medical practitioners administering or prescribing heroin or morphine should adopt for the avoidance of abuse, and to suggest any administrative measures that seem expedient for securing observance of such precautions.

   The Minister of Health, Neville Chamberlain, extended these terms of reference on 12 February 1925:

   > To consider and advise whether it is expedient that any or all preparations which contain morphine or heroin of a percentage lower than that specified in the Dangerous Drugs Acts should be brought under the provisions of the Acts and Regulations and, if so, under what conditions.

   The Report of the Committee was published on 24 February 1926.
2. Lindesmith, A. (1965) *The addict and the law*, Bloomington, Indiana: Principia Press.
3. Downes, D. (1977) 'The drug addict as a folk devil', in Rock, P. (ed.) *Drugs and politics*, New Brunswick, NJ: Transaction Books.
4. Turner, D. (1991) 'Pragmatic incoherence: the changing face of British drug policy', in Krauss, M. B. and Lazear, E. P. (eds) *Searching for alternatives: drug control policy in the United States*, Stanford, Calif: Hoover Institution Press.
5. Glaser, F. B. and Ball, J. C. (1971) 'The British Narcotic "Register" in 1970: a factual review', *Journal of the American Medical Association*, 216, pp. 177–182.
6. *British Medical Journal* (1971) 'Transatlantic debate on addiction', 7 August, pp. 321–322.
7. Berridge, V. (1978a) 'War conditions and narcotics control: the passing of Defence of the Realm Act Regulation 40B', *International Social Policy*, 7, pp. 285–304.
8. Berridge, V. (1978b) 'Professionalization and narcotics: the medical and pharmaceutic professions and British narcotic use 1868–1926', *Psychological*

*Medicine*, 8, pp. 361–372.

9. Berridge, V. (1980) 'The making of the Rolleston Report, 1908-1926', *Journal of Drug Issues*, Winter, pp. 7–28.

10. Berridge, V. (1984) 'Drugs and social policy: the establishment of drug control in Britain 1900–1930', *British Journal of Addiction*, 79, pp. 17–29.

11. See *ibid.*, p. 7.

12. Howitt, D. (1990) 'Britain's "substance abuse policy": realities and regulation in the United Kingdom', *International Journal of the Addictions*, 25, pp. 353–376, p. 355.

13. Ministry of Health (1926) *Departmental Committee on Morphine and Heroin Addiction. Report* (The Rolleston Report), London: HMSO. The Rolleston Committee made the only recommendations which involved legislative action in the following paragraphs of their report:

    > (*15*) the Home Secretary should have power to withdraw the authorisation (of a doctor to possess and supply the drugs) without conviction in the Courts, if so advised by a suitably constituted Medical Tribunal ... we recommend that Tribunals should be constituted whose function it would be to consider whether or not there were sufficient medical grounds for the administration of the drugs by the doctor concerned either to the patient or to himself, and that they should advise the Home Secretary whether the doctor's right to be in possession, to administer, and to supply the drugs should be withdrawn.

    > (*16*) any doubt there may be as to the power of the Home Secretary under the present Regulations to control the prescribing of Dangerous Drugs should be removed by suitable amendment to the Regulations ... (and) the Home Secretary should also have power, after conviction of a doctor under the Dangerous Drugs Acts, or on the advice of a Medical Tribunal, to withdraw the practitioner's authorisation to prescribe Dangerous Drugs, and we recommend that this amendment to the Regulations be also made.

    > (*18*) Doctors who do not dispense should be required to keep a simple record of their purchases of Dangerous Drugs. We recommend the Regulations are amended accordingly.

14. Berridge (1980) *op cit.*, p. 23, note 5.

15. Berridge (1978a) *op cit.*, pp. 294–5.

16. Berridge (1978a) *op cit.*, p. 297.

17. Kohn, M. (1992) *Dope girls: The birth of the British drug underground*, London: Lawrence and Wishart, p. 34.

18. PRO HO/45 10813/312966/6.

19. *Report of the Committee on the Use of Cocaine in Dentistry* (1917) London: HMSO. In paragraph 7 of the memorandum to the Report Professor Bayliss comments: 'The evils of the cocaine habit, when acquired, are undisputed. The victim becomes a complete wreck, physically, mentally, and morally. He

would, as one witness said "commit murder to get the drug." ... Although the extent of the cocaine habit may have been somewhat exaggerated, there is no doubt that it is still a serious evil and that continuation of restrictive measures is necessary in order to stop it spreading further.'

20. Berridge, V. (1978a) *op cit.*, p. 300.
21. PRO HO 45/10, 813 and 814.
22. Berridge, V. (1980) *op cit.*, p. 17.
23. Delevingne, M. (1934) 'Some international aspects of the problem of drug addiction', *British Journal of Inebriety*, 32, 125–151, p. 128.
24. Berridge, V. (1980) *op cit.*, p. 17.
25. Parssinen, T. (1983) *Secret passions, secret remedies: narcotic drugs in British society 1820–1930*, Manchester: Manchester University Press, p. 196.
26. PRO MH 58 51.
27. Berridge, V. (1980) *op cit.*, p. 18.
28. Berridge, V. (1980) *op cit.*, p. 19.
29. Rolleston Report, paragraph 11.
30. PRO HO/45 24739/416579.
31. Berridge, V. (1980) *op cit.*, p. 20.
32. Berridge, V. (1984) *op cit.*, p. 26.
33. PRO MH 58 277.
34. Parssinen, T. (1983) *op cit.*, p. 183.
35. Berridge, V. (1980) *op cit.*, p. 21.
36. Berridge, V. (1980) *op cit.*, p. 20.
37. Berridge, V. (1984) *op cit.*, p. 26.
38. Berridge, V. (1978b) *op cit.*, p. 369.
39. Rolleston Report, paragraph 88.
40. Hansard HC (28 February 1923) volume 160 column 2042.
41. Hansard Standing Committees B, C, and D, 12 March to 18 July 1923, column 311.
42. Hansard HC (28 February 1923) volume 160 column 2052.
43. *The Lancet* (1922) 'Self prescription of dangerous drugs', 9 August, p. 406.
44. PRO HO/45 13351/423410.
45. Hansard HC (29 March 1922) volume 162 column 741.
46. PRO HO/45 11285/440177.
47. Berridge, V. (1978a) *op cit.*, p. 291.
48. Berridge, V. (1978b) *op cit.*, p. 365.
49. Rolleston Report, paragraph 74.
50. Berridge, V. (1984) *op cit.*, p. 24.
51. PRO HO/45 11285 440177.
52. PRO HO/45 432, 442, 684, 886.
53. Berridge, V. (1978b) *op cit.*, p. 369.

54. PRO HO/45 451, 408.

55. Hansard HC (1 May 1922) volume 153 column 1014.

56. Hansard HC (28 February 1923) volume 160 columns 2040–2083.

57. PRO HO/144 11913/451408.

58. PRO MH 58 277; HO/144 11913/451408.

59. PRO MH 58 275.

60. Berridge, V. (1980) *op cit.*, p. 19.

61. PRO MH 58 275.

62. Berridge, V. (1980) *op cit.*, p. 20.

63. PRO HO/45 451, 408.

64. Berridge, V. (1984) *op cit.*, p. 25.

65. Berridge, V. (1978b) *op cit.*, p. 369; (1980) *op cit.*, p. 19; (1984) *op cit.*, p. 25.

66. PRO MH 58 275.

67. PRO MH 58 275.

68. Berridge, V. (1980) *op cit.*, p. 20.

69. PRO HO/144 11913/415408.

70. Berridge, V. (1984) *op cit.*, p. 24-25.

71. Berridge, V. (1978b ) *op cit.*, p. 370.

72. Parssinen, T. (1983) *op cit.*, Chapter 12.

73. *Rolleston Report*, Conclusions and Recommendations: Circumstances in which morphine or heroin may legitimately be administered to addicts, paragraph 8.

74. Sir Malcolm Delevingne (1868–1950) represented the Home Office interest in drug matters from 1913 to 1931. Criticisms of him have often been highly personalised. Berridge (1984) comments that 'his obstinacy was more than a match for the Ministry (of Health) officials'. His 'acerbic personality' was said to dominate civil servants from other government departments, a comment which overlooks the fact that this was an age when administrators took decisions quickly, and when 'consultation', as a delaying tactic, had not been developed to the fine art it is today. Berridge quotes a comment from Delevingne's obituary in *The Times* newspaper of 1 December 1950 that he was 'too much of the bureaucrat who thought that to settle a matter you had only to tie it up in a bundle of regulations, preferably of his own drafting' but omits to quote the first words of the sentence 'He sometimes gave the impression to those who did not know him of being … '.

## Chapter 2

1. *The Lancet* (27 February 1926) pp. 448–449. *British Medical Journal* (27 February 1926) pp. 391–393.

2. Ministry of Health and Department of Health for Scotland (1961) *Drug addic-*

*tion: report of the Interdepartmental Committee* (The first Brain Report), London: HMSO, paragraph 50.

3. PRO MH 58 51.

4. Trebach, A. (1982) *The heroin solution*, New Haven: University of Yale Press, pp. 96.

5. Smart, C. (1984) 'Social policy and drug addiction: a critical study of policy development', *British Journal of Addiction*, 79, pp. 31-39, p. 38.

6. Ministry of Health and Scottish Home and Health Department (1965) *Drug addiction: the second report of the Interdepartmental Committee (The second Brain Report)*, London: HMSO.

7. PRO HO/45 24761/431166/9.

8. *Report of HM Government in the United Kingdom of Great Britain and Ireland for 1935 on Opium and other Dangerous Drugs to the League of Nations.* The Chief Inspectorate's report for 1986 noted that the Inspectorate's duties had been confirmed as:

   a supervision of the licit market in controlled drugs;

   b to obtain information of use to Ministers about the scale and nature of drug misuse in the UK;

   c to promote support for Ministers in performing their role in co-ordinating Government action against drug misuse;

   d to take on specific tasks relevant to the Government's strategy which do not fall clearly within the responsibility of another Department of agency.

9. PRO HO/45 24761/431166/21 and 25.

10. *Report of HM Government in the United Kingdom of Great Britain and Northern Ireland for 1935 on opium and other dangerous drugs to the League of Nations*, Section C, paragraph 4b.

11. PRO HO/45 10813 and 10814.

12. PRO MH 58 51.

13. PRO HO/45 19983/402179.

14. PRO HO/45 537258/13a.

15. Cooke, E. (1962) 'The drug squad', *Journal of The Forensic Science Society*, 3, pp. 43–48, p. 43.

16. PRO HO/45 19983/402179 and 402144.

17. Ministry of Health (1926) *Departmental Committee on Morphine and Heroin Addiction. Report* (The Rolleston Report*)*, Paragraphs 23 and 24.

18. League of Nations (1931) Advisory Committee on Traffic in Opium and other Dangerous Drugs, Minutes of the Fourteenth Session, Volume 1, 166, Geneva: League of Nations.

19. Edwards, G. E. (1981) 'The Home Office Index as a basic monitoring system', in Edwards, G. E. and Busch, C. (eds) *Drug problems in Britain: a review of ten years*, London: Academic Press, p. 26.

20. Green, T. C. (1960) 'The incidence of drug addiction in Great Britain and its prevention', *Proceedings of the Royal Society of Medicine*, 53, pp. 921–925.
21. Spear, H. B. (1969) 'The growth of heroin addiction in the United Kingdom', *British Journal of Addiction*, 64, pp. 141–149.
22. Parssinen, T. (1983) *Secret passions, secret remedies: narcotic drugs in British society 1820-1930*, Manchester: University of Manchester Press, pp. 196–7.
23. The Rolleston Report, paragraphs 62–75.
24. Berridge, V. (1980) 'The making of the Rolleston Report 1908–1926', *Journal of Drug Issues*, Winter, 7–28, p. 22.
25. PRO MH 58 276.
26. PRO MH 58 278.
27. The Rolleston Report, paragraph 77.
28. Ministry of Health and Department of Health for Scotland (1961) *Drug addiction: report of the Interdepartmental Committee* (The first Brain Report), London: HMSO, paragraphs 44 and 45.
29. PRO MH 58 277 (Home Office memorandum to the Rolleston Committee.)
30. The Rolleston Report, paragraph 74.
31. The Rolleston Report, paragraph 67.
32. *Dan de Kar v Goodfellow*, 63 Times Law Reports 445 Divisional Court.
33. PRO HO 319 14.
34. *The Times*, 3 March 1942. Criminal Appeal Reports Volume 28 (1943) 131–137.
35. The General Medical Council (1992) *Professional conduct and discipline: fitness to practice*, Part 4.
36. Kohn, M. (1992) *Dope girls: The birth of the British drug underground*, London: Lawrence and Wishart, p. 117.
37. Sister Mildred Rebecca (1970) 'Nine decades of experience in the treatment of alcoholism and drug dependence', in Phillipson, R. V. (ed) *Modern trends in drug dependence and alcoholism*, London: Butterworths, p. 213.
38. The Rolleston Report, paragraph 68.
39. The Rolleston Report, paragraph 67.
40. Hansard HC (3 April 1952) volume 498 column 161.
41. Kohn, M. (1990) 'Grains of truth', *Weekend Guardian*, 1–2 September, pp. 14 and 15.
42. Shapiro, H. (1990) *Waiting for the man*, London: Mandarin Paperbacks, p. 106.
43. Thorpe, R. (1956) *Viper: the confessions of a drug addict*, London: Robert Hale.
44. Jeffery, C. G. (1970) 'Drug control in the United Kingdom', in Phillipson, R. V. (ed.) *Modern trends in drug dependence and alcoholism*, London: Butterworths, p. 66.
45. Spear, H. B. (1969) *op cit.*, Tables 4a and 4b.
46. Lyle, G. (1953) 'Dangerous drugs traffic in London', *British Journal of Addiction*, 50, pp. 47–58.

47. *Criminal Law Review* (1956) p. 326.
48. Section 2 of the Dangerous Drugs Act 1967 gave the Home Secretary similar powers to appoint tribunals but these were limited to dealing with contraventions of the notification and prescribing Regulations and were never used.
49. The tribunal consists of five persons, with a lawyer (always a QC) acting as chairman. The remaining four members are nominated by any of the Royal Colleges, the General Medical Council or the British Medical Association. The quorum for a tribunal is the chairman and two members. Proceedings are held in private and are similar to a court of law with the legal representatives of the Home Office and the doctor offering evidence which is subject to cross examination. The tribunal may recommend that no action is taken or that the doctor is prohibited from prescribing all or specific controlled drugs, if the latter, the Home Secretary will issue a Direction. During the interval between the start of an investigation and the issuing of a Direction, the doctor is free to continue prescribing.
50. Advisory Committee on Drug Dependence (1970) *The amphetamines and lysergic acid diethylamide (LSD)*, London: HMSO, paragraphs 50-63.
51. *British Medical Journal* (1970) 'Dangerous doctors', 21 March, p. 705.
52. Hansard HL (14 January 1971) volume 314 columns 1446-1560.
53. Advisory Council on the Misuse of Drugs (1982) *Treatment and rehabilitation*, London: HMSO, paragraph 7.36.
54. Bean, P. T. (1991) 'Policing the medical profession; the use of tribunals', in Whynes, D. K. and Bean, P. T. (eds) *Policing and prescribing*, London: Macmillan, p. 68.
55. No doctor has been referred to a tribunal since 1994 because no definition of 'irresponsible' prescribing has been agreed. The procedure may also be defective in terms of the Human Rights Act 2000.
56. General Medical Council (1992) *Professional conduct and discipline: fitness to practice*, London: General Medical Council, paragraph 44.
57. General Medical Council (1992) *op cit.*, paragraph 23.
58. House of Commons (1985) *Misuse of Drugs. Fourth Report from the Social Services Committee*, London: HMSO. Minutes of Evidence, 20 February 1985, p. 70 and table on p. 76.

## Chapter 3

1. PRO MH 58/276 (Minutes of the Rolleston Committee).
2. Hansard HC (18 February 1955) Written Answers volume 537 column 94; HL (27 April 1955) volume 192 columns 595–7.
3. Hansard HC (26 January 1956) volume 548 columns 369–371; HL (26 January 1956) volume 195 columns 616–618.

4. Bean, P. T. (1974) *The social control of drugs*, London: Martin Robertson, pp. 136–139.

5. Bartrip, P. (1996) *Themselves writ large: the British Medical Association 1832 to 1996*, London: BMJ Publishing Group, Chapter 12, pp. 304–312.

6. PRO HO/45 24817/454912.

7. House Committee on Ways and Means, 68th Congress, Hearings before the Committee on Ways and Means House of Representatives on HR 7079 A Bill prohibiting the importation of crude opium for the manufacture of heroin, 1st Session, 3 April 1924, Washington: Government Printing Office.

8. Musto, D. F. (1987) *The American disease: origins of narcotic control*, New York: Oxford University Press Inc, pp. 200 and 354–355, notes 62–65.

9. PRO HO/45 24817/454912.

10. PRO HO/45 24817/454912.

11. World Health Organization (1949) *First report of the expert committee on habit-forming drugs*, Official record of the World Health Organization, 19, 29.

12. *British Medical Journal* (1949) 15 January, pp. 107–8.

13. Ross, J. (1949) Letter, *British Medical Journal*, 15 February, p. 240.

14. Hartsilver, J. (1949) Letter, *The Lancet*, 26 March, pp. 547–548.

15. PRO MH 58 689.

16. HM Government (1946, 1948 and 1949) *The traffic in opium and other dangerous drugs*, Report to the United Nations.

17. *The Chemist and Druggist* (1949) 3 September, p. 314

18. HO/45 24817/454912.

19. PRO MH 58 689.

20. PRO MH 58 689.

21. Hansard HC (1 February 1951) volume 483 column 1056; PRO HO45 24817/454912.

22. HO/45 24817/454912.

23. *British Medical Journal* (1953) 25 July, p. 196.

24. PRO HO 319/7.

25. PRO HO 319/7.

26. Hansard HC (18 February 1955) volume 537 column 94.

27. Douthwaite, A. (1955) Letter, *British Medical Journal*, 9 April, p. 338.

28. *British Medical Journal* (1953) 25 July, p. 196.

29. Douthwaite, A. (1953) Letter, *British Medical Journal*, 8 August, p. 338.

30. PRO MH 58 68931.

31. Bartrip, P. (1996) *op cit.*, p. 306 (Resolution never reached the World Medical Association).

32. PRO HO 319/7.

33. Hansard HL (27 April 1955) volume 192 columns 595–7.

34. PRO MH 58 689.

35. Spear, H. B. (1969) 'The growth of heroin addiction in the United Kingdom', *British Journal of Addiction*, 64, pp. 245–256, Table 2a.

36. Hansard HL (8 December 1955) volume 194 columns 1231–2.

37. Donald, A. G. (1955) Letter, *British Medical Journal* 21 May, p. 1277.

38. *British Medical Journal* (1955) 18 June, Supplement, pp. 289–290.

39. Hansard HC (16 June 1955) volume 324 columns 241–3.

40. PRO MH 58 689.

41. Southwood, W. E. W. (1955) Letter, *The Lancet*, 11 June, p. 1227.

42. Laurence, D. R. (1955) Letter, *The Lancet*, 18 June, pp. 1277–1278.

43. *The Lancet* (1955) Heroin, 25 June, pp. 1311–1312.

44. PRO HO 319/7.

45. Bartrip, P. (1996) *op cit.*, p. 309. (This unleashed a further flood of protest and for the next few weeks the columns of *The Times* newspaper and the medical press were seldom without some comment on the issue, the vast majority being opposed to the proposed ban.)

46. PRO MH 58 689.

47. Conybeare, J. J. (1955) Letter, *The Lancet*, 25 June, p. 1331.

48. CP (185) 44(4), 46(1); CM(55)44.

49. *The Lancet* (1955) Heroin, 3 December, pp. 1180–1181.

50. Pringle, J. (1955) *Heroin: the BMA case against the ban*, London: British Medical Association.

51. PRO MH 58 689.

52. Hansard HC (5 December 1995) volume 547 columns 25–29.

53. PRO HO 319/7.

54. Bartrip, P. (1996) *op cit.*, p. 309 (BMA takes Counsel's advice)

55. PRO HO 319/7.

56. PRO CM (55).

57. PRO HO 319/7.

58. PRO CM (56).

59. Hansard HL (26 January 1956) volume 195 columns 616–618; HC (26 January 1956) volume 548 columns 369–371.

60. Hansard HL (13 December 1955) volume 145 columns 10–46.

61. MH 58 689.

62. *British Medical Journal* (1955) 30 April, p. 1092.

63. *British Medical Journal* (1955) 24 December, pp. 1544–1545

64. *The Lancet* (1955) Heroin, 25 June, pp. 1311–1312.

65. *British Medical Journal* (1924) 22 March, p. 535.

66. PRO HO 319/7.

67. World Health Organization Expert Committee on Drugs Liable to Produce Addiction (1958) 8th Report.

68. The *British National Formulary* is prepared jointly by the British Medical

Association and the Royal Pharmaceutical Society of Great Britain. It provides doctors and pharmacists with up-to-date information on the prescribing, dispensing and administration of medicines.

69. *British National Formulary*, Number 29, March 1995, p. 12. In issue Number 39, March 2000 (p. 12), this advice was unchanged; diamorphine is also used in the treatment of myocardial infarction (p. 120).

70. *British National Formulary*, Number 29, March 1995, p. 12.

## Chapter 4

1. Ministry of Health and Department of Health for Scotland (1961) *Drug addiction: report of the Interdepartmental Committee* (The first Brain Report), London: HMSO.

2. Bean, P. T. (1974) *The social control of drugs*, London: Martin Robertson, p. 74.

3. Stimson, G. V. and Oppenheimer, E. (1982) *Heroin addiction: treatment and control in Britain*, London: Tavistock, p. 40.

4. See Chapter 2 and Spear, H. B. (1969) 'The growth of heroin addiction in the United Kingdom', *British Journal of Addiction*, 64, pp. 245–255.

5. PRO HO 319/1.

6. PRO HO 319/1.

7. See discussion on Undertakings in Chapter 2.

8. Hansard HC (3rd April 1952) volume 498 column 161.

9. PRO HO 319/1.

10. PRO HO 319/1.

11. PRO MH 58/564.

12. PRO HO 319/1.

13. PRO HO 319/1 (Joint Home Office/Ministry of Health memorandum).

14. In 1945 the practice was abandoned of retaining an addict's card in the Addicts' Index for ten years after the last information about the addict was received, except in the case of death. Henceforth, cards were to be retained for only one year, although there are grounds for believing that this was not strictly adhered to and that the Index continued to include as 'active' some addicts about whom there had been no information for some years.

15. Spear, H. B. (1969) *op cit.*, Table 2a.

16. PRO HO 319/1 (Joint Home Office/Ministry of Health memorandum, paragraphs 15–20).

17. PRO HO 319/1 (Joint Home Office/Ministry of Health memorandum, paragraphs 20(iv) and 24).

18. HO 319/1 (Joint Home Office/Ministry of Health memorandum, paragraphs 17, 20(iii)).

19. Smart, C. (1980) 'Social policy and drug dependence: an historical case his-

tory', *Drug and Alcohol Dependence*, 16, 169–180, p. 171.

20. PRO MH 58 566.

21. Brain, R. (1961) 'The report of the Interdepartmental Committee', *British Journal of Addiction*, 57, 81–103, p. 92.

22. The first Brain Report, *op cit.*, paragraphs 37 and 24.

23. Freeman, H. (1990) 'In conversation with A. A. Baker', *Psychiatric Bulletin*, 14, pp. 386–394, p. 391.

24. Spear, H. B. (1969) *op cit.*

25. The first Brain Report, *op cit.*, paragraph 26.

26. The first Brain Report, *op cit.*, paragraph 38.

27. The first Brain Report, *op cit.*, paragraph 41.

28. PRO MH 58 568.

29. The first Brain Report, *op cit.*, paragraph 44.

30. The first Brain Report, *op cit.*, paragraph 45.

31. PRO HO 319/1.

32. *The Lancet* (1961) 'Drug addiction', 27 May, pp. 1153–1154.

33. Brain, R. (1961) *op cit.*, 92, 93.

34. Benjamin, I. (1968) 'The control of drug use in the United Kingdom', in Wilson, C. W. M (ed.) *The pharmacological and epidemiological aspects of adolescent drug dependence*, London: Pergamon Press.

## Chapter 5

1. Ministry of Health and Department of Health for Scotland (1961) *Drug addiction: report of the Interdepartmental Committee* (The first Brain Report), London: HMSO, paragraph 54.

2. *Report of HM Government in the United Kingdom of Great Britain and Northern Ireland for 1932 on opium and other dangerous drugs to the League of Nations*, paragraph 7.

3. Lyle, G. (1953) 'Dangerous drugs traffic in London', *British Journal of Addiction*, 50, pp. 47–58.

4. *The traffic in opium and other dangerous drugs. Report to the United Nations by HM Government in the United Kingdom of Great Britain and Northern Ireland*, 1947, Section V, paragraph 1.

5. *The traffic in opium and other dangerous drugs. Report to the United Nations by HM Government in the United Kingdom of Great Britain and Northern Ireland*, 1950, Section V, paragraph 1.

6. Lyle, G. (1953) *op cit.* The paper includes vivid descriptions of raids on opium dens in Soho and 'bebop' clubs in the 1940s and early 1950s as well as verbatim witness statements.

7. Kohn, M. (1992) *Dope girls: The birth of the British drug underground*, London:

Lawrence and Wishart, p. 181.

8. Howe, R. (1955) Book review, *British Journal of Delinquency*, 5, p. 244.

9. The first Brain Report, *op cit.*, paragraphs 59 and 60.

10. Hansard HC (10 July 1960) volume 643 column 22.

11. Annual Report of the Chief Medical Officer of the Ministry of Health for the Year 1954 (1955) Part 2, London: HMSO, p. 109.

12. Advisory Committee on Drug Dependence (1970) *The amphetamines and lysergic acid diethylamide (LSD)*, London: HMSO, paragraph 16.

13. Connell, P. H. (1958) *Amphetamine psychosis*, London: Chapman. Kiloh, L. G. and Brandon, S. (1962) 'Habituation and addiction to amphetamines', *British Medical Journal*, 7 July, pp. 40-43.

14. Leech, K. (1973) *Keep the faith Baby*, London: SPCK. Leech, K. (1991) 'The junkies' doctors and the London drug scene in the 1960s: some remembered fragments', in Whynes, D. K. and Bean, P. T. (eds) *Policing and prescribing*, London: Macmillan.

15. Hansard HC (4 April 1963) volume 675 column 54.

16. Hansard HC (30 January 1964) volume 688 columns 85–86.

17. Hansard HC (27 February 1964) volume 690 column 104.

18. Hansard HC (30 April 1964) volume 694 column 671.

19. Shapiro, H. (1988) *Waiting for the man*, London: Mandarin, p. 112.

20. Wilson, C. W. M. (1968) 'Sources of drugs for the drug-using culture', in Wilson, C. W. M. (ed.) *The pharmacological and epidemiological aspects of adolescent drug dependence*, Oxford: Pergamon Press, cited on p. 266.

21. Hansard HL (7 July 1964) volume 250 column 967.

22. *The Lancet* (1964) 'Drug addiction', 15 February, p. 392.

23. Hansard HC (3 February 1964) volume 688 column 121.

24. Hansard HC (10 March 1964) volume 691 column 35.

25. Hansard HC (30 April 1964) volume 694 column 635.

26. Hansard HC (22 June 1964) volume 697 columns 165.

27. Alstead, S. (1964) Letter, *The Lancet*, 15 August, p. 363.

28. Ministry of Health and Scottish Home and Health Department (1965) *Drug addiction: the second report of the Interdepartmental Committee*, London: HMSO, paragraphs 39 and 40.

29. *British Medical Journal* (1965) 'Loophole for pep pills', 20 March, p. 739.

30. Hansard HC (5 May 1966) volume 727 columns 1853–4.

31. Advisory Committee on Drug Dependence (1970) *op cit.*

32. *British Medical Journal* (1968) 'Voluntary restriction of amphetamines', 20 November, p. 533.

33. Hansard HC (30 April 1964) volume 694 column 649.

34. Hansard HC (30 April 1964) volume 694 column 673.

35. The Drugs (Prevention of Misuse) Act 1964 provided for bringing other sub-

stances under its control. There was enough evidence of the increasing use of LSD (lysergic acid diethylamide) and other hallucinogenic drugs for their being brought under the control of the Act.

## Chapter 6

1. 'Non-therapeutic addicts' refers to persons whose addiction originated other than from the administration of dangerous drugs for medical treatment of organic disease or injury.
2. Ministry of Health and Scottish Home and Health Department (1965) *Drug addiction: the second report of the Interdepartmental Committee* (The second Brain Report), London: HMSO, paragraph 8 and Appendix 1.
3. Bean, P. T. (1974) *The social control of drugs*, London: Martin Robertson, p. 79.
4. Berridge, V. (1990) 'Special issue: The British Society for the Study of Addiction', *British Journal of Addiction*, 85, p. 1058, The London Committee for the Study of Drug Addiction, 'which affiliated itself to the Society', was founded by Drs Thomas Bewley and Peter Chapple in February 1965, nine months after the Interdepartmental Committee was reconvened. They gave oral evidence to the Interdepartmental Committee on 29 October 1964.
5. Ministry of Health and Department of Health for Scotland (1961) *Drug addiction: report of the Interdepartmental Committee* (The first Brain Report), London: HMSO, paragraph 24.
6. Frankau, I. M. and Stanwell, P. M. (1960) 'The treatment of drug addiction', *The Lancet*, 24 December, pp. 1377–1379.
7. Stungo, E. (1961) Letter, *The Lancet*, 7 January, p. 56; Frankau, I. M. Letter, 21 January, pp. 168–9; Stungo, E. Letter, 28 January, pp. 228–9; Frankau, I. M. and Stanwell, P. (1961) 4 February, pp. 279–280.
8. Beckett, Dale, Personal communication.
9. Second Brain Report, paragraph 11.
10. Hewetson, J. and Ollendorf, R. (1964) 'Preliminary survey of one hundred London addicts', *British Journal of Addiction*, 60, pp. 109–114.
11. Cooke, E. (1962) 'The drug squad', *Journal of The Forensic Science Society*, 3, pp. 43–48. Sergeant Ernie Cooke was the head of the Metropolitan Police Drug Squad in 1962. In this paper (p. 45) he noted that because the heroin being trafficked in London was always in tablet form he was in no doubt that:

    > ... the supplies originate from the addict's own authorised supplies – to defray his expenses – or from supplies obtained by forged or stolen prescriptions, or by stealing the drugs from manufacturers, chemists, hospitals etc ... is there not a danger of over-prescribing dangerous drugs?

12. PRO HO 319/2. The minutes of the first five meetings of the Committee are very brief and terse and I have fleshed them out with my own recollections

and from notes and minutes by Home Office and Ministry of Health officials. If there were any minutes of the last three meetings I have been unable to locate them.

13. Second Brain Report, paragraph 6.

14. Second Brain Report, paragraph 43.

15. Second Brain Report, paragraph 42.

16. Bewley, T. (1965) 'Heroin and cocaine addiction', *The Lancet*, April 10, pp. 808–810.

17. Partridge, M. (1967) 'Drug addiction – a brief review', *International Journal of the Addictions*, 2, pp. 207–220, pp. 207 and 209.

18. *British Medical Journal* (1966) 22 January, Supplement, p. 18.

19. Second Brain Report, paragraphs 31–36.

20. *British Medical Journal* (1965) 27 November, pp. 1259–1260.

21. *The Lancet* (1965) 27 November, pp. 1113–1114.

22. Berridge (1990) *op cit.*, p. 1058.

23. *The Sunday Times* newspaper, 20 February 1966, p. 25. The article contains interviews with nine prescribers. Lady Frankau is described as 'Dr P. a white-haired Scotswoman who runs an extensive private practice in Central London'.

24. Second Brain Report, paragraph 13.

25. Hawes, J. (1965) Letter, *The Lancet*, 18 December, p. 1294.

26. Hewetson, J. (1966) 'Narcotic addiction and the Brain Committee. Report by a physician', *Anarchy* 60, 6, pp. 33–39.

27. Ollendorf, R. V. (1966) 'Drug addiction and the Brain Report', *Journal of the Liverpool Psychiatric Society*, 4, pp. 31–35.

28. Second Brain Report, paragraph 11.

29. Imlah, N. (1970) *Drugs and modern society*, London: Edward Chapman.

30. Young, J. 1971) *The drugtakers: the social meaning of drug use*, London: Paladin, pp. 206–208.

31. Glatt, M., Pittman, D. J., Gillespie, D. G. and Hills, D. R. (1967) *The drug scene in Great Britain*, London: Edward Arnold.

32. Blackwell, J. (1988) 'The saboteurs of Britain's opiate policy: over-prescribing doctors or American-style "Junkies"?', *International Journal of the Addictions*, 23, pp. 517–526.

33. Second Brain Report, paragraph 12.

34. Leech, K. (1981) 'John Petro, the junkies' doctor', *New Society*, 1 June, pp. 430–432.

35. Stimson, G. V. (1973) *Heroin and behaviour*, New York: Halstead Press, p. 26.

36. Hawes, J. (1965) Letter, *The Lancet*, 18 December, p. 1294.

37. Jeffery, C. G. (1970) 'Drug control in the United Kingdom', in Phillipson, R. V. (ed.) *Modern trends in drug dependence and alcoholism*, London: Butter-

worths, p. 67.

38. Hansard HC (8 May 1968) volume 764 column 156.

39. Hansard HC (8 May 1968) volume 764 columns 163–173.

40. Leech, K. (1991) 'The junkies' doctors and the London drug scene in the 1960s: some remembered fragments', in Whynes, D. K. and Bean, P. T. (eds) *Policing and prescribing*, London: Macmillan, p. 39.

41. Frankau, I. M. (1964) Letter, *The Lancet*, 15 August, p. 363.

42. Imlah, N. (1970) *op cit.*, p. 42.

43. Strang, J. *et al.* (1993) 'Cocaine in the UK – 1991', *British Journal of Psychiatry*, 162, pp. 1–13, p. 2.

44. Spear, H. B. and Glatt, M. M. (1971) 'The influence of Canadian addicts on heroin addiction in the United Kingdom', *British Journal of Addiction*, 66, pp. 141–149. Zacune, J. (1971) 'A comparison of Canadian narcotic addicts in Great Britain and Canada', *Bulletin on Narcotics*, 23, pp. 41–49.

45. Frankau, I. M. (1964) 'The treatment in England of Canadian patients addicted to narcotic drugs', *Canadian Medical Association Journal*, 90, pp. 421–424.

46. Spear, H. B. and Glatt, M. M. (1971) *op cit.*, p. 147.

47. Smart, C. (1985) 'Social policy and drug dependence: an historical case study', *Drug and Alcohol Dependence*, 16, pp. 169–180, p. 173.

## Chapter 7

1. Spear, H. B. (1969) 'The growth of heroin addiction in the United Kingdom', *British Journal of Addiction*, 64, pp. 245–256, Table 2a.

2. PRO HO 287 249.

3. Ministry of Health and Scottish Home and Health Department (1965) *Drug addiction. the second report of the Interdepartmental Committee* (The second Brain Report), London: HMSO, paragraph 24.

4. Smart, C. (1985) 'Social policy and drug dependence: an historical case study', *Drug and Alcohol Dependence*, 16, pp. 169–180, pp. 176 and 177.

5. The second Brain Report, paragraphs 31–36.

6. The second Brain Report, paragraph 19.

7. *British Medical Journal* (1966) Supplement, 22 January, pp. 16–19.

8. PRO HO 319/2.

9. Hansard HC (8 May 1967) volume 746 column 1997.

10. Smart, C. (1985) *op cit.*, p. 176.

11. Phillipson, R. V. (1970) 'The implementation of the second report of the Interdepartmental Committee on Drug Addiction', in Phillipson, R. V. (ed.) *Modern trends in drug dependence and alcoholism*, London: Butterworths.

12. Glancy, J. E. McA. (1972) 'The treatment of narcotic addiction in the United

Kingdom', *Bulletin on Narcotics*, XXIV, pp. 1–9.

13. Edwards, G. E. (1978) 'Some years on: evolutions of the "British system"', in West, D. J. (ed.) *Problems of drug abuse in Britain*, University of Cambridge Institute of Criminology, p. 4.

14. Leech, K. (1973) *Keep the faith Baby*, London: SPCK. Leech, K. (1991) 'The junkies' doctors and the London drug scene in the 1960s: some remembered fragments', in Whynes, D. K. and Bean, P. T. (eds) *Policing and prescribing*, London: Macmillan,

15. Hansard HC (2 August 1966) volume 733 columns 83–84.

16. Smart, C. (1985) *op cit.*, p. 176.

17. Connell, P. H. (1986) '"I need heroin". Thirty years' experience of drug dependence and of the medical challenges at local, national, international and political level. What next?', *British Journal of Addiction*, 81, pp. 461–472, p. 462.

18. First Brain Report, paragraph 36.

19. Hansard HC (29 November 1965) volume 721 columns 102, 985–986.

20. Hansard HC (31 January 1966) volume 723 column 153.

21. Hansard HC (14 February 1966) volume 724 column 910.

22. Hansard HC (28 April 1966) volume 727 column 50.

23. Hansard HC (5 May 1966) volume 727 columns 1853–1854.

24. Hansard HC (9 May 1966) volume 728 column 9.

25. Hansard HC (20 June 1966) volume 730 columns 3–4, 6.

26. Hansard HC (4 July 1966) volume 731 column 1.

27. Hansard HC (2 August 1966) volume 733 columns 83–84.

28. Leech, K. (1991) *op cit.*, p. 48.

29. Hansard HC (3 August 1966) volume 733 column 643.

30. Hansard HC (5 December 1966) volume 737 column 916.

31. Chapple, P. A. L. (1975), personal papers.

32. Hansard HC (30 January 1967) volume 740 columns 121–174.

33. Hansard HC (26 January 1967) volume 739 columns 1745–1746.

34. Hansard HC (6 April 1967) volume 744 column 526.

35. Leech, K. (1991) *op cit.*, pp. 47–50.

36. Hansard HL (20 June 1967) volume 283 column 1316.

37. Hansard HC (26 June 1967) volume 749 columns 76–77.

38. Leech, K. (1991) *op cit.*, p. 49, pp. 58–59.

39. Hansard HC (3 July 1967) volume 749 columns 1237–9.

40. Hansard HL (5 July 1967) volume 284 columns 720–753.

41. Hansard HL (19 July 1967) volume 285 columns 356–8.

42. Hansard HL (14 July 1967) volume 284 columns 1344–46.

43. Hansard HC (25 July 1967) volume 751 column 623.

44. Hansard HC (25 July 1967) volume 751 column 636.

45. Hawes, J. (1967) Letter, *The Lancet*, 22 July, p. 208.

46. Hansard HC (6 April 1967) volume 744 columns 472–536.

47. Advisory Council on the Misuse of Drugs (1982) *Treatment and rehabilitation*, London: HMSO, paragraph 4.10.

48. Hansard HC (25 January 1967) volume 740 columns 121–174.

49. Hansard HC (13 February 1967) volume 741 column 88.

50. Hansard HC (6 April 1967) volume 744 column 483.

51. Hansard HC (6 April 1967) volume 744 columns 530–531.

52. Hansard HC (6 April 1967) volume 744 column 531.

53. Hansard HL (20 June 1967) volume 283 columns 1291, 1310.

54. Hansard HC (26 July 1966) volume 732 column 248.

55. Hansard HC (4 July 1966) volume 731 column 5–6.

56. Advisory Committee on Drug Dependence (1968) *Cannabis*; (1968) *The rehabilitation of drug addicts*; (1970) *The amphetamines and lysergic acid diethylamide (LSD)*; (1970) *Powers of arrest and search in relation to drugs offences*, London: HMSO.

57. *British Medical Journal* (1967) 'Realism and addicts', 25 November, pp. 436–437.

58. *The Lancet* (1967) 'Advice on addiction', 25 November, pp. 1131–1132.

59. Hansard HC (30 January 1968) volume 757 columns 260–1.

60. Hansard HC (6 May 1968) volume 764 column 154.

61. Hansard HC (6 May 1968) volume 764 column 167.

62. Second Brain Report, paragraph 22.

63. Connell, P. H. (1986) *op cit.*, p. 463.

64. Interview: in conversation with A. A. Baker (1990) *Psychiatric Bulletin*, 14, pp. 386–396, p. 391.

65. Advisory Council on the Misuse of Drugs (1982) *op cit.*, paragraphs 4.10, 4.11.

## Chapter 8

1. Ministry of Health and Scottish Home and Health Department (1965) *Drug addiction: the second report of the Interdepartmental Committee* (The second Brain Report) London: HMSO. At paragraph 17, the Committee suggested the definition an addict 'should be on the following lines':

> A person who, as the result of repeated administration, has become dependent upon a drug controlled by the Dangerous Drugs Act and has an overpowering desire for its continuance, but who does not require it for the relief of organic disease.

2. Second Brain Report, paragraph 18.

3. Ministry of Health and Department of Health for Scotland (1961) *Drug addiction: report of the Interdepartmental Committee* (The first Brain Report), London: HMSO, paragraph 26.

4. First Brain Report, paragraph 18.

5. Second Brain Report, paragraph 31.

6. Second Brain Report, paragraph 35.

7. *British Medical Journal* (1965) 'Control of drug addiction', 27 November, pp. 1259–1260.

8. *The Lancet* (1965) 'Drug addiction', 27 November, pp. 1113–1114.

9. *British Medical Journal* (1966) Supplement, 22 January, pp. 16–19.

10. House of Commons (1985) *Fourth Report from the Social Services Committee: Misuse of Drugs*, London: HMSO, Minutes of evidence, paragraph 632.

11. Advisory Council on the Misuse of Drugs (1991) *Interim report of the Addicts Index Working Group*, Unpublished.

12. PRO MH 58 275 (Home Office memorandum paragraph 7).

13. Rolleston Report, paragraph 80.

14. Rolleston Report, paragraph 82.

15. First Brain Report, paragraph 67(2)).

16. Spear, H. B. (1991) SCODA Newsletter, February/March, p. 11

17. Second Brain Report, paragraph 19.

18. Smart, C. (1984) 'Social policy and drug addiction: a critical study of policy development', *British Journal of Addiction*, 79, pp. 31–40, p. 38.

19. Johnson, B. D. ( 1975) 'Understanding British addiction statistics', *Bulletin on Narcotics*, XXVII, pp. 49–66; (1975) 'Interpreting official British statistics on addiction', *International Journal of the Addictions*, 10, pp. 557–587.

20. Edwards, G. E. (1981) 'The Home Office Index as a basic monitoring system', in Edwards, G. E. and Busch, C. (eds) *Drug problems in Britain: a review of ten years*, London: Academic Press, p. 29.

21. First Brain Report, paragraph 26.

22. PRO HO 319 1 (Home Office memorandum para 12).

23. Mott, J. (1994) 'Notification and the Home Office', in Strang, J. and Gossop, M. (eds) *Heroin addiction and drug policy: the British system*, Oxford: Oxford University Press, p. 274.

24. Smart, R. G. and Ogborne, A. (1974) 'Losses to the addict notification system', *British Journal of Addiction*, 69, pp. 225–230.

25. Second Brain Report, paragraph 20.

26. Freeman, H. (1968) Letter, *The Lancet*, 16 March, p. 589.

27. Fullerton, A. G. 1968) Letter, *The Lancet*, 23 March, p. 640.

28. Mott, J. and Macmillan, J. (1979) 'The validity of addict notifications', *British Journal of Psychiatry*, 134, pp. 264–268.

29. *The Lancet* (1964) 'Anonymous review of Schur, E. *Narcotic addiction in Britain and America*', 22 February, p. 418.

30. Edwards, G. E. (1981) *op cit.*, p. 25.

31. Second Brain Report, paragraph 20.

32. Corkery, J. (1997) 'Statistics of Drug Addicts Notified to the Home Office, United Kingdom, 1996', *Home Office Statistical Bulletin*, Issue 22/97, paragraphs 1–4.

## Chapter 9

1. Connell, P. H. (1969) 'Drug dependence in Great Britain: a challenge to the practice of medicine', in Steinberg, H. (ed.) *The scientific basis of drug dependence*, London: J & A Churchill.
2. *The Lancet* (1967) 'Advice on addiction', 27 November, pp. 1131–1132.
3. First Brain Report, paragraph 27.
4. The Rolleston Report, paragraphs 27–28.
5. Second Brain Report, paragraph 18.
6. Second Brain Report, paragraph 22.
7. *British Medical Journal* (1966) Supplement, 22 January, pp. 16–19, p. 17.
8. Interview (1990) 'In conversation with A. A. Baker', *Psychiatric Bulletin*, 14, pp. 386–394, p. 391.
9. Advisory Council on the Misuse of Drugs (1982) *Treatment and rehabilitation*, London: HMSO, paragraph 6.23.
10. Advisory Committee on Drug Dependence (1968) *The rehabilitation of drug addicts*, London: HMSO.
11. Interview (1994) 'Conversation with Vincent Dole', *Addiction*, 89, pp. 23–30, p. 26.
12. First Brain Report, paragraph 29.
13. Partridge, M. (1967) 'Drug addiction – a brief review', *International Journal of the Addictions*, 2, pp. 207–220.
14. Hewetson, R. and Ollendorff, R. (1964) 'Preliminary survey of one hundred London heroin and cocaine addicts', *British Journal of Addiction*, 60, pp. 109–114.
15. Merry, J. (1967) 'Out-patient treatment of heroin addiction', *The Lancet*, 28 January, pp. 205–206.
16. *The Times*, 2 December 1975, Obituary for Dr P. A. L. Chapple.
17. Hansard HC (6 May 1968) volume 764 columns 163–173.
18. Smart, C. (1984) 'Social policy and drug addiction: a critical study of policy development', *British Journal of Addiction*, 79, pp. 31–40, p. 37.
19. *British Medical Journal* (1966) Supplement, 22 January, pp. 16–19, p. 17.
20. Bickford, J. A. R. *et al.* (1967) Letter, *British Medical Journal*, 18 March, p. 701.
21. Dales, M. (1967) Letter, *British Medical Journal*, 1 April, p. 53–54.
22. Heber, B. (1967) Letter, *British Medical Journal*, 1 July, p. 48.
23. *The Lancet* (1965) 'Drug addiction', 27 November, pp. 1113–1114.
24. Stimson, G. V. and Oppenheimer, E. (1982) *Heroin addiction: treatment and*

*control in Britain*, London: Tavistock, p. 216.

25. Judson, H. F. (1974) *Heroin addiction in Britain*, London: Harcourt Brace Jovanovich, pp. 90 and 91.

26. Hobson, J. A. (1956) 'The proposed legislation banning the legal production of heroin in Great Britain', *British Journal of Addiction*, 53, pp. 48–50, p. 50.

27. Hawes, J. (1967) Letter, *British Medical Journal*, 3 June, p. 641.

28. Connell, P. H. (1967) 'Importance of research', *British Medical Journal*, 20 May, pp. 499–500, p. 499.

29. Bewley, T. H. (1967) 'Advantages of special centres', *British Medical Journal*, 20 May, pp. 500–501.

30. Connell, P. H. (1967) *op cit.*

31. Chapple, P. A. L. (1967) 'Treatment in the community', *British Medical Journal*, 20 May, pp. 500–501.

32. Owens, J. (1967) 'Integrated approach', *British Medical Journal*, 20 May, pp. 501–502.

33. Lart, R. (1992) 'Changing images of the addict and addiction', *International Journal on Drug Policy*, 3, pp. 118–125, p. 123.

34. *British Medical Journal* (1967) 'Drug treatment centres', 20 May, pp. 455–456.

35. Connell, P. H. (1969) *op cit.*

36. Connell, P. H. (1991) 'Treatment of drug-dependent patients 1968–1969', *British Journal of Addiction*, 86, pp. 913–915.

37. Bewley, T. (1965) 'Heroin and cocaine addiction', *The Lancet*, 10 April, pp. 808–810.

38. Edwards, G. E. (1967) 'Relevance of American experience of narcotic addiction to the British scene', *British Medical Journal*, 12 August, pp. 425–429.

39. Glatt, M. M. (1966) 'A review of the second report of the Interdepartmental Committee on Drug Addiction', *Bulletin on Narcotics*, XVIII, No.2, pp. 29–42, p. 40.

40. Second Brain Report, paragraph 26.

41. *British Medical Journal* (1966) Supplement, 22 January, pp. 16–19, p. 17.

42. *British Medical Journal* (1967) 'Measures against drug addiction', 11 February, pp. 319–320.

43. *British Medical Journal* (1967) 'Drug treatment centres', 20 May, pp. 455–456.

44. Merry, J. (1968) 'USA and British attitudes to heroin addiction and treatment centres', *British Journal of Addiction*, 63, pp. 247–250.

45. Kosviner, A. *et al.* (1968) 'Heroin use in a provincial town', *The Lancet*, 1 June, pp. 1189–1191.

46. Camps, F. E. (1970) 'The forensic aspects of addiction', in Phillipson, R. V. (ed.) *Modern trends in drug dependence and alcoholism*, London: Butterworths, p. 199.

47. *The Lancet* (1968) 'Centres for the treatment of addiction', 10 February, pp. 288–289.

48. Connell, P. H. (1967) *op cit.*, p. 499.

49. Mullin, P. (1965) Letter, *The Lancet*, 18 December, p. 1294.

50. Glatt, M. M. (1966) *op cit.*, p. 39.

51. *British Medical Journal* (1966) Supplement, 22 January, pp. 16–19, p. 18.

52. Chapple, P. A. L. (1966) Letter, *The Lancet*, 12 February, p. 365.

53. Greenwood, J. (1992) 'Persuading general practitioners to prescribe – good husbandry or a recipe for chaos?', *British Journal of Addiction*, 87, pp. 567–575.

54. Hansard HC (6 April 1967) volume 744 column 512.

55. Hansard HC (8 May 1967) volume 746 column 1002.

56. Hansard HC (6 May 1968) volume 764 columns 156, pp. 163–173.

57. Hawes, A. J. (1968) Letter, *The Lancet*, 27 April, p. 925.

58. Hansard HC (6 April 1967) volume 744 column 532.

59. Smart, C. (1985) 'Social policy and drug dependence: an historical case study', *Drug and Alcohol Dependence*, 16, pp. 169–180, pp. 176 and 177.

60. Stimson, G. V. and Oppenheimer, E. (1982) *op cit.*, pp. 113, 205.

## Chapter 10

1. Edwards, G. E. (1969) 'The British approach to the treatment of heroin addiction', *The Lancet*, 12 April, pp. 768–771, p. 768.

2. Stimson, G. V. and Oppenheimer, E. (1982) *Heroin addiction: treatment and control in Britain*, London: Tavistock, p. 61.

3. Second Brain Report, paragraph 23.

4. Leech, K. (1991) 'The junkies' doctors and the London drug scene in the 1960s: some remembered fragments', in Whynes, D. K. and Bean, P. T. (eds) *Policing and prescribing*, London: Macmillan, pp. 52–53.

5. Bewley, T. (1965) 'Heroin and cocaine addiction', *The Lancet*, 10 April, pp. 808–810.

6. Hansard HC (30 January 1967) volume 740 columns 121–174.

7. Leech, K. (1981) 'John Petro, the junkies' doctor', *New Society*, 1 June, pp. 430–432,

8. *British Medical Journal* (1970) Supplement, 14 March, pp. 84–88.

9. *British Medical Journal* (1970) Supplement, 7 March, p. 77.

10. Tripp, M. (1973) 'Who speaks for Petro?', *Drugs and Society*, 3, pp. 12–17.

11. Stimson, G. V. and Oppenheimer, E. (1982) *op cit.*, pp. 186, 195.

12. *British Medical Journal* (1968) 'Voluntary restrictions of amphetamines', 30 November, pp. 532–533; 'Control of amphetamine preparations', Supplement, pp. 572–573.

13. Advisory Committee on Drug Dependence (1970) *The amphetamines and lysergic acid diethylamide (LSD)*, London: HMSO, paragraphs 50–52.

14. Godber, G. (1968) Letter, *British Medical Journal*, 23 March, p. 754.

15. Hansard HC (6 May 1968) volume 764 columns 170–171.

16. Advisory Committee on Drug Dependence (1970) *op cit.*, paragraph 40.

17. De Alarcon, R. (1972) 'An epidemiological evaluation of a public health measure aimed at reducing the availability of methylamphetamine', *Psychological Medicine*, 2, pp. 293–300.

18. Hawks, D. *et al.* (1969) 'Abuse of methylamphetamine', *British Medical Journal*, 21 June, pp. 715–721.

19. *Pharmaceutical Journal* (1969) pp. 202, 257.

20. *British Medical Journal* (1969) 'Abuse of drugs', 21 June, pp. 710–711.

21. Leech, K. (1991) *op cit.*, pp. 52, 53.

22. Edwards, G. E. (1978) 'Some years on: evolutions in the "British system"', in West, D. J. (ed.) *Problems of drug abuse in Britain*, University of Cambridge Institute of Criminology, p. 11.

23. Leech, K. (1991) *op cit.*, p. 52.

24. Rathod, N. H. (1972) 'The use of heroin and methadone by injection in a New Town', *British Journal of Addiction*, 67, pp. 113–122.

25. Kosviner, A. *et al.* (1968) 'Heroin use in a provincial town', *The Lancet*, 1 June, pp. 1189–1191.

26. McSweeney, D. and Parr, D. (1970) 'Drug pushers in the UK', *Nature*, 228, pp. 422–424.

27. Jones, J. (1967) 'Drugs and teenagers', *Journal of the Forensic Science Society*, 7, pp. 12–16.

28. Bennie, E. H., Mullin, P. and Balfour Sclare, A. (1972) 'Drug dependence in Glasgow 1960–70', *British Journal of Addiction*, 67, pp. 101–105.

29. Journal Interview 28. (1990) Conversation with Raj Rathod, *British Journal of Addiction*, 85, pp. 1239–1245.

30. Jaffe, J. (1987) 'Footnotes in the evolution of the American national response: some little known aspects of the first American Strategy for Drug Abuse and Drug Traffic Prevention', *British Journal of Addiction*, 82, pp. 587–600, p. 592.

31. Anumonye, A. and McClure, J. L. (1970) 'Adolescent drug abuse in a north London suburb', *British Journal of Addiction*, 65, pp. 25–34.

32. *British Medical Journal* (1968) Supplement, 13 July, p. 66.

33. Owens, J. (1967) 'Integrated approach', *British Medical Journal*, 20 May, pp. 501–502. Nyman, M. (1969) 'Addiction Unit – All Saints Hospital', *British Hospital Journal and Social Service Review*, 1 August, pp. 1451–1452. Judson, H. F. (1974) *Heroin addiction in Britain*, New York and London: Harcourt Brace Jovanovich, pp. 88–91 and p. 107.

34. *British Medical Journal* (1966) 'Birmingham City Council Health Committee action against drugs', 19 March, p. 748.

35. Owens, J. (1967) *op cit.*, p. 501.

36. Owens, J. and Nyman, M. (1972) 'Drug abuse as a community mental health

problem', *The Journal of the Queen Elizabeth Medical School*, Spring, pp. 9–11.

37. Marks, J. (1988) Letter, *British Medical Journal*, 9 January, p. 132.

38. Judson, H. F. (1974) *op cit.*, p. 90.

39. Hansard HC (6 May 1968) volume 764 column 154.

40. Strang, J., Ghodse, H. and Johns, A. (1987) 'Responding flexibly but not gullibly to drug addiction', *British Medical Journal*, 28 November, p. 1364.

41. O'Bryan, L. (1985) 'The cost of Lacoste', in Henman, A. *et al.* (eds) *The big deal*, London: Pluto Press.

42. Edwards, G. E. (1978) *op cit.*, p. 10.

43. Griffith, P., Gossop, M. and Strang, J. (1994) 'Chasing the dragon: the development of heroin smoking in the United Kingdom', in Strang, J. and Gossop, M. (eds) *Heroin addiction and drug policy: the British system*, Oxford: Oxford University Press, pp. 123–124.

44. Aitken, D. (1978) Discussion, in West, D. J. (ed.) *Problems of drug abuse in Britain*, University of Cambridge Institute of Criminology, p. 46.

45. Edwards, G. E. (1978) *op cit.*, p. 10.

46. Cox, B., Shirley, J. and Short, M. (1977) *The fall of Scotland Yard*, Penguin Books, Chapter 2, pp. 84–181.

47. Lewis, R. (1994) 'Flexible hierarchies and dynamic disorder – the trading and distribution of illicit heroin in Britain and Europe 1970–1990', in Strang, J. and Gossop, M. (eds) *Heroin addiction and drug policy: the British system*, Oxford: Oxford University Press.

48. British Medical Association (1997) *Therapeutic uses of cannabis*, Amsterdam: Harwood Academic Publishers.

## Chapter 11

1. Connell, P. H. and Strang, J. (1994) 'The creation of the clinics: clinical demand and the formation of policy', in Strang, J. and Gossop, M. (eds) *Heroin addiction and drug policy: the British system*, Oxford: Oxford University Press, p. 174.

2. Glancy, J. E. McA. (1972) 'The treatment of narcotic dependence in the United Kingdom', *Bulletin on Narcotics*, XXIV, pp. 1–9.

3. Power, R. (1994) 'Drug trends since 1968', in Strang, J. and Gossop, M. (eds) *Heroin addiction and drug policy: the British system*, Oxford: Oxford University Press, p. 38.

4. From 1968 to 1975 two or three annual national clinical conferences were convened by the Department of Health, with the London consultants meeting more frequently. These conferences provided the treatment centre consultants with the opportunity to be kept up to date with the current drug scene by the Drugs Inspectorate and to discuss treatment policies, practices

and treatment. After 1975 the London consultants held their own informal meetings with invited observers from the Department of Health and the Home Office. I attended most of these meetings until 1986. Since the early 1980s provincial treatment centres have also held regular meetings.

5. Connell, P. H. (1991) 'Treatment of drug-dependent patients 1968–1969', *British Journal of Addiction*, 1991, pp. 913–915.

6. Glancy, J. E. McA. (1972) *op cit.* Stimson, G. V. and Oppenheimer, E. (1982) *Heroin addiction: treatment and control in Britain*, London: Tavistock, p. 100.

7. Connell, P. H. *et al.* (1970) Letter, *British Medical Journal*, 16 May, p. 422.

8. Strang, J. *et al.* (1994) 'Prescribing heroin and other injectable drugs', in Strang, J. and Gossop, M. (eds) *Heroin addiction and drug policy: the British system*, Oxford: Oxford University Press, p. 203.

9. Bewley, T. (1967) 'Advantages of special centres', *British Medical Journal*, 2, pp. 498–499, p. 499.

10. Chapple, P. A. L. and Gray, G. (1968) 'One year's work at a centre for the treatment of addicted patients', *The Lancet*, 27 April, pp. 908–911. Chapple, P. A. L. (1967) 'Treatment in the community', *British Medical Journal*, 20 May, pp. 500–501, p. 501.

11. Gardner, R. and Connell, P. (1970). 'One year's experience in a drug-dependence clinic', *The Lancet*, 29 August, pp. 455–458.

12. Strang, J. *et al.* (1994) *op cit.*, p. 198.

13. Mitcheson, M. (1994) 'Drug clinics in the 1970s', in Strang, J. and Gossop, M. (eds) *Heroin addiction and drug policy: the British system*, Oxford: Oxford University Press, p. 179.

14. Strang, J. *et al.* (1994) *op cit.*, pp. 198 and 203.

15. Stimson and Oppenheimer *op cit.*, p. 101.

16. Strang, J. *et al.* (1994) *op cit.*, p. 199.

17. Mitcheson, M. (1994) *op cit.*, p. 180.

18. Burr, A. (1983) 'The Piccadilly drug scene', *British Journal of Addiction*, 78, pp. 5–21, p. 8.

19. Royal College of Psychiatrists (1987) *Drug scenes*, London: Gaskell, p. 64.

20. Connell, P. H. (1967) 'Importance of research', *British Medical Journal*, 20 May, pp. 499–500.

21. Mitcheson, M. (1994) *op cit.*

22. Hartnoll, R. L. *et al.* (1980) 'Evaluation of heroin maintenance in controlled trial', *Archives of General Psychiatry*, 37, pp. 877–884.

23. King Edward's Hospital Fund for London (1975) *Drug dependency discussion group: liaison and co-ordination*, KFC Reprint No. 974.

24. Release Newsletter (1976), 3, Number 2.

25. Madden, J. S. (1989) 'The decline of long-term prescribing to opioid users in the United Kingdom', *British Journal of Addiction*, 82, pp. 457–459.

26. Advisory Council on the Misuse of Drugs (1982) *Treatment and rehabilitation,* London: HMSO, Paragraph 4.16. and Recommendation 28.

27. Advisory Council on the Misuse of Drugs (1982) *op cit.,* paragraph 4.19.

28. Advisory Council on the Misuse of Drugs (1982) *op cit.,* paragraphs 7.21–7.24 and Recommendation 23.

29. Report of the Medical Working Group on Drug Dependence (1984) *Guidelines of good clinical practice in the treatment of drug misuse,* London: Department of Health and Social Security.

30. Willis, J. (1983) Letter, *British Medical Journal,* 11 August, p. 500.

31. Bishop, B. P. *et al.* (1976) 'A city looks at its problems of drug abuse by injection', *British Journal of Psychiatry,* 129, pp. 465–471.

32. Bewley, T. H., James, I. P. and Le Fevre, C. (1972) 'Maintenance treatment of narcotic addicts (not British nor a system, but operating now)', *International Journal of the Addictions,* 7, pp. 597–611.

33. Mitcheson, M. (1994) *op cit.,* p. 182,183.

34. Trebach, A. (1982) *The heroin solution,* New Haven: Yale University Press, quoted on page 191.

35. *The Lancet* (1967) 'Advice on addiction', November 25, pp. 1131–1132.

36. Advisory Council on the Misuse of Drugs (1977) *The first interim report of the Treatment and Rehabilitation Working Group,* London: HMSO.

37. Royal College of Psychiatrists (1987) *op cit.,* pp. 65 and 66.

38. Stimson, G. V. (1978) 'Treatment or control? Dilemmas for staff in drug dependency clinics', in West, D. J. (ed.) *Problems of drug abuse in Britain,* University of Cambridge Institute of Criminology, pp. 66 and 67.

39. Strang, J. (1989) 'The British system: past, present and future', *International Review of Psychiatry,* 1, pp. 109–120, p. 113.

40. Judson, H. F. (1974) *Heroin addiction in Britain,* New York and London: Harcourt Brace Jovanovich, p. 41.

41. Judson, H. F. (1974) *op cit.,* pp. 91–94.

42. Chapple, P. A. L. (1967) 'Treatment in the community', *British Medical Journal,* 20 May, pp. 500–501. Owens, J. (1967) 'Integrated approach', *British Medical Journal,* 20 May, pp. 501–502.

43. Glatt, M. M. (1966) 'A review of the second report of the Interdepartmental Committee on Drug Addiction', *Bulletin on Narcotics,* XVIII, pp. 29–42, pp. 34 and 38.

44. Ghodse, A. H. (1978) 'Treatment versus Control, discussion', in West, D. J. (ed.) *Problems of drug abuse in Britain,* University of Cambridge Institute of Criminology, p. 71.

45. Stimson, G. V. and Oppenheimer, E. (1982) *op cit.,* p. 97.

46. Mitcheson, M. (1994) *op cit.,* pp. 178 and 179.

47. Judson, H. F. (1974) *op cit.,* pp. 95 and 96.

48. *The Lancet* (1977) 'Drug-dependence clinics', 19 February, pp. 405–406.
49. Advisory Council on the Misuse of Drugs (1982) *op cit.*, paragraphs 4.12 and 4.17.
50. Edwards, G. E. (1970) 'Place of treatment professionals in society's response to chemical abuse', *British Medical Journal*, 25 April, pp. 195–199.
51. Advisory Council on the Misuse of Drugs (1982) *op cit.*, Chapter 8.
52. Mitcheson, M. (1994) *op cit.*, p. 189.
53. *The Lancet* (1982) 'Drug addiction: British system failing', 9 January, pp. 83–84.
54. *Addiction* (1994) Conversation with Vincent Dole, 89, pp. 23–29.
55. Mitcheson, M. and Hartnoll, R. (1978) 'Conflicts in deciding treatment within drug dependency clinics. Discussion', in West, D. J. (ed.) *Problems of drug abuse in Britain*, University of Cambridge Institute of Criminology, p. 79.
56. Connell, P. H. (1969) 'Drug dependence in Great Britain: a challenge to the practice of medicine', in Steinberg, H. (ed.) *The scientific basis of drug dependence*, London: J & A Churchill.
57. Advisory Council on the Misuse of Drugs (1982) *op cit.*, paragraph 4.10.
58. Strang, J. (1989) *op cit.*, p. 112.
59. Trebach, A. (1982) *op cit.*, pp. 174 and 175.
60. Farrell, M. *et al.* (1994) 'Methadone maintenance treatment in opiate dependency', *British Medical Journal*, 309, pp. 997–1001.

## Chapter 12

1. Hewetson, J. and Ollendorff, R. (1964) 'Preliminary survey of one hundred London heroin and cocaine addicts', *British Journal of Addiction*, 60, pp. 109–112.
2. Mitcheson, M. *et al.* (1970) 'Sedative abuse by heroin addicts', *The Lancet*, 21 March, pp. 606–607.
3. Mitcheson, M. (1994) 'Drug clinics in the 1970s', in Strang, J. and Gossop, M. (eds) *Heroin addiction and drug policy: the British system*, Oxford: Oxford University Press, pp. 184 and 185.
4. Hansard HC (20 February 1970) volume 798 column 1454.
5. Reed, J. L. *et al.* (1970) Letter, *British Medical Journal*, 28 March, p. 817.
6. Tylden, E. and Saville, C. *et al.* (1970) Letter, *British Medical Journal*, 4 April, p. 49.
7. *British Medical Journal* (1971) Supplement, 31 July, p. 74.
8. Bishop, B. P. *et al.* (1976) 'A city looks at its problems of drug abuse by injection', *British Journal of Psychiatry*, 129, pp. 465–471.
9. Advisory Council on the Misuse of Drugs (1982) *Treatment and rehabilitation*, London: HMSO, paragraphs 7.27 and 7.28. and Recommendation 24.
10. Marjot, D. (1978) Letter, *British Medical Journal*, 6 May, p. 1214.

11. Bewley, T. H. (1980) 'Prescribing psychoactive drugs to addicts', *British Medical Journal*, 14 August, pp. 497–498.

12. Marks, J. and Leaver, J. (1982) 'How best to manage drug addicts?', *British Medical Journal*, 1 May, pp. 1335–1336.

13. Gilman, M. (1988) 'DIY Diconal?', *Mersey Drugs Journal*, 1 (5), p. 15.

14. *The Chemist & Druggist* (1979) 10 March, p. 294.

15. Hartnoll, R., Lewis, R. and Bryer, S. (1984) 'Recent trends in drug misuse', *DrugLink*, Spring, No. 19, pp. 22–24.

16. Hewett, C. (1987) 'A cocaine explosion?', *DrugLink*, 2, p. 7.

17. British Medical Association (1968) 'Control of amphetamine preparations', *British Medical Journal*, 30 November, pp. 572–573.

18. Griffiths, P., Gossop, M. and Strang, J. (1994) 'Chasing the dragon: the development of heroin smoking in the United Kingdom', in Strang, J. and Gossop, M. (eds) *Heroin addiction and drug policy: the British system*, Oxford: Oxford University Press.

19. Burr, A. (1984) 'The illicit non-pharmaceutical heroin market and drug scene in Kensington Market', *British Journal of Addiction*, 79, pp. 337–343,

20. Burr, A. (1984) *op cit*. Glatt, M. M. (1979) Letter, *British Medical Journal*, 14 April, p. 971.

21. Lewis, R. (1994) 'Flexible hierarchies and dynamic disorder – the trading and distribution of illicit heroin in Britain and Europe 1970–1990', in Strang, J. and Gossop, M. (eds) *Heroin addiction and drug policy: the British system*, Oxford: Oxford University Press.

22. Advisory Council on the Misuse of Drugs (1982) *op cit.*, Appendix F, Table 4.

23. *The Lancet* (1979) Drug addiction: time for reappraisal, 11 August, pp. 289–290.

24. Hansard HL (30 October 1979) volume 402 column 353–355.

25. Hansard HC (21 December 1979) volume 976 columns 1066–1984.

26. Hansard HL (30 October 1979) volume 402 column 362–363.

27. Hansard HC (21 December 1979) volume 976 columns 1079.

28. Wagstaff, A. and Maynard, A. (1988) *Economic aspects of the illicit drug market and drug enforcement policies in the United Kingdom*, Home Office Research Study 95, London: HMSO.

29. Ditton, J. and Speirits, K. (1981) *The rapid increase in heroin use in Glasgow during 1981*, Background Paper No. 2, Department of Sociology, University of Glasgow. Pearson, G. (1987) 'Social deprivation, unemployment and patterns of heroin use', in Dorn, N. and South, N. (eds) *A land fit for heroin?*, London: Macmillan Education Ltd. Parker, H., Newcombe, R. and Bakx, K. (1987) 'The new heroin users: prevalence and characteristics in Wirral, Merseyside', *British Journal of Addiction*, 82, pp. 147–157.

30. Gilman, M. and Pearson, G. (1991) 'Lifestyles and law enforcement', in

Whynes, D. K. and Bean, P. T. (eds) *Policing and prescribing* London: Macmillan, p. 97.

31. *The Lancet* (1982) 'Drug addiction: British system failing', 9 January, pp. 83–84.


## Chapter 13

1. Advisory Council on the Misuse of Drugs (1982) *Treatment and rehabilitation,* London: HMSO, paragraph 1.1.
2. Department of Health and Social Security (1982) *op cit.,* paragraph 5.5.
3. Department of Health and Social Security (1982) *op cit.,* paragraph 11.1.
4. Department of Health and Social Security (1982) *op cit.,* paragraph 4.20.
5. Department of Health and Social Security (1982) *op cit.,* paragraph 5.13.
6. Department of Health and Social Security (1982) *op cit.,* paragraphs 7.6–7.13.
7. Bewley, T. H. (1980) 'Prescribing psychoactive drugs to addicts', *British Medical Journal,* 16 August, pp. 497–498.
8. Ghodse, A. H. (1983) 'Treatment of drug addiction in London', *The Lancet,* 19 March, pp. 636–639.
9. Connell, P. H. and Mitcheson, M. (1984) 'Necessary safeguards when prescribing opioid drugs to addicts: experience of drug dependence clinics in London', *British Medical Journal,* 10 March, pp. 767–769.
10. Report of the Medical Working Group on Drug Dependence (1984) *Guidelines of good clinical practice in the treatment of drug misuse,* London: DHSS.
11. Department of Health and Social Security (1982) *op cit.,* paragraph 7.37.
12. Advisory Committee on Drug Dependence (1970) *The amphetamines and lysergic acid diethylamide (LSD),* London: HMSO, paragraph 64.
13. Department of Health and Social Security (1982) *op cit.,* paragraph 7.36.
14. Department of Health, Scottish Home and Health Department, Welsh Office (1991) *Drug misuse and dependence: guidelines on clinical management,* London: HMSO, paragraph 1.2.3.
15. Connell, P. H. and Mitcheson, M. (1984) *op cit.,* p. 767.
16. *The Lancet* (1965) 'Drug addiction', 27 November, pp. 1113–1114.
17. Ashton, M. (1981) 'Conference (almost) agrees on central funding, licensed GPs and more detoxification', *DrugLink,* Information Letter, No. 15, pp. 6–7, p. 6.
18. Ashton, M. and Shapiro, H. (1981) 'More thoughts on licensing, funding and detox – and new thoughts on the law', *DrugLink,* Information Letter, No. 16, pp. 12–15.
19. Rathod, N. H. (1979) Letter, *The Lancet,* 29 September, pp. 695–696.
20. *The Lancet* (1979) 'Drug addiction: a time for reappraisal', 11 August, pp. 289–290.
21. Department of Health and Social Security (1982) *op cit.,* paragraph 4.2.
22. Department of Health and Social Security (1982) *op cit.,* paragraph 6.7.

23. Department of Health and Social Security (1982) *op cit.*, paragraph 5.13.

24. Ashton, M. (1984) 'The response to the Treatment and Rehabilitation Report', *DrugLink*, Information Letter, No. 19, pp. 16–21.

25. Department of Health and Social Security (1982) *op cit.*, paragraphs 7.17 and 7.18.

26. Ashton, M. (1984) *op cit.*, p. 20.

27. Department of Health, Scottish Home and Health Department, Welsh Office (1991) *op cit.*, p. 5, paragraph II.2.

28. House of Commons (1985) *Fourth Report from the Social Services Committee Session 1984–85, Misuse of Drugs*, London: HMSO, paragraph 50.

29. *Government Response to the Fourth Report from the Social Services Committee Session 1984–85* (1985) London: HMSO, paragraph 68.
(Editor's note: In March 2000 the Home Office issued a consultation document, 'Changes to the Misuse of Drugs Act: Licensing of Controlled Drugs Prescribed in the Treatment of Addiction'. This proposed that any doctor, including general practitioners, who treated addicts should be licensed to prescribe any controlled drug in Schedule 2 or 3 of the Misuse of Drugs Act 1971 Regulations made in 1985 (which ensure that appropriate exemptions are made from the offence provisions of the Act) except methadone liquid or mixture on an NHS prescription and to prescribe injectable forms of any controlled drug in Schedule 2. This is 'to reinforce the clinical standards set out in the Guidelines (*Drug misuse and dependence – guidelines on clinical management* (1999)) and to tackle the problems caused by inappropriate prescribing, especially overdose death and leakage of prescribed drugs on to the illicit market'. Some criticisms of the proposals are similar to those made to the earlier proposal: licensing alone will not bring about appropriate prescribing and will end the flexible British prescribing system; the Royal College of General Practitioners rejected the proposal; general practitioners will be discouraged from treating addicts; the prescribing of methadone alternatives will be stifled; pharmaceutical companies will be inhibited from carrying out research for better drugs to treat addicts (see *DrugLink* (2001) 15, 25).)

30. Department of Health and Social Security (1982) *op cit.*, paragraphs 7.12 and 7.13.

31. Beckett, D. (1983) Letter, *British Medical Journal*, 9 July, p. 127.

32. Bewley, T. H. (1980) *op cit.*, p. 497.

33. Bewley, T. H. and Ghodse, A. H. (1983) 'Unacceptable face of private practice: prescription of controlled drugs to addicts', *British Medical Journal*, 11 June, pp. 1876–1877.

34. *The Lancet* (1980) 'Drug addiction: British system failing', 9 January, pp. 83–84.

35. Burr, A. (1983) 'The Piccadilly drug scene', *British Journal of Addiction*, 78, pp. 5–19.

36. Strang, J. (1982) Personal view, *British Medical Journal*, 27 March, pp. 972.
37. Department of Health and Social Security (1982) *op cit.*, paragraph 7.13.
38. *British Medical Journal* (1966) 21 January, Supplement, p. 18.
39. House of Commons (1985) *op cit.*, Minutes of Evidence, paragraph 503.
40. Dally, A. (1981) Personal view, *British Medical Journal*, 26 September, p. 857.
41. Willis, J. (1983) Letter, *British Medical Journal*, 18 August, p. 500.
42. Dally, A. (1982) Letter, *British Medical Journal*, 1 May, p. 284.
43. Bewley, T. H. and Ghodse, A. H. (1983) *op cit.*
44. Strang, J. (1982) *op cit.*
45. *The Lancet* (1980) *op cit.*
46. Beckett, D. (1983) Letter, *British Medical Journal*, 9 July, p. 127.
47. Dally, P. (1983) Letter, *British Medical Journal*, 13 August, p. 500.
48. Hartnoll, R. and Lewis, R. (1983) Letter, *British Medical Journal*, 13 August, p. 500.
49. Robertson, A. B. (1983) Letter, *British Medical Journal*, 9 July, p. 126.
50. Burr, A. (1983) 'Increased sales of opiates on the black market in the Piccadilly area', *British Medical Journal*, 24 September, pp. 883–885, p. 885.
51. Dally, A. (1983) Letter, *British Medical Journal*, 22 October, p. 1219.
52. Beckett, D. (1983) Letter, *British Medical Journal*, 22 October, p. 1219.
53. Strang, J. (1981) Personal view, *British Medical Journal*, 1 August, p. 281.
54. General Medical Council (1985) Annual Report, pp. 5–6.
55. House of Commons (1985) *Fourth Report from the Social Services Committee Session 1984–85, Misuse of Drugs*, London: HMSO, p. 68.

## Chapter 14

1. Edwards, G. E. (1979) 'Ten years working of the revised response', *British Journal of Psychiatry*, 134, pp. 1–13, p. 1.
2. Parker, H., Bakx, K. and Newcombe, R. (1988) *Living with heroin*, Milton Keynes: Open University Press.
3. Scottish Committee on HIV infection and Intravenous Drug Misuse (1986) *Report on HIV infection in Scotland*, Edinburgh: Scottish Home and Health Department.
4. Advisory Council on the Misuse of Drugs (1982) *Treatment and rehabilitation*, London: HMSO.
5. Strang, J. and Clement, S. (1994) 'The introduction of community drug teams across the UK', in Strang, J. and Gossop, M. (eds) *Heroin addiction and drug policy: the British system*, Oxford: Oxford University Press, p. 206.
6. Lindesmith, A. (1957) 'The British system of narcotics control', *Law and Contemporary Problems*, 22, pp. 141–153.
7. Schur, E. M. (1963) *Narcotic addiction in Britain and America: the impact of*

*public policy*, London: Tavistock Publications.

8. Royal College of Psychiatrists (1987) *Drug scenes*, London: Gaskell, p. 62.

9. Gillespie, D. *et al.* (1967) 'Drug dependence and abuse in England', *British Journal of Addiction*, 62, pp. 155–170, p. 161.

10. Edwards, G. E. (1978) 'Some years on: evolutions in the "British system"', in West, D. J. (ed.) *Problems of drug abuse in Britain*, University of Cambridge Institute of Criminology, p. 6.

11. Ministry of Health (1926) *Report of the Departmental Committee on Morphine and Heroin Addiction* (The Rolleston Report), London: HMSO, paragraph 24.

12. Edwards, G. E. (1978) *op cit.*, pp. 1–2.

13. The Rolleston Report, *op cit.*, paragraph 71.

14. Pearson, G. and Gilman, M. (1994) 'Local and regional variations in drug misuse: the British heroin epidemic of the 1980s', in Strang, J. and Gossop, M. (eds) *Heroin addiction and drug policy the British system*, Oxford: Oxford University Press, p. 103.

15. Wilson, J. Q. (1990) 'Against the legalisation of drugs', *Commentary*, 89, pp. 21–28, p. 23.

16. Edwards, G. E. (1978) *op cit.*, pp. 2, 3 and 13.

17. James, I. P. (1965) Letter, *The Lancet*, 7 August, p. 288.

18. Blackwell, J. (1988) 'The saboteurs of Britain's opiate policy: over-prescribing physicians or American-style "Junkies"?', *International Journal of the Addictions*, 23, pp. 517–526.

19. Gillespie, D. *et al.* (1967) *op cit.* Glatt, M. M. *et al.* (1967) *The drug scene in Great Britain*, London: Edward Arnold.

20. Hewetson, J. and Ollendorf, R. (1964) 'Preliminary survey of one hundred London heroin and cocaine addicts', *British Journal of Addiction*, 60, pp. 109–112.

21. Spear, H. B. (1969) 'The growth of heroin addiction in the United Kingdom', *British Journal of Addiction*, 64, pp. 245–255, Tables 4a and 4b.

22. Young, J. (1971) *The drugtakers: the social meaning of drug use*, London: Paladin, pp. 206–7.

23. Connell, P. H. (1969) 'Drug dependence in Great Britain: a challenge to the practice of medicine', in Steinberg, H. (ed.) *The scientific basis of drug dependence*, London: J & A Churchill.

24. Connell, P. H. (1991) 'Treatment of drug-dependent patients 1968–1969', *British Journal of Addiction*, 86, pp. 913–915.

25. Ashton, M. (1984) 'The response to the treatment and rehabilitation report', *DrugLink*, Information Letter, Spring, No. 19, p. 19.

26. Connell, P. H. (1969) *op cit.*, p. 298.

27. Connell, P. H. (1975), quoted by Strang, J. *et al.* (1994) 'Prescribing heroin and other injectable drugs', in Strang, J. and Gossop, M. (eds) *Heroin addiction and*

*drug policy the British system*, Oxford: Oxford University Press, p. 193.

28. Pringle, J. (1955) *Heroin: the BMA case against the ban*, London: British Medical Association.

29. Edwards, G. E. (1969) 'The British approach to the treatment of heroin addiction', *The Lancet*, 12 April, pp. 768–771, p. 770.

30. Glatt, M. M. (1966) 'A review of the second report of the Interdepartmental Committee on Drug Addiction' (The second Brain report), *Bulletin on Narcotics*, XVIII, April–June, pp. 29–42, p. 39.

31. Bewley, T. H. (1967) 'Advantages of special centres', *British Medical Journal*, 20 May, pp. 458–459. Connell, P. H. (1967) 'Importance of research', *British Medical Journal*, 20 May, pp. 459–460.

32. Hansard (25 July 1967) HC volume 751 column 633.

33. Connell, P. H. (1967) *op cit.*, p. 499.

34. Connell, P. H. (1969) *op cit.*, p. 295.

35. *The Lancet* (1965) 'Drug addiction', 27 November, pp. 1113–1114, p. 1113.

36. Owens, J. (1967) 'Integrated approach', *British Medical Journal*, 20 May, pp. 501–502, p. 501.

37. Ministry of Health and Department of Health for Scotland (1961) *Drug addiction: report of the Interdepartmental Committee* (The first Brain Report), London: HMSO. In paragraph 36 the Committee defined stabilised addicts as those 'who have been taking small and regular doses for years show little evidence of tolerance and are often leading reasonably satisfactory lives'.

38. Connell, P. H. (1986) '"I need heroin". Thirty years' experience of drug dependence and the medical challenges at the local, national, international and political level. What next?', *British Journal of Addiction*, 81, pp. 461–472, p. 462.

39. Bewley, T. H. (1965) 'Heroin and cocaine addiction', *The Lancet*, 10 April, pp. 808–810, p. 810.

40. Bewley, T. H. (1967) *op cit.*.

41. Glatt, M. M. (1969) 'Rehabilitation of the addict', *British Journal of Addiction*, 64, pp. 165–182, p. 170.

42. Stimson, G. V. and Ogborne, A. C. (1970) 'Survey of addicts prescribed heroin at London clinics', *The Lancet*, i, 1163.

43. Gardner, R. and Connell, P. H. (1970) 'One year's experience in a drug-dependence clinic', *The Lancet*, 29 August, pp. 455–458.

44. Glatt, M. M. (1966) *op cit.*

45. Glatt, M. M. (1969) *op cit.*, p. 169.

46. Merry, J. (1968) 'USA and British attitudes to heroin addiction and treatment centres', *British Journal of Addiction*, 63, pp. 247–250, p. 250.

47. Oppenheim, G. B. *et al.* (1973) 'Outpatient treatment of narcotic addiction. Who benefits?', *British Journal of Addiction*, 68, pp. 37–44.

48. Edwards, G. E. (1969) *op cit.*, p. 770.

49. Chapple, P. A. L. and Marks, V. (1965) Letter, *The Lancet*, 7 August, pp. 288–289.

50. Connell, P. H. (1969) *op cit.*, p. 298.

51. Edwards, G. E. (1969) *op cit.*, p. 769.

52. Connell, P. H. (1969) *op cit.*, p. 297.

53. Connell, P. H. (1991) *op cit.*, p. 914.

54. *British Medical Journal* (1967) 'Drug treatment centres', 20 May, pp. 455–456, p. 456.

55. Willis, J. H. (1983) Letter, *British Medical Journal*, 13 August, p. 500.

56. Glancy, J. E. McA.(1972) 'The treatment of narcotic dependence in the United Kingdom', *Bulletin on Narcotics*, XXIV, pp. 1–9.

57. Mitcheson, M. (1994) 'Drug clinics in the 1970s', in Strang, J. and Gossop, M. (eds) *Heroin addiction and drug policy: the British system*, Oxford: Oxford University Press, p. 178.

58. Connell, P. H. (1969) *op cit.*, p. 295.

59. Stimson, G. V. and Oppenheimer, E. (1982) *Heroin addiction: treatment and control in Britain*, London: Tavistock, p. 100.

60. Berridge, V. (1990) 'Special issue: The British Society for the Treatment of Addiction 1884–1988', *British Journal of Addiction*, 85, p. 1058.

61. Connell, P. H. (1986) *op cit.*, p. 462.

62. Marjot, D. (1987) 'Heads up – or heads down?', *British Journal of Addiction*, 82, pp. 317–318.

63. Connell, P. H. (1987) 'Heads up – or heads down? A reply to David Marjot', *British Journal of Addiction*, 82, p. 558.

64. Edwards, G. E. (1969) *op cit.*, p. 770.

65. Advisory Council on the Misuse of Drugs (1982) *Treatment and rehabilitation*, London: HMSO, paragraph 4.10.

66. Connell, P. H. (1967) *op cit.*, p. 500.

67. Advisory Council on the Misuse of Drugs (1982) *op cit.*, paragraph 8.1.

68. Advisory Council on the Misuse of Drugs (1990) *Problem drug use: a review of training*, London: HMSO, paragraph 2.10.

69. Smart, C. (1985) 'Drug dependence units in England and Wales. The results of a national survey', *Drug and Alcohol Dependence*, 15, pp. 131–144, p. 143.

70. James, I. P. (1968) Letter, *The Lancet*, 7 December, p. 1239.

71. Field, L. H. (1968) Letter, *The Lancet*, 21 December, p. 1350.

72. Haldane, F. P. (1969) Letter, *The Lancet*, 4 January, p. 925.

73. The Rolleston Report, *op cit.*, paragraph 43.

74. First Brain Report, *op cit.*, paragraph 34.

75. *The Lancet* (1982) *Drug addiction: British system failing*, 9 January, 83–84, p. 83.

76. Thorley, A. (1981) 'Longitudinal studies of drug dependence', in Edwards, G. E. and Busch, C. (eds) *Drug problems in Britain: a review of ten years*, London: Academic Press, p. 162.

77. Stimson, G. V. and Oppenheimer, E. (1982) *Heroin addiction: treatment and control in Britain*, London: Tavistock, p. 252.

78. Advisory Council on the Misuse of Drugs (1982) *op cit.*, paragraphs 9.3 and 9.6. (Editor's note. The Task Force set up by the Department of Health in 1995 to review services for drug misusers found that 'The largest single challenge the Task Force faced was the lack of existing UK research on drug treatment effectiveness' so that it 'had to rely on literature reviews of international findings'. Department of Health (1996) *The Task Force to Review Services for Drug Misusers. Report of an Independent Review of Drug Treatment Services in England*, London: Department of Health, p. 98.)

79. Connell, P. H. (1986) *op cit.*, p. 470.

80. Stimson, G. V. and Oppenheimer, E. (1982) *op cit.*, p. 216.

81. Gardner, R. (1970) 'Methadone misuse and death by overdosage', *British Journal of Addiction*, 65, pp. 113–118, p. 113.

82. Editor's note. A fresh set of guidelines was issued in 1999 by the Departments of Health in England and Wales and Scotland.

83. White Paper (1995) *Tackling drugs together*, London: The Stationery Office, p. 22.

# Index

membership 81, 97, 104, 106, 136
meetings 104–10
origins 90–7
Report and recommendations 33,
110–12, 116, 179, 194–5
Brain Committee, second
on addiction 190
convening of 125–33
evidence collected 131
and maintenance prescribing 249,
250
meetings 134–7, 138–41
membership 133, 136
reactions to Report 141–3
Report and recommendations 121,
133, 137–41, 176, 179–80, 195, 202–3,
299–300
terms of reference 133
Braine, Bernard 153, 158–9, 168, 206,
271
Branthwaite, Dr R. W. 28, 29
Brass, Sir Leslie 84, 84–5
Brecher, Edward viii
Brennan, Dr 260, 261
Bridgeman, W. C. 12
Bristol, drug use 243, 263
British Drug Houses Ltd 244
*British Journal of Addiction* 192
British Medical Association (BMA)
and 1921 Regulations 8
addiction survey 103
and amphetamines 120–1, 123, 219,
221, 222
and attempts to ban heroin 65, 66,
70, 75, 77–8, 79–81, 83, 87
and barbiturates 257
and Brain Committees 100, 141–2,
150, 285
and cannabis 234
and Diconal 265
and doctor addicts 14, 16–17

and doctor licensing 152–3, 205–6,
209, 282
and doctors' rights 44–5
and drug inspection 39–40
on GPs 306
and medical tribunals 43–4, 55, 317
and notification 152–3, 177
*British Medical Journal*
on 2nd Brain Report 141
and addiction research 192
on amphetamine control 121–2
and attempts to ban cocaine 87–8
and attempts to ban heroin 70, 75,
77, 79
on British system 1
on implementation of Brain
recommendations 170–1
on notification 176
on private prescribing 285
on Rolleston Report 33
on treatment of addicts 198–9, 203,
302
British National Formulary 89, 259,
263
British Pharmacopoeia Commission
72–3, 75–6
Brock, L. G. 30
Brooke, Henry 118, 119, 120
Brouet, Prof. Georges 80
Browdy, Dr M. W. 214, 220
Buchanan, Sir George 66
Burley, S. H. E. 104, 105, 107, 110, 115
Burr, Angela 240, 285, 288
Burroughs, William 144
Burroughs Wellcome & Co. 259

**C**
Cahal, Dr Denis 244–5, 259, 263
Campaign on the Use and Restriction
of Barbiturates (CURB) 258–9
Campbell, Sir David 83, 109